HEARTBEAT

OMNIBUS
VOLUME
II

Constable Along the Lane
Constable Through the Meadow

HEARTBEAT

OMNIBUS
VOLUME
II

Nicholas Rhea

ROBERT HALE · LONDON

© This omnibus edition Nicholas Rhea 1993
First published in Great Britain 1993

ISBN 0 7090 5234 0

Robert Hale Limited
Clerkenwell House
Clerkenwell Green
London EC1R 0HT

Printed in Great Britain by
St Edmundsbury Press Limited,
Bury St Edmunds, Suffolk
Bound by WBC Bookbinders Limited

CONSTABLE ALONG THE LANE

1

How shines your tower, the only one
Of that special site and stone!
                    Edmund Charles Blunden, 1896–1974

Among the unpaid benefits in the life of a village policeman is
that of leisurely patrolling the beautiful lanes which pattern and
serve our countryside. Every season has its delights and my
patrols took many forms. Sometimes I toured the villages and
hamlets in the section car, at other times I depended upon my
official-issue small, noisy but reliable Francis Barnett motor
cycle. But by far the most pleasant and rewarding way of
performing my duty was to meander among the cottages and
along the lanes on foot. The seasons did not matter – every day
had its own charm, but this allowed precious time to see the
sights, smell the perfumes and hear the sounds of England's
living and ever-changing countryside. There were times when
my slow pace made me feel part of the surrounding landscape.

By comparison, the car and motor cycle were speedy and
functional as they presented the image of a busy police-officer
going about his vital work with the aid of modern technology.
The latter was in the form of an official radio fitted to both the
car and the motor cycle. The crackle of that radio, the zooming
off into the unknown to go about some urgent mission, plus the
polished livery of the police vehicles with the occasional flash of
blue light or sound of a multi-tone horn, served to nurture an
essential aura of efficiency and style.

Early morning patrols by car or motor cycle were generally
spent in the eternal search for cups of tea, people to talk to and

5

the occasional evidence of criminal activity of the rural kind. If I am to be honest, our missions were seldom urgent, unless executed in response to a traffic accident; the truth is that those pastoral wanderings enabled us to see a great deal of the changing landscape and the people who lived and worked there. The car, but more often the motor cycle, carried me through the hills and valleys, across the moors and dales, past ruined abbeys and crumbling castles and along the highways and byways, invariably on a route which had been pre-arranged by a nameless senior officer.

In fixing our routes, he would try to incorporate several villages and hamlets within, say, a three or four hour patrol, where we halted hourly in nominated villages. There we had to stand beside the telephone kiosk in case we were required. Someone in the office would ring us on those telephones if necessary. The fact that we were equipped with radios did not change that ancient routine because hourly points at telephone kiosks had been a feature of rural patrolling for generations. The system could not be abandoned simply because we now had radios! Senior police officers do tend to be belt-and-braces types, especially where their patrolling subordinates are concerned.

In my rural bobbying days, they liked to know what their village constables were doing at every moment of their working lives. It was an admirable method of stifling initiative but it also revealed their lack of confidence in themselves and a corresponding lack of trust in us. Nonetheless, the system did ensure that every tiny hamlet, as well as the more populated areas, received a regular visit from a uniformed officer, particularly at odd hours of day and night. As a piece of positive policing, they were valueless but they did keep our supervisory officers content in the belief that they had us just where they wanted us. And the public did see us going about our endless missions and probably wondered why we were passing at such peculiar times when nothing had happened.

But from my point of view, I did enjoy the early morning routes, as we called them, especially in the spring and summer, even if I had to drag myself out of bed at 5 a.m. at least once a week. But when the sun was shining, the birds were singing and the air was redolent with the scents of new blossom, it provided experiences I would not have missed for the world. I saw nature and the countryside at its beautiful best and the freshness of the morning made me glad to be alive and to be working in such amenable surroundings. To patrol with an accompaniment of the fabulous dawn chorus; to see young animals and birds enjoying their first taste of life and to hear the season's first cuckoo never ceased to thrill.

But even in such bucolic circumstances, it's nice to dodge the official system. As I started those routes from my hilltop police house at Aidensfield, I did so in the happy knowledge that there were several calling places on my patch. There I could enjoy a break from the routine or a spot of refreshment and human companionship. Farms and bakeries provided early morning buns and cups of tea which were most welcome during a tour of duty. In addition, the tiny police station at Ashfordly also provided sanctuary.

So far as Ashfordly Police Station was concerned, I had to be very careful; like all my rural colleagues, I had to enter without the resident sergeant hearing me, because if Sergeant Blaketon was woken by one of his tea-seeking constables, he would rapidly and effectively make his displeasure known and we would thereafter be denied that calling place.

For an erring constable, life would be hell for a short time thereafter, and so we all adopted a simple technique. We would park our motor bikes some distance away and walk to the police station. This silent approach was most effective. After 6.30 a.m. however, the doors were open because that's when Polly, the station cleaner, arrived. Approaching sixty-five, she was iron-haired with grey eyes and the clean, fresh complexion of a countrywoman. She fussed over our little station as if it was her own immaculate home; she polished the furniture and brass-work; she cleaned out the fireplace; emptied waste-paper baskets and, if the cells had been occupied, she cleaned them and aired the blankets. And if Alwyn's chrysanthemums were in the cells, she would make sure they were tended.

Polly's strength lay in the fact that when one of the rural constables was performing an early morning route, she knew he was abroad because she could decipher the contents of the duty sheet. Knowing he'd love a cup of tea, she always had the kettle ready.

This little ritual meant that at some stage between 6.30 a.m. and 7.30 a.m. (when Sergeant Blaketon usually left his bed), Polly would put the kettle on and brew a pot of hot tea, as a result of which the early patrolling constable would pay a visit to the police station. There he would enjoy tea, biscuits and a chat with Polly. If Sergeant Blaketon happened to wake early to try and catch us, Polly would hear him moving upstairs and would stand her mop in the front porch as a warning that Blaketon was likely to appear. This was the signal for us to head into the lanes of Ryedale and to the next kiosk on our agenda, thirsty but devoid of any slanderous criticism from our supervisory officer.

Sometimes, though, Sergeant Blaketon would surprise everyone by creeping downstairs in his slippers. To cope with that eventuality, we always carried some reports or papers which provided us with an excuse for being indoors. 'I've just popped in with these papers, Sergeant,' would be our excuse, at which he would retort, 'Well, don't hang about here, stopping Polly from working and don't loiter when on duty!'

But by and large, those many little subterfuges worked to our advantage. The police office at Ashfordly became a regular haven of refuge, one which was particularly welcome during winter patrols. During those dark and chilly mornings, when our fingers, toes and ears were frozen, Polly always had a blazing fire and her splendid cups of tea to warm us. But through every spring, summer, autumn and winter for years, Polly had been there with her fire, her cups of tea, her awareness of the sergeant's movements and, in times of need, her warning mop at the door.

Then a crisis came to Ashfordly Police Station.

Polly retired.

We made a fuss over her departure and had a farewell party in one of the local pubs. Sergeant Blaketon made a nice speech and presented her with a portable radio we had bought for her.

That we missed Polly was never in doubt, but for a few idyllic days afterwards, we did honestly believe we could encourage any new cleaner to be as thoughtful and accommodating as Polly. But Sergeant Blaketon had quietly made his own decision about the kind of person who would be suitable for the appointment and we were to learn to our sorrow that his ideas did not correspond with ours.

My first encounter with the new cleaner came that April. The appointment had been made only days before and upon my first tour of duty afterwards, I was performing one of those early morning routes. I had started at 5.30 a.m. from my police house at Aidensfield, and had made my first point at Elsinby at 6.05 a.m. with my second at Briggsby at 6.35 a.m. As Ashfordly lay only a five minute ride from Briggsby, there was time for a quick visit to the police station before my 7.05 a.m. liaison with another in my allotted chain of telephone kiosks.

If my colleagues had done their work efficiently, the new cleaner would have lit the fire; the kettle would be boiling and it would be known that a lonely, patrolling constable was in need of tea, warmth and amiable companionship.

As I made my lonely vigil outside Briggsby's kiosk, I wallowed in anticipation of a hot cup of tea. The early spring morning was, in Yorkshire terms, 'nobbut a fresh 'un', the real meaning of that description being that the morning was extremely cold. Indeed it was, for April can produce some very chilly northern mornings; it can also produce some memorable April showers, and in both achievements it excelled itself that morning.

As I stood shivering beside my motor cycle with the cheerful singing birds for companionship, I wondered momentarily whether I was in the right job. After all, other folks were still in bed or had warm cars to carry them about their work. As I pondered upon the unfairness of a constable's life, the heavens opened.

In a matter of minutes, the beautiful blue morning sky had been obliterated by a mass of swiftly moving black clouds, some with delightful silvery edges. As they succeeded in shutting out the rising sun, they opened their taps. Huge dollops of heavy rain lashed the earth from that sombre ceiling and in seconds, the roads and fields were awash with urgently rushing water and dancing raindrops. In seconds, brown rivulets were gushing from the fields and roaring along the lanes.

In my heavy motor cycling gear, I was reasonably prepared

for most kinds of weather, but on this occasion, water ran down my neck and into my boots as the pounding rain bounced off my helmet and battered my face which was already sore from the effects of a chill morning breeze. The downpour persisted for several minutes, then the monstrous black clouds moved to a new venue upon their journey of misery and the sun came out.

Brilliant and warm, it caused the roads to dry a little and the birds to resume their singing. As I climbed aboard my motor bike little clouds of steam began to rise from the tarmac, but as I kicked the bike into life, I wondered if the rain had waterlogged the electrical essentials. But it started without any trouble and I chugged over the hills to enjoy the dramatic vista as I dropped into Ashfordly. As I motored sedately into the valley, I could see the beautiful effects of that awesome shower – the glistening pools in the fields as they reflected the morning sun; the patches of rising mist as the water evaporated in the bright coolness of that day; the sheer greenery of the panorama before me and the freshness of the new spring colours. It was as if the landscape had had its morning bath.

But I was cold as the pervading dampness soaked into my clothes beneath my motor cycle suit. The one salvation was that a few minutes drying out before the lovely fire in Ashfordly Police Station would cure that problem. On the final run-in, I drove through some running rivulets, some lingering pools of muddy residue which the downpour had produced. Very soon, my boots, legs and machine were spattered with mud.

When I arrived at the police station, therefore, I was soaked externally with the mud and residue of the roads, and internally with rain that had flowed down my neck. I coasted the final few yards to avoid arousing Sergeant Blaketon and having parked the little motor bike, I switched off the radio. With visions of hot tea before me, I prepared to enter the warm office.

I was surprised when a powerful voice bellowed 'Out!' It was a voice I did not recognize.

I stood for a moment in the porch, stamping my feet on the doormat and I must admit that I did not immediately connect the voice with my arrival. I continued to stamp in an effort to shake off the surplus water and then the inner door opened.

I was confronted by a short, thick-set fellow with a bull-like neck and cropped hair. It was still black but shaven so close that it looked like a well-worn black lead brush. Two piercing grey eyes stared at me from the depths of the heavy, pale features of a man dressed in a long, brown dust-coat. He'd be in his middle fifties, I guessed, and was only some 5 feet 5 inches tall. But he looked and behaved like a bulldog.

'Out!' he ordered. 'Get out of here!'

I stood my ground, still shaking off the after-effects of that shower. 'Who are you?' I demanded. 'You can't tell me to get out. I'm not even in yet!'

'And you're not coming in, not like that. I've cleaned the floor, I'm not having muck dropped and paddled all over. Taken me hours to get it something like, it has, so clear off.'

'Who are you?' I asked again, having stopped shaking off the water as he stood in the centre of the doorway to effectively block my entry. It would require a strong physical action to shift him, I reckoned.

'Forster. Jack Forster, I'm the new caretaker.'

'Caretaker? Cleaner, you mean.'

'Caretaker,' he affirmed. 'I takes care of this police station, so I'm a caretaker. Now, if you want to come in, you'll have to go into the garage and get rid of that mucky suit. Leave it there to dry off and make sure your feet are clean. I'm not having you lot messing up my floors. So you and your mates can all get that into your heads right from the start. I don't clean floors so that folks can muck 'em up again.'

'I'm soaked, I want to dry myself in front of the fire,' I said. I wanted to see if there was any compassion in that squat, powerful frame.

There wasn't.

'Not here,' he continued to block the doorway. 'Yon fire's not lit. I'm not lighting that fire while I'm working, it makes me too hot when I'm polishing. It's laid, but I'm not lighting it today. So you've no need to come in, have you?'

'I've got some official business to conduct,' I said. 'Telephone calls to make, reports to read. I'm on duty,' and I stepped up towards the door, but he stood his ground, determined.

'Then take them mucky clothes off,' he said. 'Otherwise, I'll get Sergeant Blaketon to issue an order saying no motor bike

11

suits allowed in here. I'm not having my floors messed up, no way. Look at you mud, water, muck everywhere!'

I was in a momentary dilemma. He had no right to bar an officer from his own police station, but I was acutely aware that if I physically moved him aside, he might lodge a complaint. He seemed the kind of person who might claim he'd been assaulted by a policeman. Time and time again in police circles, we met cleaners and similar operatives who used their mundane tasks as a source of petty power over others; cooks, cleaners, domestics, car washers there was always one who lusted after power and who liked to exercise his or her own brand of dominion over others. This man was of that breed, and the fellow was here, in Ashfordly, blocking my route into the office.

If I ignored his demands, he would, without any shadow of doubt, run to Sergeant Blaketon. He would then take great delight in banning us from using the office as a refuge and tea-room. This meant that I had the future welfare of myself and my colleagues to rapidly consider as I stood dripping before this little Hitler. The options flashed through my mind as I watered the floor of the outer porch. Already, I had created a distinctive pool of mud.

But as I swiftly considered the alternatives, I concluded that, under no circumstances, must a trumped-up cleaner be allowed to succeed in banning me or my colleagues from the station. That fact must be established immediately.

I was tempted to use bad language to express my views, but realized this could also be used as ammunition when this fellow made his inevitable complaint to Sergeant Blaketon.

'Mr Forster, by standing there, you are obstructing a police-officer in the execution of his duty,' I said with as much pomposity as I could muster, and thrust him aside as I pushed into the office. I don't think that accusation would have convinced a court, but my action took him by surprise. Any threat of greater authority, I knew, would compel him to retreat. He did, but he was not finished.

'You'll regret this, you'll be disciplined!' he began to shout as he backed into the office. 'I'll have Sergeant Blaketon informed of this, so help me!'

Once inside, I made a great show of ringing up Divisional

Headquarters, reading circulars, checking my in-tray, reading notices and generally doing all the routine chores which were expected during a formal visit of this kind. And all the time I dripped mud and water along my circuitous route across Forster's floor. I felt some guilt but justified my conduct because of his uncompromising attitude. He followed me around, red-faced and angry, fuming at the mess I was leaving in my wake, and threatening all manner of actions from my superior officers. I decided not to stay for tea. The atmosphere was not conducive to a relaxing visit, and the fire was unlit anyway. It was laid out with regimental accuracy with the fire-irons arranged in sequence upon the hearth and the coal heaped neatly upon the paper and sticks. Those portions of the clean floor gleamed like polished silver. I was reminded of my days in the RAF, doing National Service, when we polished the floors of our billets to such a standard that no one dare walk on them. We moved around by sliding on little mats made from old blankets, one to each foot.

That ensured the floor was always polished and saved us lots of time on Bull Night. Now, this floor was heading that way. But, having messed it severely, I left. I found a welcoming bakery where I warmed myself as I enjoyed a nice bun and a mug of hot tea, and soon I was glowing amid the scents of newly-baked bread and cakes.

Later, I discovered that Forster had complained to Sergeant Blaketon. To give the sergeant some credit, he had not spoken to me about the affair of the muddy visit which perhaps revealed something of his disdain for the nature of the grumble, but he did resort to his normal tactic – he displayed a typed instruction on the police station notice-board. Each of us had to read and initial it.

Sergeant Blaketon was prone to issuing typed instructions through the medium of the station notice-board. We learned that the degree of his anger was reflected in the method of typing – a notice produced in black lower case type was routine. This might embrace matters like holiday dates, special duty commitments and so on. A black notice in upper case type was more important – that could include warnings not to use the office telephone for private calls or to make sure our monthly returns were submitted on time.

A notice typed in red was rather more serious. If it was in lower case red type, it was of considerable import – such as 'Members will refrain from revving up their motorcycles outside the station at 2 a.m.' or 'Members *will* repeat *will* study all Force Orders and *will* repeat *will* initial each copy when it has been perused.'

We were never instructed to 'read' papers and documents – always, we had to *peruse* them, and we were always classified as 'members' in Sergeant Blaketon's vocabulary. I never did find out of what we were members.

But a very important notice was always typed in red upper case letters. For example, 'MEMBERS WILL STUDY THE ACCOMPANYING PHOTOGRAPH OF THE CHIEF CONSTABLE AND WILL ACKNOWLEDGE HIM IN THE STREET BY SALUTING' or 'MEMBERS WILL *NOT* REPEAT *NOT* USE OFFICIAL VEHICLES FOR COLLECTING GROCERIES OR FISH AND CHIPS.'

After my first meeting with Jack Forster, therefore, an instruction did appear on the station notice-board. In lower case red type, it said, 'Members will take every care to keep the police office clean and tidy at all times and should not enter in soiled motor cycle protective clothing unless unavoidable owing to the exigencies of duty.'

The 'exigencies of duty' was a marvellous phrase for making exceptions to most rules, and when this notice appeared, the story of my meeting with Forster became widely known. So did the reason for the appearance of this order, and from that time forward, we discovered more of his tactics. He objected to smokers putting cigarette-ends in ashtrays; he disliked tea or coffee cups being left unwashed; he objected to paper containing crumbs of food being placed in the waste-bins; he wanted all lights switched off when the office was empty; he objected to out-of-date posters being left on the notice-board and apple cores on the mantelshelf.

In fact, he objected to everything and everyone. He seemed to have a passion for cutting official expenditure which probably explained his unwillingness to light the fire, his passion for switching off lights and his theory that much of the paperwork in the office was not necessary. I think he based this judgement upon the amount of waste paper which accumulated in the waste-bins. The outcome of his arrival was that the office *did* remain clean and tidy, chiefly because we rarely went in. There was no longer any pleasure in visiting our little section headquarters and the result was that the lanes around Ashfordly were very regularly patrolled. We made very frequent visits to establishments like hotels and bakeries which offered warmth and occasional refreshment, and we also made use of each other's homes.

In one sense, the social life of our happy little section was enhanced because we saw more of each other and of each other's families, but it was clear that Sergeant Blaketon was growing concerned about our unwillingness to make regular visits to the office. To circulate our paperwork, we tended to rely upon his visits to us, rather than our visits to him. To counter this, he compiled an instruction, in red lower case type, about the matter.

It read, 'Rural members *will* repeat *will* visit the Sectional Office at Ashfordly at least once during each tour of duty. It is essential that all members keep up to date with correspondence, local procedures, new legislation, Force orders and internal instructions. This instruction is effective immediately.'

And we all had to initial it and comply. Thereafter, we made these token visits to collect our mail and to obey Sergeant Blaketon's order, although most of us managed to make our visits when Jack Forster, whom we nicknamed Jack Frost because of his chilly nature, had completed his daily stint. He worked from 6.30 a.m. until 9.30 a.m. each morning consequently avoidance was not difficult, except when working an early route.

But overall, the effect of his presence could not be ignored. We moved around the clean, tidy office as if it was a showroom of some kind, hardly daring to touch the furniture or leave footprints on the floor. We cursed Jack for his cussedness, and we cursed Sergeant Blaketon for engaging him. I must admit that I often wondered whether poor old Blaketon had really foreseen what the outcome of Forster's appointment would be.

Some of us did try discreetly to frustrate or annoy Jack. We did paddle upon his floors; we did leave waste paper lying about; we did spill tea or coffee from our flasks and we did make the office look as if it was a place of work and not a disused museum.

But the real punishment for Jack arrived late one night; it was something that could never have been planned and it was doubly pleasing because it could be logged under that wonderful heading 'Exigencies of duty'. I was pleased too, because I was the officer involved. I felt that some kind of poetic justice had descended upon Jack Frost.

It so happened that I was not working one of those motor cycle routes, but was performing a full tour of night duty in Ashfordly. A complete week of night duty came around every six months or so, when we worked from 10 p.m. until 6 a.m. the following morning.

I was patrolling on foot in the outskirts of Ashfordly. It was 1.30 a.m. and I was looking forward to my meal break which was scheduled for 2 a.m. I would take that break in Ashfordly Police Station, careful not to dirty the place because of Jack's ferocious responses.

During patrols of that nature, we kept our eyes open for villains and villainy of every kind, from drunken drivers to car thieves, from burglars to cattle thieves, from runaways to tearaways. So when I saw a small, rusty Morris pick-up inching slowly along Brantsford Back Lane without any lights, my suspicions were immediately aroused. It was moving jerkily and rather noisily towards me, and so I decided to investigate.

My first job was to halt it so I stepped into the lane and flashed my powerful torch at the vehicle, waving it up and down in the manner then used to halt motor vehicles.

Always wary that vehicles of this condition might not have brakes, it was unwise to stand right in front of them. The procedure was to keep clear as they came to a halt, and then move in to continue the investigation. But there were no problems as the slow-moving pick-up came to a halt with my torch shining into the driving-seat.

The driver, a thin-faced individual with thick, dirty hair, looked pale and ill and he awaited me with a suggestion of resignation on his face. I opened the driver's door, removed the keys from the ignition switch and said, as all policemen do, 'Now then, what's going on here?'

'Summat's gone wrong wi' t'electrics,' he said in a hoarse whisper. 'Sorry, Officer. Ah know Ah shouldn't have drove, but Ah had ti git 'ome . . . '

At that point, there was a tremendous rumpus in the rear and some heavy object caused the pick-up to rock and sway, so I hurried to the back. A massive pig, a Large White sow, was struggling to climb over the tailboard, and as I reached the back, she half-tumbled, half-climbed from the vehicle into the road. Fortunately, she did not gallop off; judging by her massive size she would have difficulty even in walking, so she stood close to the vehicle, snuffling around the rear wheels. I saw that she had a rope attached to one leg but there was no way I could get her back into that vehicle. He must have had a ramp of some kind for her to climb up.

It was then that the contents of a crime circular of some weeks ago echoed in the recesses of my mind. There'd been regular thefts of livestock in the area over a period of months and some livestock owners had reported seeing a small, darkened vehicle leaving the scene late at night . . .

I grabbed the end of the rope and clung to it, then said, 'This pig. Is it yours?'

The fellow in the pick-up made a non-committal response. I followed with a request for his name and address, and asked where he had obtained the pig. He produced more non-committal and indecipherable replies.

'Come along, out you get,' I said. 'Leave the van here. We'll talk about this at the police station.'

'No, Officer, Ah can explain . . . '

'In the police station!' I had made up my mind to question this fellow in the security of the station. The van was in a quiet lane, and was parked on the verge where it was not a danger to other traffic. After noting its make, size, colour and registration number, I discovered it was not taxed either. There'd be a catalogue of traffic offences here, so I seized the driver's arm with one hand and kept the pig's rope in the other. 'Police station!' I said as I guided man and pig towards Jack Forster's shining palace.

The fellow shuffled along, sometimes groaning and sometimes uttering words which I did not understand. I jollied the huge sow along the road by slapping her ample back from time to time as she waddled contentedly through the streets. She was clearly domesticated and seemed unflustered by this turn of events.

Sometimes, she would stop for a snuffle in the hedge bottoms but she was no real trouble. Her companion was no trouble either as he walked, with some support from me, towards the station.

Sergeant Blaketon was having a day off, so I knew I must not arouse him. I told my captive to hang on to the pig's rope, which he did, as I unlocked the door of the office. As I switched on the light, the big sow hurried inside, dragging the man with her, and I followed, closing and locking the door for security.

'Has thoo arrested me?' was the man's first question as the lock went home.

'Yes,' I said, for I did not want him to leave. Had I said, 'No, you are just helping with enquiries,' he might have decided not to assist with the many enquiries I must make.

'What for?' he asked.

'Suspicion of stealing that pig,' I said. 'So where did you get it?'

He sighed. 'Aye, all right, Ah took it. From a sty ovver Brantsford way. Don't know whose. If that truck o' mine hadn't brokken . . . '

I cautioned him and wrote his admission in my notebook, then obtained his name and address, age and occupation. He was Cecil Matthews of 56 Roselands Road, Ashfordly, forty-three years old and a general dealer. Having checked this, I said, 'Right, I'll have to get a sergeant to see you. So it's the cells for you and for that animal!'

I searched him, listed his belongings and placed him in Cell No 1, and then, by putting on the light of Cell No 2, persuaded the waddling, grunting sow to go in there. She seemed to like places that were well-illuminated because she went straight in. It was the Female Cell anyway, which I felt was appropriate, although it was very bare now that it did not house Alwyn Foxton's chrysanthemums. He was replenishing his stock, I

18

think. Having locked up my two prisoners, I rang Eltering Police to contact the duty sergeant.

It was now after 2 a.m. I told my story and he said he'd come immediately. I made a cup of tea and took some in for my prisoner, then settled down for my break. I had sandwiches, a piece of cake, an apple and a cup of tea, then Sergeant Bairstow arrived.

'Now, Nicholas old son. Where's the prisoner?'

'In the cells,' I said. 'He's admitted pinching the pig. I got a voluntary out of him. He can't remember whose it is, but it's from somewhere near Brantsford.'

'Ah! A nice easy cough then? Good for you. Right, I'll have words with him, then I'll charge him and bail him out from six o'clock. You stay here in the office until six, and then send him home. I'll bail him to Eltering Court for next Friday.'

'Right, Sergeant.'

'And the pig? Where is it?'

'In No 2 cell, Sergeant,' I said. 'There was nowhere else . . . '

'The van? Why not leave it where it was?' he cried.

'It got out,' I explained. 'And there's no way to get it back in. It's docile enough . . . '

'Right, the minute somebody comes on duty at Brantsford, get them to find out whose it is, and have the bloody thing collected. We can't keep pigs in the cells . . . '

'Yes, Sergeant.'

And so the official procedures for prosecuting Cecil Matthews were put into action. Sergeant Bairstow dealt with him kindly but firmly, and then we placed him back in the cell until six o'clock. Sergeant Bairstow departed about three o'clock, leaving me in the office until my relief came on duty at six.

Each half-hour I peeped into the prisoner's cell to check that he was safe, but around four-thirty, he started to produce some ghastly noises. He began calling for help. I went in, wary that it might be a trick of some kind, but it was clear that the man was ill. Beads of perspiration stood out on his forehead and his face was a dull, pasty green colour; he was holding his stomach and was doubled up with pain.

I rushed to the telephone and dialled for Doctor Williams for I had no wish to have a man die while in my custody. After explaining the problem, he said he would come immediately, in spite of the hour. When he arrived only minutes later, a dour, heavy man, I showed him into the cell; he recognized Cecil and after a brief examination, said in his lilting Welsh voice, 'Stomach trouble, Constable, it is.'

'Is it serious?' I was genuinely worried.

'Not so that it will kill him, you know, but he'll be very ill for a while. Gastric troubles, of long standing they are. Now, I have something in my bag which might be of help . . . leave him to me . . . '

I left the cell, glad to be away from the suffering man, but I then became aware of more awful noises, this time from the adjoining cell. Screeching, heavy snufflings and gruntings, painful cries. I hurried to the door, but was unable to open it. When I slid back the inspection hatch, I could see that the huge sow was lying against the door, holding it shut as she uttered the most pained and piercing of cries. It sounded like many pigs in distress.

I was in two minds whether to ask the doctor for advice, but felt he might be offended; even so her cries were agonizing and so I decided to call the vet. Not giving me time to explain the somewhat unusual story, he said he would come immediately.

When he arrived, he made an initial examination through the inspection hatch and smiled.

'She's farrowing, giving birth,' he said. 'Soon, the place will be full of little pigs . . . '

I groaned. 'How many?' was all I could ask.

'Ten or twelve perhaps. She's a Large White, so she'll have a lot. Large Whites always do, Constable. Some achieve twenty a farrow. Yours is she?'

I explained in detail how she came to be here, and he laughed. 'Well, there's a bonus for the loser. He's lost one and will gain many. Now, if you don't mind, I'll hang on until she's produced them all, just in case there are complications. She'll roll clear of that door sooner or later, maybe to have a drink from that loo in the corner of the cell.'

'Will you have a cup of tea?' I offered him.

'Love one,' he said. 'Three sugars.'

I went off to make a cup of tea, and when I returned, I found Doctor Williams having a hearty laugh with the vet, a man called Harvey. We sat and discussed the patients, Doctor Williams saying that Cecil's stomach would result in him being sick all over the cell along with some uncontrollable diarrhoea, and the condition would persist until his gastric trouble had eased. Mr Harvey said the pig would make a mess too, what with giving birth and exercising her bowels . . .

And as I sat there, I wondered what Jack Forster would make of it all when he arrived at half past six. But I was off duty at six. I decided not to wash the cups either.

2

When I was at home, I was in a better place
But travellers must be content.

William Shakespeare, 1564–1616

Having been compelled to spend more time patrolling the lanes
around Aidensfield and Ashfordly, it was inevitable that I
should become more deeply acquainted with Arnold Merryweather's rattling old buses. In their faded purple and cream
livery, the pair of them were a familiar sight in Ryedale. They
provided a vital means of transport and an equally valuable
method of communication for many of the villagers. Those
without cars relied upon Arnold's buses to carry them to work
or to the shops or merely on visits to relatives and friends; it was
impossible to envisage a contented rural life without the service
that Arnold provided.

His buses were never off the road, a fact which meant that on
several occasions, I had to speak to Arnold about the condition
of his vehicles. In his rustic and carefree way, he managed to
ignore the laws which governed the operation of passenger
vehicles. He seemed to think that the laws which applied to
large companies and city transport did not apply to his little
business.

He would use the aged buses as delivery vehicles and would
carry parcels, goods and even livestock to market; I've even
known him use a bus as a breakdown vehicle. Because they were
always in use, their maintenance became somewhat suspect. In
addition, his willingness to help others often led to him flouting
or even breaking the law. Never did I prosecute him, although I

found it necessary to constantly remind him of his statutory responsibilities. And, in his own way, he did try.

'Aye, Mr Rhea, Ah'll see to it,' he would say. 'One o' these days, Ah'll get it fixed' or 'Ah'll get Hannah to make sure it doesn't happen again.'

But he seldom did get it fixed, whatever it was, and he relied on Hannah, his huge conductress, to exercise her own judgement over the events which occurred on board the service bus.

Miss Hannah Pybus, with her loud voice, masculine appearance and authoritative manner, kept order and, in her own way, helped Arnold's business to thrive. Unattractive though she was, there was always a hint of romance between Hannah and her boss. Thick-set Arnold, with his mop of ginger hair now greying slightly as he progressed towards his sixties, seemed an ideal partner for the tall and equally thick-set Hannah. Her heavily-freckled face and mop of sandy hair complemented his features and even if she did walk along his aisles with the swaying gait of a sailor, we all knew there was some attraction between them.

But their romance never blossomed. I think this was because Arnold spent all his working days either behind the wheel or in the depot in Ashfordly effecting repairs. In addition, his limited leisure time was spent in the Brewer's Arms telling Irish bus jokes and drinking Guinness.

His only contact with Hannah was on board his bus. After work, she would mount her trusty cycle to ride home to Thackerston. Occasionally if the weather was bad, Arnold would place her cycle in the bus and take her home, but he never went in. He never took her to a restaurant, the theatre or cinema, or even to the local pubs. One reason was that his only mode of transport was his bus! Hannah would say, 'If you think you're taking me to the pictures in that, you've another think coming!' The result was that not once, to my knowledge, did Arnold enjoy a social outing with the formidable Hannah.

For those who have not been introduced to Arnold's bus service through my *Constable around the Village*, he operated along the picturesque lanes and through the pretty villages between Ashfordly and York. Each day, one of his groaning coaches, furnished with wooden seats bolted on iron frames would leave at 7.30 a.m. and weave its slow way through Briggsby, Aidensfield, Elsinby and beyond until it arrived in York.

It made a return journey, and then a second trip from Ashfordly to York, making a final return trip at 5.15 p.m. On Fridays, Arnold's other bus made a special run to Galtreford because it was market day and lots of rural folk regarded that as a day out.

During these runs, Arnold carried the village workers into the city where he did bits of shopping and ran errands for those who could not make the journey. He collected eggs *en route*, delivered laundry, and performed a whole series of useful deeds, many of which probably infringed the various laws which governed the use of public service vehicles.

Arnold's helpfulness is illustrated in an incident in which he came to the aid of the constabulary. The same incident also highlights the importance of a village policeman's knowledge of his patch and the things that occur on it. In this case, that knowledge involved the route, timing, halting places and general *modus operandi* of Arnold's bus service.

Just after eight o'clock one Wednesday morning, I received a frantic telephone call from Abraham Godwin, an animal feeds salesman who lived in Aidensfield.

'Mr Rhea,' he panted into the mouthpice, 'my car's been stolen, just now. Less than a minute ago . . .'

The urgency of his voice propelled me into action, although I had just got out of bed, having worked until two o'clock that same morning. I was not feeling on top of the world. In less urgent circumstances, I would have adopted the well-proven procedures of having details of the car immediately circulated to all our patrols. I'd have then recorded the details in a statement before filing the event in the criminal records and stats. files. It would rest upon some other distant police officer to locate the vehicle when eventually it was abandoned.

But as the thief had just struck, it didn't make sense to follow the normal procedures. With only a minute's start, it might be possible to catch the villain.

I'm sure that thought was also in Godwin's mind.

'Which way did it go?' I asked.

'Towards Elsinby. The thief's dumped another in my drive, Mr Rhea, an old Ford,' he panted.

'Right, what's your car number?' I asked.

'DVN 656C,' he said. 'A red Hillman . . . you know it.'

'I do, but my colleagues don't. So,' I said, 'I'll come to see you soon, but I've work to do right now if we're to catch him.'

And I slammed down the telephone. I knew it was utterly futile dressing in my motor cycle gear to give chase. That would take several minutes. In the meantime, the stolen car, especially if driven by a thief, would be racing away and I would never catch it. It was time for immediate, albeit unorthodox, action.

I looked at my watch. It was five minutes past eight and I knew that Arnold's bus would be trundling towards York. If I was right about the habits of an opportunist car thief, he would also be heading for the city, either to vanish there or to steal another car to continue his journey. The fact he'd dumped one in Godwin's drive suggested he was hitching lifts through the countryside by stealing a succession of available cars.

I looked at my map. I tried to recall the day I'd once used Arnold's bus on its circuitous journey into York and reckoned his bus would, at any moment, be calling at Hollin Heights Farm.

He called regularly to collect a load of eggs and actually took the bus into the farmyard to do so. I rang Jim Harker, the farmer, and he answered.

'It's PC Rhea,' I said. 'Has Arnold's bus got to your spot yet?'

'Just coming doon oor lane, Mr Rhea.'

'It's urgent that I speak to him,' I tried to stress the urgency of this call, but I knew old Jim Harker could not rush. That was something he found impossible.

'Ah'll tell him,' said Jim, and I heard the handset being placed on a hard surface. I could only wait. But surprisingly, only a minute or so passed before someone picked it up.

'Merryweather,' said the voice.

'Arnold,' the relief must have been evident in my voice. 'It's PC Rhea. I need help.'

'Fire away, Mr Rhea, Ah've time to listen while they're loading t'eggs.'

Once before, I'd advised Arnold not to carry loads of eggs on his bus because it was illegal but there was no time to worry about that. I explained that Godwin had just had his car stolen and that it seemed to be heading towards York. I began to describe it, but Arnold said, 'I know it, Mr Rhea, that red Hillman.'

'I wondered if you could halt it, Arnold,' I said. 'I know there might be a risk, but if . . . '

'If that car comes up behind me, Mr Rhea, Ah'll stop him. Then Ah'll call you,' and the phone was replaced.

It was a long shot, but it might work. I now made the necessary formal circulation of the stolen car's particulars by ringing our Control Room and Divisional Headquarters. I arranged for the CID to visit Godwin's home to examine and fingerprint the dumped vehicle and executed all the formalities that were associated with a reported crime.

Having done this, I hurried down to Godwin's house, explaining to Mary that if Arnold rang, she should contact me there. To save time, I drove down in my own private car. Godwin, extremely upset at the audacity of the thief, was still in a state of anxiety, but I suggested he take me into the kitchen where I asked his wife to brew some coffee. The performance of a mundane domestic chore often removes a good deal of tension; besides, I hadn't had my breakfast.

Godwin explained that after starting his car, he had driven it on to his forecourt where he had left the engine running to warm thoroughly. After locking the garage, he'd gone into the house to collect his briefcase and papers. While doing that, a strange car had entered in his drive and driven on to the lawn. A slim youth in his early twenties and dressed in a pale green sweater and jeans, had then jumped out and had got straight into the waiting Hillman. Then he'd driven off at speed towards Elsinby and York. For sheer cheek and opportunism, this theft was almost unique.

It took me a while to complete the necessary crime report forms. I required the engine and chassis numbers in addition to the more obvious details, and explained it was necessary if the car was altered or broken up; parts of it might still be identifiable and for that reason, our C.10 Branch, the stolen car experts, would need those kind of details.

I made a rapid examination of the dumped and ancient Ford,

noted its number on Godwin's phone, rang the details to Control Room. Efforts would be made to trace its owner and the source of the theft, if indeed it had been stolen. All this took about three-quarters of an hour, and then the telephone rang. It was Mary, slightly breathless.

'Arnold's stopped that car,' she said. 'He rang from Woodland Hall, that's about a mile the other side of Craydale. He's got your thief; he's at the entrance to the Hall. He says can you go straight away, so he isn't too late into York?'

Godwin beamed with pleasure at the news, but I was worried about the state of his car. Thieves have no respect for the vehicles they use so carelessly and so it was with some apprehension that I asked Godwin if he would come with me and drive his own car home. He agreed.

Twenty minutes later we arrived to be confronted by the results of Arnold's remarkable bus-driving skill. The thief had been trapped too, so my arrest was easy.

Afterwards, I learned how Arnold had contrived this. While driving his bus and its assortment of passengers out of Craydale, he'd noticed the red Hillman approaching from behind. When the speeding car was level with the rear of his bus and overtaking it, Arnold had eased over to his offside, keeping pace with the car. The car, now with a very anxious driver at the wheel, had been forced to move over and as the vehicles sped along, Arnold's mighty bus had moved still further to its wrongside. In that way, it had literally forced the stolen Hillman off the road and into a shallow ditch.

It had been trapped on one side by the high dry-stone walls of Woodland Hall and on the other by the bus. The driver had become a prisoner, and the Hillman had suffered some minor damage to the offside front mudguard.

Afterwards, I discovered that Arnold had given his passengers a running commentary to explain his odd behaviour, but as his bus had drawn to a halt beside the trapped car, a young passenger had leapt out. Quickly, he had placed two large stones from the Hall's wall behind the wheels of the car, very effectively preventing it from reversing to freedom.

The bus's position across the road meant that traffic could pass by, although some did stop to enquire if they could be of assistance at the 'accident' but Arnold had declined. And so, thanks to Arnold, we caught a car thief.

I submitted a report to the Chief Constable about Arnold's actions. In gratitude Arnold was presented with a 'thank you' letter and a helmet badge mounted on an oak plaque. The press publicized the tale too, which gave him and his coach service some useful publicity, but this was minor praise in comparison with the hero status he was awarded by the local people and regular customers.

On another occasion, Arnold used his bus as an ambulance. I happened to be using the bus at the time. It was a Tuesday.

Arnold had eased his groaning old coach to a halt outside the gate of Ridding Farm on the moors above Elsinby, where Aud Mrs Owens boarded it for her weekly trip to York market. Inevitably, Arnold and his passengers had to wait as the diminutive figure of Mrs Owens pottered up the long track laden with baskets.

That Tuesday, however, we noticed two figures making their slow and painful progress towards the bus. One was Mrs Owens and the other was her husband, Kenneth, who seldom appeared in public. His life was spent almost entirely on the farm; he had no car and no wish to see what lay beyond the boundaries of his spread. He led a life of self-sufficiency and seclusion.

As the couple approached Arnold's bus, it was evident that Kenneth was hobbling painfully.

I saw he was using a home-made crutch. It was simply a broom upturned, the head tucked under his right armpit and the shaft supporting his limping progress. His right leg, which wore a wellington boot, was held awkwardly aloft in a kind of sling which had been created by tying a length of rope about the sole and ankle of the wellington, then up and around his neck and shoulder. It kept his foot off the ground.

Kenneth's age was a matter of debate. He would be well over fifty, probably nicely into his sixties. Today, he wore some soiled corduroy trousers which bore evidence of many years of work and milking cows, and a rough, grey denim jacket, hereabouts called a kytle. A battered, flat cap decorated with a patch of cow hairs sat low upon his head and concealed most of his thin, weary face. The cow hairs were from his habit of resting his head on the flanks of the cows as he milked them.

His wife gave little support as poor old Kenneth made his slow, difficult way towards the bus. I was about to offer my help, but Mrs Owens anticipated this by calling, 'Leave him be! He'll manage best on his own.' Kenneth had a very difficult job manoeuvring himself up the steps into the coach, but with some help from Arnold and Hannah, and some cursing from his little wife, he made it and hopped into a seat. There he sank onto the wooden framework with an audible sigh of relief.

'And what's up wi' thoo, Kenneth?' asked Arnold as he slammed the bus into gear and began to guide it away.

"E fell off an haystack,' said Mrs Owens. "E reckons 'e's brokken 'is leg. 'E should 'ave been watching what 'e was doing, that's what Ah say.'

'Where are you taking him then?' It was Hannah's turn now as she hovered with her ticket-machine.

"Ospital,' was the reply.

'He can't walk from the bus station . . . ' said Hannah.

'Nay, so you can tak 'im, it's only down a few side streets,' she said. 'Tak him on t'way in,' she shouted at Arnold. 'Leave him there. Ah'll see to t'milking and t'hens tonight.'

Hannah looked at Arnold who was now in the driving-seat with his back to this little drama, but he simply said, 'Aye, right-ho.'

'So that'll be one return to York and back, and one to York only, for 'im,' Mrs Owens ordered her tickets.

'Are you leaving him?' Hannah asked.

'Might as well,' said Mrs Owens. "E's nobbut a nuisance about the spot like this, suffing and sighing from morning 'til night, and Ah shall 'ave his hens ti feed and eggs to collect, then there's t'cows to muck out and milk . . . 'e's as well off in 'ospital oot o' my road.'

The subject of this discussion sat and said nothing as he gazed out of the window of Arnold's coach, his injured leg sticking into the aisle and his broom standing like a sentinel as he clung to it.

'Do you think he's broken his leg?' Hannah asked as he spun the handle of her ticket-machine.

'Aye, Ah reckon so,' said Mrs Owens. 'There was a mighty

crack when 'e landed and his foot wobbled a bit. So Ah made 'im keep 'is welly on, and then 'e couldn't walk on it cos his foot end went all sloppy. After a day or two like that, we reckoned it was brokken. So Ah thowt we'd better get him seen to.'

'When did it happen?' asked Hannah aghast.

'Thursday or Friday last week it would be. Ah've not 'ad a day's work out of him since, so Ah thowt Ah'd better tak 'im to 'ospital.'

We overheard this curious exchange, but the placid Arnold simply drove on and collected more people along the route. In York, he diverted his bus from its journey and drove through some side streets until his bus full of people arrived at the Casualty Department of York City Hospital.

There, a repeat performance occurred as Mrs Owens, with help from several passengers, including Arnold, Hannah and myself, manipulated Kenneth and his brush off the bus. Once he was established on his feet outside, Mrs Owens pointed to a sign which announced, 'Casualty Department'.

'In there,' she ordered Kenneth and got back on to the bus.

'Aren't you staying?' asked Hannah.

'Ah am not!' said the redoubtable lady. ''E's old enough to fend for 'imself and Ah've no time to fuss over a thing like that. Ah've got work to do in town. So come on, Arnold, let's be off,' and she made her way to a seat.

Arnold hesitated for a few moments to make sure poor old Kenneth completed the short journey, but a nurse discovered him and eased his final yards into the building. Arnold then continued his journey.

On his first return trip, with Mrs Owens still somewhere in York, Arnold did make a second detour and personally called at the hospital to enquire about poor old Kenneth. He learned he had suffered a broken leg and that he would be allowed home when the doctor was satisfied the bone was healing and that the plaster cast was performing its function.

When Mrs Owens caught the bus on its second return run, she said, 'Ah'll write 'em a note, Arnold, to see 'ow 'e's getting on, and when 'e's fit to come 'ome, mebbe you'll call and pick 'im up?'

'Right,' said Arnold, not wishing to cause a flutter in the

Owens' household by saying an ambulance would bring home the injured farmer.

Kenneth was brought home in due course and I found him hobbling about the premises with his pot leg as he fed the pigs and mucked out the cows.

He seemed quite content and said very little about his sojourn into city life. I realized that country folk like Kenneth and his wife were so self-reliant that they rarely ever asked anyone for help. If they wanted something doing, they did it themselves; their method of coping with Kenneth's broken leg was an example of that independence.

Arnold's bus service, however, called at another market once a week; this time on Fridays at the small market town of Galtreford. Arnold's second coach was utilized, with a relief driver as a rule.

I heard that when this bus travelled via Galtreford, there was a good deal of wheeling, dealing, buying and selling on board before the bus actually arrived. By studying the Public Service Vehicles (Conduct of Drivers, Conductors and Passengers) Regulations 1936, I learned it was illegal to beg, sell or offer for sale any article in the vehicle . . .

But, in rural areas, one closes one's eyes to a great deal, and really, I felt, this problem was not really mine. It could be argued that the enforcement of such rules was really the responsibility of the Traffic Commissioners, not the police.

So the minor infringements continued and they helped everyone aboard to feel content and happy. In fact, a trip to Galtreford market on Arnold's bus seemed to be a very jovial and happy affair.

Judging by the accounts which came to my notice, it was more of a party than a domestic outing or a bus trip. Songs were sung, for example, and drinks were handed around, albeit never to the driver when he was behind the wheel.

My very discreet enquiries led me to believe that a trip to market was a very sociable occasion which included community singing. This was led by two Aidensfield characters nicknamed Bill and Ben. In their late forties, they were inseparable and had been pals since their schooldays. They went everywhere together. Bachelors with no regular means of financial support, they went to Galtreford market every Friday.

Their real names were Arthur Grieves and Bernard Kingston; Arthur was 'Bill' and Bernard was 'Ben'. Each lived in a small rented cottage and undertook casual work in the area. They found employment on farms at potato picking time, harvest time and hay time; they took jobs on building sites, or washed windows – in fact, they would do anything anywhere for a small fee. They always worked together and it was their unhampered life-style that allowed them the freedom to go to market each Friday.

Arthur (Bill) was the elder by a few months and had lived in Aidensfield since birth. His mother, widowed in her twenties, had reared him but had died before I was posted to this beat. He was a dour character who said very little, and whose main interests appeared to be darts and dominoes at the Brewer's Arms.

A stocky man, he had a square, weathered face with skin as tough as leather and thinning hair which encircled a tanned bald patch. In his mode of dress, he always appeared smart because he constantly wore a dark suit, a white shirt, a dark tie and black shoes, but closer examination would show that the suit was a little threadbare, the shirt could have done with washing and ironing while the tie bore evidence of several pub snacks and spilled beer. But from a distance, he looked fine.

Ben was more casual; taller than his friend by perhaps three inches, he was lean and angular, with a good head of dark, curly hair and a loping gait. Always untidy, his clothes generally seemed too wide or too long; sometimes he wore a grey suit, sometimes a pleasing sports jacket and flannels and occasionally, he would appear in casual wear such as jeans or a bright-squared shirt which made him look like a Canadian timberjack.

Ben was rarely seen without a smile on his face; he always appeared to be happy with the world, and as he lived with his aged parents, he never had to worry about cooking his own meals or washing his own clothes.

All that kind of chore was done for him, and it was perhaps the influence of his mother which explained the size of his clothes. Maybe she still treated him as a growing boy who required clothes just a fraction too large so he could grow into them. I think she failed to realize he had matured. Like Bill, he spent a lot of his time in the Brewer's Arms playing darts and dominoes.

Close as their bachelor friendship was, there was never a suggestion there was anything sinister or unsavoury in their behaviour, and no one even considered theirs was a homosexual relationship. It wasn't; they were two heterosexual men who loved a good time and who, in reality, had never grown up. Theirs was a life of casual ease with no responsibilities.

This eternally juvenile aspect of their existence had led to their outings at Galtreford market; ever since leaving school, they had made the weekly trip on Arnold's bus. Their mission was to wander around the market and then adjourn to one or other of the local pubs to sample the ale, play darts or dominoes and meet some of their acquaintances, especially those of the female sex.

When Bill and Ben got among the women, there would be banter and chatter, but nothing else; certainly no dates and no real courtships arose from these carefree meetings.

On the return journey these lads, as everyone called them in spite of their age, would lead the community singing on Arnold's bus. The more I heard about this outing, the more I thought I'd like to experience a trip to Galtreford market. I did not want to catch Arnold by identifying possible breaches of the many bus laws, but felt I'd like to experience the in-bus entertainment which seemed to cheer all those who travelled that route. I knew that singing on a bus was only illegal if it annoyed the passengers, and was sure this did not – how could it annoy if everyone joined in?

My opportunity came one Friday when I was having a day off duty. It was my long weekend. I had Friday, Saturday and Sunday off duty, a welcome sequence which came around once every seven weeks. On this date, it coincided with Mary's turn to have the local children's play-group at our house.

Several mums with tiny tots took turns in hosting a play-group; it allowed some of those harassed young ladies to take time off from their children, to enjoy a short shopping spree or to have their hair done and relax in other ways. Even though our four youngsters, aged between one and five, would make a class of their own, we both knew it was beneficial for them to mix with others of their age before starting primary school. So we joined that lively group.

On that Friday, it was made plain that if I remained at home, I'd be in the way. Because Mary might need the car to ferry home some of the visiting children, I felt the occasion presented me with an ideal opportunity to disappear by jumping onto Arnold's bus and experiencing the delights of Galtreford market.

And so, as I stood at Aidensfield bus stop at half past nine that morning, I was joined by Bill and Ben. As we waited, no one said a word and eventually others joined the little queue, including a large brown and white spaniel.

Eventually, Ben looked at me, his curiosity getting the better of him. He asked, 'Gahin ti market then, Mr Rhea?'

'Yes,' I said. 'I've heard a lot about this outing, so I thought I'd come along.'

'Then stick wiv us, Mr Rhea, we'll show you what's what, me and my mate. Do you play dominoes? We could do with a third hand.'

'You're on,' I said as Arnold's bus came into view.

The little queue clambered aboard and from the outset, it was evident that Bill and Ben had their own seat. The spaniel pushed its way through the queue and slid beneath one of the other seats from where it eyed everyone, almost as if it expected to be ejected. But it wasn't.

Bill and Ben's seat was the first one inside the door, a prime position because it allowed Ben to pass comments about everyone who entered and, if necessary, to lend a helping hand to any aged person. As there was no conductress on this bus, (Hannah had travelled into York on the other one), their help was appreciated, even when spiced with bawdy remarks.

Ben's running commentary included remarks like 'Howway, Mrs Preston, we can't hang about all day just 'cos thoo's gitten arthritis' or 'If thoo taks onny longer gittin in, Elsie, this bus'll run oot o' petrol,' or 'Now then, Phyllis, leaving t'old man again, are we? Ah'll bet 'e's chuffed about that. 'E'll have that

34

little milkmaid in ti mak 'is coffee this morning, mark my words!'

It was all part of the on-going entertainment and Ben held forth with his chatty line of banter at each stop. The driver was one of Arnold's pool of part-timers and he bore the chatter in silence as he accepted the fares and guided the old bus towards Galtreford. It pulled into the market-place, halted with a groan of brakes, and everyone, including the spaniel, spilled out on to the cobbles to go their separate ways. It was just ten-thirty.

'Now then, Mr Rhea,' said Ben, as I waited for their next move. 'What's thy plans for today?'

'I have no set plans,' I said. 'I think I'll just have a look around, and then think about something to eat.'

'Right,' said Ben, who appeared to be spokesman for both. 'Then thoo'll have a game o' dominoes with us, eh? In t'King's Head. We allus 'ave a mooch about till twelvish, and then settle in for t'day with dominoes. There's sandwiches, pork pies, pickled eggs and crisps in t'King's Head. We need a third hand, today. Thoo'll be there, eh?'

'Right,' I said, and off they went, with the spaniel trailing behind.

I wandered around the colourful open-air stalls, listening to the banter of the traders and looking at second-hand books, antiques, furniture, crockery and all the other regular offerings of this busy little market. I enjoyed a coffee in one of the pubs which turned its bar into a coffee shop on market day mornings, and in no time, the town hall clock was striking twelve.

Somewhat apprehensively, I entered the King's Head, a fine looking coaching inn just off the market-place, and spotted Bill and Ben seated at a table with the domino box already before them. Four pints stood beside it, and the spaniel lay beneath the table, apparently asleep.

'Yan o' them's yours.' At my approach, Ben indicated the beers with a wave of his hand. 'Flossie'll be here in a minute.'

'Play this game much, then, Mr Rhea?' asked Bill, eyeing the box of dominoes as he spoke.

I shook my head. 'Not a lot, we used to play at our training-school, or during break-times when we were on nights.'

'Then you do know a bit about it. We play fives and threes, threepence a knock,' Ben informed me.

'Fine,' I said.

'And it's Nick, isn't it?' Then he leaned across and whispered, 'We shan't let on thoo's a bobby, so thoo's among friends!'

'Thanks,' I said, with genuine appreciation. It would be nice, being away from my own patch and being anonymous for a while, but I did wonder who Flossie would be. Then a heavily-made up woman arrived and sat down, sipped from one of the pints, and said, 'Who's your friend, lads?'

'Nick,' said Ben. 'Pal of ours.'

'Hello Nick,' she said, and took a heavy draught. 'Right, highest for off.'

Bill upturned the box and spread the dominoes face down upon the table and he selected a six four. He had to play first. I was still wondering about Flossie who could have been any age between thirty and forty-five.

She was a brassy woman with a husky voice and very heavy make-up which was adorned with rich, red lipstick and nail varnish. But to this day, I don't know who she was or where she came from, or what she did for a living. But she could drink pints of beer with the best of the men, and I was to learn that she could play dominoes too.

As the game progressed, each of us bought at least one round of pints, and then we had a kitty to take us up to bus time. In between, we had sandwiches, pickled eggs and a pork pie each, which we shared with the spaniel, and the afternoon vanished in a haze of clicking dominoes and coins, shouts of delight, lots of spots totalling five or three or multiples thereof, and several pints of strong Yorkshire ale. Because, on market days, the pubs are open all day, we drank quite a lot.

I think I lost about six shillings and ninepence in all, but it was a very entertaining and relaxing way of spending a day. We all said farewell to Flossie, and at five-thirty returned to the bus stop, with the spaniel at our heels.

'We enjoyed that, Mr Rhea, thoo'll etti come again,' said Ben.

'It'll be a long time before I get another Friday off,' I

managed to say. 'But when I do, I'll come along. Thanks for inviting me to join your game.'

'Flossie'd die if she knew you were a bobby,' laughed Ben. 'But she's good fun.'

'Where's she from?' I asked.

'No idea,' he said. 'No idea.'

And then the bus pulled in.

'If thoo hadn't bought all them taties and carrots, Mrs Baxter, thoo'd git onto this bus a bit faster,' once more Ben launched into his commentary. 'By, Mrs Harrison, Ah'll bet thoo's spent all this week's wages on that there kettle, and I happen to know there's nowt wrang wi' that awd 'un o' yours. Ah'll bet thoo reckons yon's a bargain. But what's your Fred gahin ti say? He nivver likes spending a penny . . . he's as tight as a duck's . . . '

Bill and Ben settled on their special seat, the spaniel slid beneath another and I occupied one mid-way along the aisle. Then, as the old bus creaked away from the market, the singing started.

Led by Ben and a woman whom I did not know, it seemed that the entire complement of passengers joined in a happy programme of real sing-along songs like 'Mother Kelly's Doorstep', 'Ilkley Moor Bah't 'At', 'Maybe It's Because I'm a Londoner', 'Blaydon Races', 'Shine on Harvest Moon' and many more of that popular range. Bill and Ben produced bottles of beer from their pockets and so did several of the other passengers, women included, and a party atmosphere was rapidly generated.

The spaniel joined in by howling as some of the notes reached a high pitch, and I reckoned my own awful voice would not be condemned. So I joined in the noise too.

We would be around half-way home, when the bus eased to a halt in Pattington. As it began to brake, Bill stood up and Ben clambered down the steps.

He jumped out as the bus halted, and so did Bill; the spaniel followed and so, because I now considered myself a member of their party, I did likewise. Others followed and said their cheery goodbyes, and the bus pulled away. We watched it leave as it echoed to the sound of happy singing; by now, the Merryweather Coaches Mobile Choir were well into 'Home, Home on the Range'. As it vanished around the corner *en route* to Aidensfield and Ashfordly, Bill, Ben, myself and the dog stood on the side of the road in silence. No one said a word. I have no idea how long we remained there in our little group, but I wondered if this was part of their market day ritual.

At length, I said, 'Well, what now?'

Ben looked at Bill.

'Thoo got off,' he said. 'Why?'

'Ah didn't,' countered Bill. 'Ah just stood up to find my handkerchief. Thoo was t'one ti get off. Ah just followed.'

'Ah thought thoo was getting off!'

'And Ah thought thoo was getting off.'

'And I thought you were both getting off,' I added.

The dog wagged its tail.

'Thoo was getting ready to get off!' snapped Ben.

'Nowt o' t'sooart,' retorted Bill. 'Ah just stood up to dig deep for my handkerchief, then thoo jumped off.'

'Ah just jumped off because Ah thought thoo was gahin ti jump off . . . '

And so we stood there like three stupid charlies, the bus now weaving its ponderous way through the distant lanes as the spaniel looked at us for guidance.

'It's a long walk back to Aidensfield, Mr Rhea,' said Bill slowly, reverting to the formal mode of address now that our day was drawing to a close.

The walk home was about six miles, many furlongs of which were steep rising hills, but there was no alternative. How on earth we came to be here still seemed something of a mystery, but we started our long walk. The spaniel seemed to be enjoying this part of the day, for it frolicked in the hedgerows and along the floral verges of the long, winding lane.

'At least your dog's happy about it,' I said to Ben as we got into our stride.

'It's not my dog, Mr Rhea,' said Ben.

'Nor mine,' added Bill.

'Well, it isn't mine,' I felt I had to clarify that point. 'Whose is it?'

Ben shrugged his shoulders. 'No idea,' he said. 'But he's a

grand little chap, reet good company. He comes wiv us ivvery Friday on that bus, follows us aroond t'market and then 'as a pork pie in t'pub. He likes yon pie and comes home on t'bus as well. He nivver pays a fare, 'cos nobody claims him, but Aud Arnold doesn't mind.'

I could have inspected the spaniel's collar to determine the identity of his owner, but he was some distance ahead of us now, sniffing and fussing about the roadside vegetation. To be honest, there seemed no point in worrying about his owner – clearly, this dog was his own master, just like Bill and Ben, and he would go home in his own good time. They were three of a kind, carefree and content, with no responsibilities and no one to answer to. They went where they pleased; they did as they liked, and thoroughly enjoyed their method of existence.

I began to wonder whether I was envious of them as we strode out of Pattington. But once away from the cottages, Bill, Ben and I were subjected to the effects of the beer and desperately found ourselves having to attend to the needs of nature. We found a tall and sheltering hawthorn hedge, climbed over a five-bar into a field and stood behind that hedge like three sentinels as we watered the undergrowth to the accompanying sounds of intense relief. The spaniel joined us by cocking his leg against the gatepost.

Thus satisfied, we renewed our walk home, and had walked but half a mile when it started to rain. Instead of complaining or attempting to shelter, the happy pair began to sing 'April Showers' in the style of Al Jolson. The dog howled as they reached the higher notes and the rain intensified with every passing minute.

I was pleased no one knew me, for we must have seemed a strange quartet of men and beast. But I enjoyed walking along with this strange, happy-go-lucky trio of market-attenders; perhaps I did feel just a hint of jealousy over their carefree way of life.

As I contemplated their mode of existence, and as the increasingly heavy rain saturated my clothes and hair, I began to wonder what Mary would think when she realized I hadn't come home on the bus. A meal would be ready and she would be tired after hosting all those children, so I pondered upon her reaction when eventually I did walk into the house, weary, beery and wet.

Explanations would not be easy but I was pleased I didn't have to make my excuses to Sergeant Blaketon. I was reminded of an old piece of Yorkshire wisdom which goes, 'Being late home from t'market often spoils a good bargain.'

I lengthened my stride and joined the singing of 'April Showers'.

When other lips and other hearts
Their tales of love shall tell.

Alfred Bunn, 1796–1860

To those who have never been, North Yorkshire's image is seldom that of a land of sylvan beauty. They don't think of it as being graced by charming villages full of thatched cottages and peaceful ponds. But North Yorkshire's Ryedale, reclining on the southern edge of the North York Moors, can shatter those illusions, if indeed they lurk in the mind. For Ryedale is a valley of thatched cottages, peaceful inns and village ponds. There are charming woodland glades, ruined castles and abbeys, quiet streams and a countryside so gentle that it would be more in keeping with the south or the west of England.

One of the most photographed of England's thatched cottages is to be found here; it graces many a box of chocolates and country calendar. There are thatched inns too and many of the villages boast interesting collections of thatched homes. Some are remote and some are positioned at the side of our main roads. Some have been modernized and some have had their thatch removed, while several are the old-fashioned cruck houses.

Most are single-storied and contain oak beams which are dark with age. They derive from the early long-houses of the dales, being built with little architectural skill, but with the essentials of rural life in mind. Quite often, the family lived at one end and their livestock at the other, but these lowly homes were functional and cheap both to construct and maintain.

Cruck houses, many of which still stand, were constructed from early in medieval times until late in the seventeenth century. Pairs of oak trees were used, each pair being shorn of their branches until a tall, straight trunk remained. These were positioned with the thick portion on the ground, and the tips were then drawn together and linked with a 'ridge tree' to form a letter A. When standing upright, one or two spars were fixed to them so that the 'A' shape had two or even three crosspieces.

Several of these 'A' shapes were used, each erected some five yards from the other, and they formed the framework of the cottage. They were linked lengthwise to one another by more beams and spars. Stone walls, a flagstone floor and a thatched roof completed the building, and many of these stand today.

When I arrived at Aidensfield to occupy the hilltop police house with its lovely views of the valley, I found great delight in locating these delightful cottages. At one time, I considered making a register of them, purely for my own interest, but somehow, never found the time. Perhaps this interest in old houses coincided with a sudden interest in buying and reno-vating ancient country cottages. People everywhere wanted to buy them and occupy them, and there was a ready market for all kinds of ancient piles.

Wealthy people from the cities bought all manner of hovels and spent much time and lots of money 'doing them up'. Some of the results were horrific, but it is fair to say that many were tastefully restored and brought back to life when, without this surge of interest, they might have been left to fall into total ruin.

Perhaps rural folk did not appreciate the architectural or historic significance of these little homes. They allowed them to be sold off, seldom making a bid to buy them. For them, the houses were often 'That awd spot up t'rooad that's tummling doon and leeaks like a coo shed'.

As I toured the lanes of Ryedale, therefore, I became aware of all the thatched cottages in their various locations and in their various stages of repair or disrepair. From time to time, I saw our local thatcher at work – we called him a theeaker – and marvelled at his casual skills. Sometimes the cottages would be completely gutted and rebuilt, with all their ancient oak interior woodwork and flooring being removed and replaced with modern fittings.

But occasionally, someone would come along and buy a remote thatched cottage, then proceed to restore it in its original form, albeit with modern benefits such as damp-proofing, up-to-date plumbing, central heating and electricity. When done properly, such a house could be a delight, a real gem.

It was during my patrols along the lesser known byways around Aidensfield that I discovered Coltsfoot Cottage, a pretty country home if ever there was one. Tucked behind a tall, unkempt hawthorn hedge and almost hidden among a paddock thick with tall rose bay willow herbs, it had a thatched roof, whitewashed walls and tiny Yorkshire sliding windows. These were, and indeed still are, a feature of some moorland and Ryedale cottages.

Owned .by one of the local estates, it had for years been occupied by an elderly man who paid the tiniest of rents and who therefore lived in a rather primitive manner. His toilet was an earth closet; he had no hot water and no electricity and the floors were sandstone flags. The estate had offered to implement a full modernization scheme but old Cedric had declined.

Having lived in the house since birth, he had no wish to change either it or his way of life. Dark, damp and neglected, it was a tumbledown old house and was known to date to the seventeenth century. But the interior was lovely; dark oak beams, an inglenook, tiny cosy rooms and a position of almost total seclusion gave it the status of a dream cottage. It was the kind of house that the country cottage-seekers of that time were desperately hunting, and was probably more attractive because it was so very ripe for modernization.

From the quiet lane which passed the front gate, it appeared to be unoccupied and derelict, although there was a patch of garden which produced hollyhocks, delphiniums and several varieties of rose. Some of these climbed the walls and smothered the thatched porch with colour in the summer, mingling so beautifully with the honeysuckle.

When Cedric died, the estate decided that it would be too expensive to bring the cottage up to contemporary standards.

The subsequent rents would never justify the expense and so it was placed on the market. And even as the estate agent's 'For Sale' signs were being erected, a wealthy insurance broker from London chanced to be passing.

With commendable speed and decisiveness he bought it; the price being very low due to its lamentable condition. But, like so many townspeople of the time, his great wish was to own a picturesque and isolated cottage wherein he could live a life of rural bliss far from the pressures of his high-flying career. It was a place he could 'do up'; it needed thousands of pounds and many man-hours spending upon it, but the new owner of Coltsfoot Cottage was prepared to do all that. He wanted the perfect hideaway and he had found it.

In my role as the village policeman, I had to be aware of events on my patch, and so I kept a discreet eye on the empty cottage.

I did not want it to be vandalized or occupied by unauthorized visitors such as squatters who might come across it and establish a commune there. But within weeks of the purchase, the new owner began to make his impact. He came every weekend and sometimes during the week; he did a lot of the work himself, although he did employ contractors for the specialized tasks. The theeaker came to re-thatch the roof; a plumber came to install hot and cold water, a bathroom, shower and central heating while the electrician wired the house for lights and power.

A damp-course was installed; the garden was cleared; the walls were re-pointed and whitewashed and the woodwork was either varnished or painted. The exterior rubbish was cleared with the assistance of a JCB, and a drive and parking area constructed to accommodate his Rover and her MGB. This was laid with gravel which crunched when anyone walked across it, and then a small conservatory was added at the rear, partly as a draught-proofing scheme and partly to grow flowers and cacti.

Within a year, Coltsfoot Cottage had been transformed. Happily, roses still climbed up the white walls and trailed across the porch; but now, with its new roof of clean thatch and sparkling exterior, it was the ideal dream cottage. Modern, clean but incredibly beautiful, I would have loved to have been the owner, but such things were not for constables. This man had money, and he knew how to use it.

During his weekend visits, I learned his name was James Patrington; once or twice as I patrolled past his gate on my little Francis Barnett, I would stop for a chat, ostensibly to pass the time of day and to make him aware that I was keeping an eye on his premises. Frequently, I found him in the garden dressed in a pair of old grey trousers, a holey brown sweater and wellingtons. Sometimes, his wife was there too and one day they invited me in for a coffee.

They were a handsome, friendly couple; he was in his mid-forties and a shade less than six feet tall. Stockily built, he was balding and had once had a head of thick, black curly hair, evidence of which lingered about his neck and curled over his collar. Round-faced with dark, intelligent eyes, he smoked a heavy pipe which never seemed to leave him, and told me he was a partner in a firm of City insurance brokers.

His wife, Lucy, would be in her late thirties and was almost as tall as her husband; slim and elegant, she had dark hair too, and this was showing signs of premature greying, something she did not try to hide and which therefore made her most attractive. She had very slender hands, I noticed, the kind one would expect in a piano player and her peach-complexioned face always bore a pleasant smile.

I was to learn that she ran a fashion shop in Chelsea and that its demands did not permit her to come to Coltsfoot Cottage every weekend. James, however, always seemed to be there from late on a Friday evening until late on a Sunday evening. I knew that he worshipped the cottage and he asked me to keep an eye upon it during his absence. This I was happy to do. I was supplied with both his business and home address, and his telephone number at both places in case of problems.

'Come and see my cacti,' he invited one Saturday afternoon when I called. He was alone and led me into the conservatory at the rear where I saw hundreds of tiny plant pots. All were neatly labelled with obscure names and some plants bore incredibly beautiful flowers. 'I grow these for fun, I suppose,' he said. 'I sell some, but I reckon that I've every known variety here and at my other home . . . '

And so I became on good terms with the Patringtons. I cannot claim friendship, however; the relationship was that of the village bobby and those who lived on his patch, a friendly albeit business-like acquaintanceship. But both of them always made me welcome and sometimes, I felt, when James was alone, he was glad of someone to talk to. Gradually, he did make his own friends in the area, people of the same professional class to which he belonged, and I would see him *en route* to the local inns or restaurants, or perhaps heading for a cocktail party or drinks gathering at one of the homes in the area.

Lucy, when she came, did not often leave the cottage. Sometimes, she drove up from London with James and sometimes, if she had to return early, she would drive up alone in her red MGB. Clearly, her own commercial interests kept her very busy and when she did come to Coltsfoot Cottage, she wished for nothing more than a quiet weekend before the blazing log fire in its oak-beamed inglenook, and perhaps a pleasant dinner with James at one of our splendid local inns or restaurants.

They came and they went, not interfering in the village activities, but simply enjoying the unhurried pace and solitude offered by Coltsfoot Cottage. Incomers though they were, they had rescued the old house from destruction and decay, for I'm sure that no local person could or would have raised the capital necessary to buy and renovate it.

Once the Patringtons were established, I saw less of them; every so often, though, I would receive a telephone call from James advising me that he would not be at Coltsfoot that coming weekend and asking if I would keep an eye on the cottage during my patrols. It would be about two years after he had bought the cottage, that their pretty little home hit the headlines of the national newspapers. It happened like this.

High on the hills behind Aidensfield lies the Yorkshire and North of England Sailplane Club, one of the busy gliding clubs of this area. Gliding is very popular from here because the lofty moors provide ideal conditions for launching these engineless aircraft. The thermals created by the ranging hills and dales give the light aircraft a tremendous uplift on rising currents of air, while the views from aloft are staggering in their range and beauty, and the peace they signify.

Since the war, gliding in these elegant sailplanes has become more and more popular and the thriving club now has its own landing strip, runway and control tower, along with administrative and social buildings. There is also a caravan site for its members. By the time I arrived at Aidensfield, the prestige of this club had become such that it hosted events which were of considerable importance in the gliding world – these included both local and national championships, as well as club gliding events and social functions.

During the long, lazy summer which marked the Patringtons' second anniversary in Coltsfoot Cottage, the club hosted the British Long Distance Sailplane Championships. This attracted a host of enthusiasts to the area who were accommodated at local hotels, inns, boarding-houses and cottages. They swamped the nearby caravan sites and their presence brought wealth to the area. These people had money and cheerfully spent it.

Many of them were from the world of business and commerce and I wondered if James Patrington had joined the Club. As I patrolled my beat during the two weeks of the Championships, I could imagine him soaring aloft in a glider as he enjoyed the solitude and silence of the skies above the North York Moors. Perhaps he was involved, perhaps he wasn't. I did not know.

But, like all previous sailplane championships, there were problems. The more regular of these problems involved a glider coming to earth in an unexpected place. With so many competitors and so many engineless aircraft in the sky, I suppose it is inevitable that some of them fail to remain aloft or cannot make the return journey back to base. The result was that over the two weeks of this event, some six or seven gliders crash-landed around the Club premises. Fortunately, none of these resulted in serious injury to the pilot or anyone else.

I witnessed one of these crash landings. I was patrolling my patch one Saturday afternoon and had parked my Francis Barnett in Crampton. I was performing a short foot patrol around that village and had just emerged from the village shop when my attention was drawn to a whistling sound overhead. And there, floating dangerously low over the village, was a gleaming white glider. It didn't need an expert to realize that it had lost its necessary height, and that it was coming rapidly to earth. To be honest, it was the sort of thing the local people had come to expect and Ryedale does possess many suitable places upon which to safely land.

With the wind hissing about its framework, it came frighteningly low over the chimneys and pantile roofs and it was banking as it circled in a desperate search for a safe landing site. Beyond the village there were flat fields and indeed, there is a disused wartime airfield – I felt sure the pilot was urging his downward floating craft towards that.

As I hurried between the cottages to watch the pilot's frantic efforts to both save the village from danger and to safely bring down his aircraft, I lost sight of the glider. It disappeared behind a row of cottages as I realized it could never regain the air. It was far too low; it had lost all its altitude.

I hurried to my motor cycle, activated the radio and called my Control Room.

'Delta Alpha Two-Nine,' I radioed. 'Location Crampton. It appears that a glider has crash-landed in the vicinity of Crampton – am investigating. Over.'

'Received Two-Nine. Please provide sit-rep as soon as possible. Control out.'

With several villagers watching with interest, I motor cycled out of Crampton towards Brantsford, for that road led into a bewildering array of narrow lanes and tiny hamlets. The glider was last seen heading in that direction; I was sure it had come down somewhere in that maze of lanes and fields, or even on the disused airfield. It could not have flown far and there was no sign of it in the air.

As I drove along the lane which ran through the old disused airfield, there was no sign of the glider, so I turned left and chugged along, sometimes standing on the footrests so that I could peer over the hedges into the large fields at either side. I was now heading for Seavham.

I drove through the hamlet and remained alert for any signs or news that the glider had landed nearby. But there was no one in the street and the Post Office was closed. At least ten minutes had elapsed since my sighting, so I continued through the village and turned left at the end, passing the oval pond which was overlooked by two pretty thatched cottages.

This lane took me on a circular route back to Crampton and I felt that the aircraft couldn't have travelled much further. It hadn't.

As I crested a gentle rise in the lane, I could see its tail sticking into the air like that of a diving whale and I could distinguish one crooked wing behind a copse of sycamore trees. I accelerated now, anxious to save life if that proved necessary, and within a minute was drawing up at the scene of the crash.

I was horrified.

The glider had come down squarely on the top of Coltsfoot Cottage. The nose had penetrated the newly-thatched roof and had thrust piles of straw on to the earth around the house.

Both the nose and fuselage were hidden deep inside the walls, while one wing had cracked off completely and was lying in the garden. The other was sticking out of the cottage, its fuselage-end deep inside the walls and the slender tip rising awkwardly to the sky like a huge broken feather. And the tail stuck up too, like a sentinel.

For one fleeting moment, I thought it looked like a giant white seagull sitting on a nest, but this was serious. I parked my motor cycle on the road outside and ran into the grounds. My first contact was with a woman.

She was comforting James Patrington as he sat on the lawn.

She saw me approaching.

'Thank God,' she said.

'Anyone badly hurt?' was my first question.

'This gentleman's wife,' she said. 'We were driving past at the time . . . we saw it all . . . my husband's rushed her in his car to the hospital. Brantsford Cottage Hospital . . . she had a knock on the head . . . '

'And the pilot?'

'Him as well, he was bleeding from his face and leg . . . my husband's taken him as well, this gentleman isn't badly hurt. Just shocked, I think. No one's badly hurt.'

The first aid training I'd received told me that shock alone could be a severe medical problem, so I radioed Control Room and provided a brief outline of the incident, then asked for an ambulance to take James to hospital as well, for a check-up. The good news was that no one was seriously hurt.

From this point, there would be all kinds of official bodies to inform; all that action would be undertaken by the Force Control Room who would operate from a pre-arranged set of instructions for dealing with crashed aircraft.

My priority now was to ensure that James received immediate medical attention, and that there was no immediate danger from the aircraft or the house. Happily, there was no aircraft fuel to worry about and there were no fires burning in the house. That reduced the fire risk enormously but it couldn't be ruled out. I decided to keep everyone away from the house and to preserve the scene against the sightseers who would inevitably arrive.

As I marshalled my thoughts I made sure that all the relevant services were notified and that attention was given to the people and the premises. But I could have wept at the sight of the cottage. Perhaps, because it was a thatched roof, it could be repaired fairly easily and likewise because it was a soft landing, there had been no serious injury. It looked a real mess.

Later from home, I rang Brantsford Cottage Hospital to learn that James had suffered severe shock and had been detained. The pilot, a man called Alastair Campbell from Edinburgh, had a broken leg and severe bruising. He had also been detained. I then asked about Mrs Patrington, but the hospital had no record of her. When I added that she was a victim of the glider crash, I was told she had been removed to Scarborough General Hospital for treatment.

As I looked up the telephone number of Scarborough Hospital, my own telephone rang. When I picked up the receiver, a woman's voice asked, 'Hello, is that PC Rhea?'

'Speaking,' I acknowledged. 'Who's that?'

'Lucy Patrington,' she responded. 'I've just heard the news on the radio, is it true? That a glider's crashed into our cottage?'

I must admit that I was thrown completely off my stride by this call and for a moment, I did not reply. Was she really ringing me to ask this, or was she in hospital, dazed perhaps? I wondered if the shock of the event had caused her to lose all memories of the crash. Maybe she'd been unsettled by the trauma of the event?

'Hello,' she said anew.

'Oh sorry, Mrs Patrington,' I apologized, 'I was completing something . . . er . . . yes, I'm afraid it is true . . . James is in the Cottage Hospital at Brantsford now, but he's not hurt. Just a check visit. I was about to call and ask after you,' I rabbited on. 'Now, are you fit to be released . . . I mean, should you be out of bed . . . ?'

'Released, Mr Rhea?' she cried. 'What on earth are you talking about? I'm in my shop in London, and James has gone to Scotland for a weekend seminar . . . '

Then her voice trailed away and I knew I had let some sort of cat out of some sort of bag.

'James has not gone to Scotland, has he?' She put to me in no uncertain terms.

'All I know,' I told her, 'is that he was at the house when the glider came down. Maybe he stopped off *en route* to Scotland? I can confirm that a glider has landed on your roof, and no one is seriously hurt, although there is a good deal of damage . . . '

'The news said a woman had been taken to hospital, Mr Rhea,' she pressed me.

'She had gone before I arrived . . . I don't know who she was. I am, at this moment, trying to find out who she is and the extent of her injuries. Perhaps it was someone from the village, visiting the cottage . . . ' Rather irrationally and without any real reason, I found myself defending James Patrington.

'Perhaps it was that bitch of a secretary of his,' she snapped. 'It serves them right!' and she slammed down the telephone.

So because something fell out of the sky, James Patrington's little secret had been revealed to the whole world and a few weeks later, the now deserted cottage, still in its damaged condition, was once again put on the market. I never saw James and Lucy again.

I often wonder if he had his cottage insured.

I was more directly involved in another story of love which came about because of a broken romance. This one was almost as unlikely as the Patrington saga.

At three o'clock one morning, my telephone rang. It was downstairs in the office attached to my house, and its continuous shrilling gradually penetrated my sleep. As I staggered downstairs, I rubbed my eyes and tried to shake myself into clarity of action before I lifted the noisy instrument. It was a call from a kiosk.

'PC Rhea, Aidensfield,' I announced, shivering as my bare feet grew cold upon the bare composition floor.

At the other end of the line, coins were inserted and the pipping ceased, then all I could hear was sobbing. I waited for a brief moment, hoping that the person would say something, but the sobbing continued.

'Hello?' I called into the phone. 'Hello, this is the police.'

It continued and I realized Mary had joined me; she stood at my side, wrapping her dressing-gown tightly around her slim body. She'd had the sense to put on her slippers.

'What is it?' she asked. With late calls of this nature, it was natural to think it was a personal family crisis of some kind.

'Somebody sobbing. Listen,' and I passed the handset to her. She listened and passed it back.

'Hello,' I tried again and increased the volume of my voice this time. 'Hello, this is PC Rhea speaking.'

'I want to come and see you,' said a faint voice, a female voice, through the sobbing.

'Who is it?' I asked, holding the handset so that Mary could hear both sides of the conversation.

'I must come,' continued the voice. 'Now, or I'll jump under the train . . . '

'What train? Look, who are you? I want to help you.' I had detected a note of real desperation in that voice and did not think it was a joke of any kind. 'Where are you?' I added.

'Newcastle Railway Station,' she sobbed, 'and if you don't say yes, I'm going to jump off the platform . . . '

Mary was hissing in my ear.

'For heaven's sake say yes,' she snapped. 'Don't string her along, don't make it appear you're not going to help . . . '

'But . . . ' I began as my suspicious police mind began thinking all manner of thoughts.

'Do it,' said Mary.

'Look,' I said to the caller, 'I'll welcome you, we'll welcome you, my wife and I. You can come and see me. But how . . . '

'I can get the next train to York.' Even now, the sobbing sounded less dramatic.

'Yes, all right,' I said, 'I'll meet you there, at York Station.'

'Thank you, oh, thank you,' breathed the voice, sniffing as the sobs subsided. 'Oh thank you . . . '

The pips sounded and the call was abruptly ended.

I stared at my handset and asked Mary, 'Well, what do you make of that?'

She shrugged her shoulders. 'One of your ex-girl-friends getting worked up about something? A blast from the past? Or have you been misbehaving when you've been away on your various courses? Maybe you've broken someone's little heart?' There was a trusting twinkle in Mary's eye, but I knew that this call could have been misconstrued in all kinds of ways.

'I don't know who she is or what she wants!' I began a weak protest . . .

'Then you'll have to go to York and find out. Bring her here,' said Mary. 'She sounds as if she needs help and friendship, whoever she is and whatever she's done.'

There are times when one is thankful for a marvellous, understanding wife who possesses oceans of common sense, and this was such a time. Policemen especially require wives who have all the qualities of angels coupled with a high measure of earthly common sense. So, in response to Mary's advice I nodded in agreement and said, 'OK, I'll have a cup of tea and get dressed. I'll drive to York to meet our mystery lady.'

It was then that I realized it was a Sunday and it should have been my day off. However, I checked the arrival times of trains from Newcastle and as I drove into York in my own car, I wondered whether this was classed as police duty. Was this a private matter or could I claim that I had used my car for emergency duty purposes?

If such thoughts seemed petty, this is not so because if I had an accident on this trip, it would be vital to my future security as to whether or not it was a 'duty' commitment. But there was nothing I could do about the technicalities of the situation at this stage; I would worry about those kind of things after I had met my damsel in distress.

And so it was, that shortly after 4.30 a.m. that chill but sunny

Sunday morning, I was standing on York Station awaiting the Newcastle train. I must admit that I wondered whether I was a fool or not, or whether this was some curious prank, but on reflection I knew I had no alternative but to turn out. I had to discover for myself the reality of the situation.

The train was about ten minutes late. A few minutes after its arrival, as I stood at the ticket-collector's barrier, I noticed a young woman heading my way. I did not recognize her. In her late teens or early twenties, she was pretty without being beautiful, and had mousy hair which straggled down to her shoulders. She was dressed in a rather crumpled, short tartan skirt, a dark green velvet top and white blouse. She wore no stockings or tights and was waif-like in many ways. As she drew closer, I could see that her pale face bore a hint of freckles, but other than some pale lipstick she wore no make-up. She had no luggage or topcoat but did carry a black handbag.

After passing through the barrier, she managed an embarrassed smile as she came nervously towards me. She was like a naughty child who was anticipating a telling-off by an angry parent.

'Hello.' Clearly she knew who I was. She stood before me like a lost kitten.

'Hello,' I returned, racking my brains in an attempt to recall her name or where we'd met. In those few brief moments, I failed. I had no idea who she was.

'I'm sorry . . . for all this . . . ' she began in an accent which I did not recognize as either Yorkshire or Tyneside. 'I was silly . . . I'll go back. I'm all right now.' She turned to walk away from me.

'No,' I said, still baffled. 'Don't go. You need help, don't you? Look, my car's outside and my wife has got a cup of tea ready. The buffet's closed, I'm afraid, so we can't talk here.'

'No,' she said, 'I'm all right now, honest. I can go. I'll go back to Newcastle on the next train . . . I was silly . . . I'm confused . . . I'm a nuisance to you.'

'No,' I said, 'my wife wants to meet you and I want to know what all this is about. So, come along. No arguing! I'm here because I want to help you.'

She hesitated momentarily, then followed me to my waiting

car. Without a word, she climbed into the passenger-seat and settled down as I drove through York's deserted streets.

'Well,' I said as we cleared the town, 'so what's all this about? How about a name to start with?'

'Tessa,' she said. 'Teresa, really, but everybody calls me Tessa. Tessa Underwood.'

'I'm still baffled,' I admitted. 'I don't recall that name. Tell me about the phone call, Tessa. You wanted help, so why did you ring me? I don't know you.'

'It all sounds so silly now, Mr Rhea,' she used my name quite normally. 'It really does. After the train ride, I came to my senses. It was so silly . . . I feel a right fool, I do, bothering you like this, when you don't know me . . . '

'It wasn't silly at three o'clock this morning, Tessa. It was very serious then, and it could be serious again so let's hear about it.'

And so, during the half-hour trip from York to Aidensfield, I managed to drag the story from her. Brought up in Staffordshire, her parents had been killed in a road accident about four years ago, when she was seventeen. For a time, she'd lived with an aunt, but had fallen out with her. So eighteen months ago, she had moved to Newcastle-upon-Tyne where she now worked as a shorthand typist in a factory on a new industrial estate.

She lived alone in a little flat which she rented and, apart from Mark, her boyfriend, and some of the girls at work, she knew no one. Some of the girls at work had made fun of her because of her curious accent, but three days ago, her boyfriend had left her.

At this stage, the tears started again; I was tempted to halt the car and comfort her but felt it wiser to continue. I exhorted her to continue. Through her sobs, she said Derek left her for a married woman he'd met in a night club, a real old scrubber according to Tessa. All attempts at reconciliation had failed; Tessa, with no parents to turn to and no relations other than the awkward aunt, felt she could not confide in anyone. She was alone in the world; she'd felt unloved and unwanted.

In her own way, she provided me with a graphic account of how her misery and loneliness had turned into a suicidal determination. Burdened with her worries in the early hours of this very morning, she had gone down to Newcastle Central railway station with a determination to throw herself under one of the speeding expresses. Even now, as she re-told her story among floods of tears, she wondered how she could have contemplated such a thing.

'I wasn't thinking straight,' she said. 'It was horrid. I was . . . oh . . . so silly, so miserable and sad, lonely . . . it was Saturday night, you see, and everyone goes out with friends and I had none, only Derek, and he'd left me . . . I had no one Mr Rhea. No one. If you hadn't said you'd see me . . . '

'But I did. I said you could come to see me and here you are. If that action has stopped you from doing something silly, then I'm delighted. Now, do you think you've got rid of those awful thoughts?'

She nodded and wiped her eyes. 'I'll be all right now.'

'But,' this was the point that still puzzled me, 'why ring me? Of all the people who would have helped – the local police, for example, the Salvation Army, the Church! And you rang me!'

She produced a thin smile and looked embarrassed. 'It was so good of you, I mean, you could have said no and . . . '

'And you might have jumped in front of a train?'

'You didn't ignore me, Mr Rhea . . . I'm . . . well . . . '

'I know. But, Tessa, I don't know you. I still can't understand why you rang me?'

She hesitated. We were now drawing close to Aidensfield and in the growing light of dawn, I could distinguish my police house on its lofty site which overlooked the ranging and beautiful countryside. By now, it was after five o'clock and the lights of some houses were showing as smoke rose from our chimney. Mary had prepared a welcome for this girl.

'Can you remember a car breaking down outside your house, about a year ago?' Tessa asked, smiling at the memory.

Vaguely, I did recall the incident.

'Me and . . . that boy . . . well, we'd had a day out on the moors in his car, and when we came along the road somewhere in this area, we found a small suitcase lying in the road. So we picked it up and thought we'd better report it to the police. Well, yours was the first police station we saw. So we stopped and Mark, that's him, made me bring it in.'

I was now recalling the incident with more clarity.

'He didn't want to bring it in, so I did. I handed it to you and you made a note of it in case the loser came asking.'

'She did, I remember,' I said. 'She was most grateful – it had fallen off a roof-rack. So that was you, was it? You look so different!'

'I've changed – I've lost my puppy fat for one thing, and I've had my hair cut.'

'So you remembered me from that little incident?'

'Well, you remember Mark's car? When I went back to the car after bringing in the suitcase it wouldn't start. Mark tried and tried, so you ran him down to a garage in the village and got a set of plugs or something for the engine.'

'Points,' I corrected her. 'A set of points. Yes, and we put them in, me and your friend. I remember it now.'

'Well,' she was still trying to reach the end of her story, 'I remembered how helpful you were . . . '

'It was nothing,' I said.

'But you see, I wasn't used to policemen helping me, Mark neither. But, well, I kept the receipt you gave me for that suitcase. It was in my handbag, it has been there ever since. You know what women are for carrying stuff around and well, last night when I was so unhappy and depressed, I was rifling through my bag, getting rid of his letters and things on the station. I was putting things in the rubbish bin, you know, getting rid of everything, then I found that receipt. It had your number on as well. So I rang – and here I am.'

'I'm pleased you rang if it meant so much,' I was sincere. 'Well, we're almost home.'

'I'll go straight back,' she said. 'I shouldn't have come. I've been a silly, stupid nuisance and I've thought things out on that train, sensibly I think. I had time . . . '

'At least come in and have some breakfast,' I offered. 'And you are welcome to stay until you get yourself completely sorted out.'

And so she did. At Mary's invitation, she stayed three days and Mary was marvellous with her. Tessa was lovely with our children too, and that girl and our family are still good friends. She still calls, albeit now with a new husband and two lovely children of her own.

But her presence in our house did cause a flutter of interest and some speculation in the village. Mary and I decided we must not tell anyone of her real reason for being with us, and so we were faced with questions like, 'Is that the wife's sister then?' or 'Been arrested, has she?' or 'Is she a policewoman in disguise, watching summat in Aidensfield?'

In all cases, we simply said she was a friend who was staying for a day or two.

But I often wonder whether that event was part of my police duty or not. I think not, for I never mentioned it to any of my superiors.

4

Little deeds of kindness, little words of love
Help to make the earth happy, like the heaven above.

                                                    Julia Carney, 1823–1908

There was great excitement in Ashfordly one Friday morning in June. It arose because BBC radio had decided to broadcast its 'Good Morning' programme from a mobile studio in the market-place. It was to be a live broadcast from the North Region, and would be on the air from 7 a.m. until 9 a.m. At that time, the 'Good Morning' series visited a different town or village each week and the series had a dedicated following.

It was natural that the people of Ashfordly were excited and delighted that their charming market town had been selected and in due course, a list of candidates for interview was drawn up. Personalities from all walks of life were procured and the interviews would be interspersed with music and reports about a selection of the interesting places in the locality.

Late on the Thursday afternoon beforehand, the BBC's entourage arrived and the galaxy of technicians and production staff established themselves and their vehicles at the pre-arranged place. The little town awaited the honour of tomorrow's spell of publicity, while the participants grew more nervous as their hour of glory approached. The police, as always, had their role to play.

In addition to keeping a protective eye on the vehicles and their loads of expensive equipment during the preceding night, they had to maintain a discreet presence on the day itself. We had to be there just in case someone tried to gatecrash the proceedings or otherwise make a nuisance of themselves.

As an outdoor audience was anticipated in the vicinity of the mobile studio, there would be a degree of crowd control and some car-parking to supervise. Duties of this kind were undertaken in conjunction with every crowd-pulling event and the BBC's 'Good Morning from Ashfordly' was no exception. As our duty rota had been compiled some weeks in advance, I was delighted to find that I was to perform an early morning patrol that Friday. My duties were from 6 a.m. until 9 a.m. and I was therefore allocated a foot patrol in the town centre so that a uniformed police presence would be evident.

I looked forward to the work.

I left home at six o'clock on my Francis Barnett, arrived at Ashfordly Police Station at 6.15 a.m. and left my motor cycle there. I also left my motor-cycling weather-proof clothes and donned my uniform cap as I set about my patrol. Even at that early stage of the morning, a small crowd of onlookers had gathered but they stood at a respectful distance and appeared to be causing no bother. The technicians were hard at work setting up and checking their sophisticated equipment while the producer of the programme had gathered the programme participants in a separate caravan for a final briefing.

I did not intrude. I could see that things were moving apace so I kept in the background, watchful but discreet. The minutes ticked away and then, as seven o'clock approached, much of the crowd melted away.

I realized they would be going home to hear the broadcast and I wondered if Sergeant Blaketon would be listening. He had not yet made an appearance and I did wonder if he was just a wee bit upset because he was not one of the selected personalities . . . But I reckoned he would be tuned in as he enjoyed his breakfast.

I knew that I could listen to parts of the broadcast in a friendly bakery just behind the market-place. Confident that my presence was not required, I sidled away and entered the bakery by a side door. I was assailed by the marvellous whiff of new bread as the manager noticed my entry. He pointed to the kettle and then to a radio perched on a shelf.

I got the message. They were listening as they worked, and I was invited to join them and to make myself a cup of tea; they were already drinking theirs. I asked if anyone required a refill, but they were content and made hand signals to inform me of the fact, so I made myself a cup and stood in silence beneath the radio. At seven, the broadcast started with the announcer sounding bright and breezy as he introduced the programme and gave a brief résumé of Ashfordly's topography and the delights in store.

Then he said, 'And here am I, in the middle of the market-place awaiting my guests. And in my rush to get everything ready this morning, I forgot to bring some sugar for my tea! We've no sugar in the studio, folks, but perhaps someone will fetch a spoonful along . . . '

No one in the bakery made a move, and so I decided to help out. After all, I reasoned, everyone else was glued to their radios at home, and would hate to move away in case they missed something. If everyone took this attitude, no one would provide the sugar! And so I thanked the bakery staff for the tea and left. The shops which stocked sugar would not yet be open, so I hurried to the police station, located the tin of sugar we used in our own tea-swindle, and poured some into a milk bottle.

Rather than carry it through the streets in my uniform I donned my crash helmet, popped the bottle of sugar into the pannier of my motor cycle and scooted the few yards back to the market-place. Lifting the machine on to its stand, I removed the bottle of sugar and walked across to the BBC's collection of vehicles. At the door of the studio, I found an assistant, handed over the sugar with my compliments and left.

I returned to my bike, placed the crash helmet upon the saddle and resumed a normal patrol. And that, I thought, was that. It was my good deed for the day. Twenty minutes later, I was in the local newsagent's shop, a courtesy visit during my patrol, and I heard the broadcast issuing from their radio.

Miss Phyllis Oakworth, a leading light in Ashfordly WI for fifty years, had just been interviewed, and the announcer was once again in full flow.

And to my horror, I heard him say, 'I am delighted that my plea for some sugar has been answered. I've now got enough for myself and my guests. For this, my thanks go to the local constabulary in Ashfordly who rushed a supply to our studio by police motor cycle. Now there's an example of co-operation between the police and the public – if you need help, just ask an Ashfordly policeman. Well done, Officer, whoever you were, you've saved the day. I think your policemen are wonderful, Ashfordly. And now to our next guest . . . '

'You?' asked Ken, the newsagent.

I nodded and grimaced at the unwarranted publicity, but he just laughed. 'Nice one,' he said and continued his work among the morning papers.

I left the shop and wondered who, among the dozens of my senior officers, had heard that; furthermore, I wondered what their reaction would be. Could my action be construed as too frivolous for a police officer? But as the morning passed and the local folks listened to their own town, its people and its attractions being so professionally scrutinized, my worries began to evaporate.

Then, at quarter to nine, I noticed the tall, smart but severe figure of Sergeant Blaketon as he moved towards me across the market square. Rigidly upright and with military bearing, he came towards me, an impressive man in his immaculate uniform. He was prominent among the crowd which had grown larger due to the arrival of some workers who were due to start their day's toil at nine o'clock.

They had paused for a moment before disappearing into their offices and places of work, and the broadcast was drawing to a close in those final minutes.

'All correct, Rhea?' he asked. I noticed the more-serious-than-usual expression on his face as he arrived at my side.

'All correct, Sergeant,' I responded in the traditional manner.

'No problems? Trouble from the crowd? Parking?'

'No, Sergeant.'

'No crimes, no pickpockets in the crowd, no thieves at work as everyone's attention was diverted by this affair?'

'No, Sergeant,' I said, hoping that no one had taken the opportunity to steal a bike or to take someone's wallet. That sort of thing just did not happen in Ashfordly, I felt, and so I was confident in my bland assessment of the situation.

'No overnight break-ins? Car thefts? Broken windows not discovered?'

'No, Sergeant,' and my answer must, by this time, have sounded quizzical. He was going on a bit, I felt, certainly more than usual. In normal circumstances, my 'All Correct' speech would have been sufficient, but he was probing now. I realized he was leading up to something; judging by the expression on his face, it was something serious. I began to wonder if a crime *had* been reported or if some incident had occurred. If so, I was not aware of it and that could infer that I had neglected my duty.

Somewhat worried by his attitude, we made a brief perambulation of the market square and I noticed that the crowd was now dwindling as the people finally went to their places of work.

'If you have been so vigilant, Rhea, and have had such a positive command of the situation, how is it that you have found the time to be entertained by a radio programme?'

'Sergeant?'

He came to a halt in a quiet recess near the town hall and we stood together as he mustered his speech. 'The sugar, Rhea. There am I, sitting at my breakfast-table, when I learn that one of my constables has heard a plea for sugar from this lot here, these broadcasting people. That alone indicates that the constable in question must have been neglecting his duty, that he was failing to work his beat in accordance with instructions . . .'

'I . . . ' I couldn't believe what I was hearing.

'And furthermore,' his voice rose to stifle any comment I might make, 'there is the question of the misuse of police vehicles, that is, the use of an official motor cycle and fuel, to say nothing of police time, to convey the sugar from the police office to these broadcasting people, and there is also the question of the ownership of the sugar, eh Rhea? Was it yours to give away? Was it your personal property? Or was it sugar which belonged to the Police Authority? Was it sugar from a fund of some kind?'

'But, Sergeant . . . '

'And on top of all that, Rhea, how do you think the public will react to this? Will those listeners, those thousands or even millions of them out there, think that Ashfordly Police have nothing better to do than to act as delivery men for the BBC?

63

We will be the laughing-stock of police forces, Rhea, we will be the butt of jokes from our city counterparts who are coping with murders and mayhem. They will now believe that we occupy our duty time by running cupfuls of official sugar from police stations to broadcasting people who then announce it to the world . . . '

Sergeant Oscar Blaketon was on top form. All his prejudices and formal police attitudes were emerging as he stood there in the recess near the town hall, giving vent to his concern.

'But, Sergeant . . . '

'And Rhea, let us now suppose that the Superintendent or even the Chief Constable himself was listening to that programme! What are they to think about it all, Rhea? How am I to justify your actions; your highly unofficial and thoughtless actions; your neglect of duty in this very public manner; your misuse of police property . . . '

'Sergeant, I thought . . . '

'I don't care what you thought, Rhea. What I do care about is what you did. And what you did could amount to a breach of the Discipline Code with the severest of repercussions for you and for the force . . . '

I must admit I had not for one moment thought of that aspect. Anyone else, in any sort of job or profession, would have done the same, so why should the police be any different? But, according to Blaketon's interpretation of the Police (Discipline) Regulations, it did seem that I had fallen foul of those rules, and I knew him well enough to realize that he would have checked the provisions of that code before coming to speak to me. He was not the man to leave such detail to chance.

As he continued his diatribe, I visualized the punishments that could be imposed for such breaches of the Discipline Regulations. There was dismissal from the force, with an alternative of a requirement to resign; there was reduction in rank (which didn't apply to me because, as a constable, I was at the bottom of the scale); a reduction in pay; a fine; a reprimand or a caution.

I began to feel pale and sick and started to worry about my future, both in the immediate and long term. I knew the Dis-

cipline Code was strict and that some supervisory officers rein-
forced it to the letter . . .

'So, Rhea,' said Blaketon as he concluded his lecture, 'you
will submit a report about his incident. In triplicate. And it will
be on my desk not later than twelve noon today.'

'Yes, Sergeant,' I said, with evident meekness.

Having delivered his lecture, he strode away, grim-faced,
awesome yet somehow majestic in his unassailable attitude.
With my mind ranging across the problem I had now created for
myself, I watched the BBC technicians begin to dismantle their
equipment and decided I was no longer required. I went across
to my motor cycle and mounted it.

A voice called to me from the assembled BBC personnel.
'Thanks for the sugar, Officer!'

'Cheers!' I responded with a wave of my hand and knew I
dare not tell them of Blaketon's reaction or of my impending
ordeal. Communication with journalists about internal police
matters was another disciplinary offence, so I left it at that.
Dejected and worried, I started the Francis Barnett and
motored slowly back to Aidensfield.

Over breakfast, I told Mary all about it and she thought it was
a ridiculous attitude, but at ten o'clock I settled in my office to
type the report. I knew it must be totally factual and that I
should not try to make excuses; I therefore decided on a plain,
simple and honest account of my sugar mission. I would set it
out in chronological order.

At twenty minutes past ten, my telephone rang.

'PC Rhea, Aidensfield,' I announced.

'Just a moment,' said a woman's voice at the other end of the
line, 'I have the Chief Constable for you.'

I nearly fell off my chair. The Chief! I saw myself being
summoned immediately to Police Headquarters to account for
my actions. I saw myself writing out my resignation and looking
for another job. My heart thumped as I waited for the great man
to speak.

I tried to marshal my thoughts in an attempt to justify my
actions. I clung to the telephone, nervous and worried, as his
secretary connected me.

'Chief Constable,' I heard his crisp response.

'PC Rhea, Aidensfield, sir,' I answered.

'Ah, Rhea. I have been in touch with your Divisional Headquarters and they tell me that you were the constable on duty at Ashfordly this morning.'

'Yes, sir,' I admitted, quaking.

'And am I right in thinking that you were responsible for supplying some sugar to the BBC during that morning broadcast?'

I swallowed. So he had been listening, just as old Blaketon had feared.

'Yes, sir,' my voice must have sounded faint and weak as I croaked my reply.

'Bloody good show!' he said. 'That was an excellent piece of public relations, Rhea. It gave the police a sympathetic and human image, and I was delighted it was my force which had done it. Excellent, well done. I just wanted you to know that I was delighted, and so was the Government Inspector. He heard the broadcast too and was delighted. He has just called me.'

And so, in one single moment, all my worries and tensions evaporated.

'It's good of you to ring, sir . . . ' I managed to splutter.

'Not at all. It's the least I could do. Keep up the good work, Rhea,' and he ended our conversation.

I sat in my chair as a feeling of release swept over me. Now, I had the perfect ending for my report to Sergeant Blaketon.

To conclude it, I added this sentence, 'At 10.20 a.m. today, I received a telephone call from the Chief Constable who had heard the broadcast in question. He congratulated me on my actions and stressed the public relations value of the publicity. The HMI also expressed his pleasure in similar terms and had conveyed his appreciation to the Chief Constable with a request that it be transmitted to me.'

At half past eleven, I signed my report and drove into Ashfordly with it. Sergeant Blaketon was on the telephone as I walked into the office, so I placed my report on his desk and walked out.

Never again did he refer to the matter.

On another occasion, it was the police who needed assistance and I found myself involved in that episode too. The ingredients were an ancient ruined abbey, a religious service, some severe car-parking problems and a stubborn Yorkshire farmer.

In the spring of the year, Ashfordly Police Station received a visit from Father Geoffrey Summerson, the Roman Catholic parish priest. Sergeant Bairstow was on duty at the time and warmly received his visitor.

Father Summerson was a small man who had passed his sixtieth birthday; he had been at Ashfordly for many years and ran a happy, busy little parish. He was constantly involved in events and happenings in the town and his diminutive, but powerful personality made him popular with all faiths and even with those who professed no known religion.

His frail figure, with a somewhat gaunt and hungry appearance, belied a bundle of energy which he used for the good of both the town and his parishioners. At first sight, he looked humourless and severe, with a sallow skin drawn tight over thin, high cheekbones. Small, pale eyes glinted from behind rimless spectacles and his hands were never still. He was fond of gesticulations; constantly emphasizing his words with sweeping gestures or meaningful movements of his thin arms and surprisingly long and slender hands. They were the hands of an artist or musician but I do not know whether he possessed either of those talents.

That day, however, he arrived at the police station on foot, clad in his dark grey suit and dog collar. I was on the telephone at the time, receiving a long, involved message about warble fly. I saw the priest being invited into the sergeant's office and guessed it indicated a matter of some importance.

I concluded my call and at a wink from the sergeant, put on the kettle for some coffee.

'Well, Father,' Sergeant Bairstow was always happy and cheerful, 'what can we do for you this bright, spring morning?'

'Good of you to see me, Sergeant,' began the priest. 'It's about Waindale Abbey. It is within your province, isn't it?'

'Yes,' said Bairstow. 'It's on our patch.'

Waindale Abbey is one of several beautiful ruins dotted around the area. Wrecked by the Commissioners of Henry VIII during the Reformation, it sits beside the gentle River Wain where its impressive location and magnificent broken outline give testimony to its dramatic past. Today, it is a popular tourist attraction where its mellow stone and lofty columns give no hint of the role it once played in the economic life of the locality.

'This year marks the thirteenth centenary of the foundation of the Abbey,' began the priest. 'It is one of the oldest ruins in the land and dates to the earliest times of Christendom in this country. So,' he went on, 'we – that is the hierarchy of the Catholic Church, with the blessing of members of the Anglican faith I might add – have decided to mark the occasion. We are going to hold a Concelebrated Mass with the bishop and priests of this diocese. It will take place in the ruins and the proposed date is 24 August, that's the Feast of St Bartholomew, patron saint of the Abbey.'

'So that will mean a considerable influx of people and vehicles, Father?'

'Yes, I estimate there'll be well into tens of thousands. Bus loads, cars, foot and cycle pilgrims, priests, nuns and laity – they'll come from all the northern parishes and even further afield. That is why I am here, to give you due notice, so that you can make your own plans.'

I took them a cup of coffee each and settled down in the front office to enjoy one too. They continued their chat and I could hear every word. It was not a confidential meeting.

'We appreciate adequate warning, Father, then we can arrange our duties to cope. Will you want a police presence inside the Abbey grounds, do you think, or merely on the outside to cope with the traffic and crowds?'

'Certainly on the outside, Sergeant. As for the interior, well, I imagine our pilgrims will behave, although a discreet police presence is never amiss.'

'I'll mark the date in our duty diary,' said Sergeant Bairstow. 'You'll not have the time of the service yet?'

'No, those matters are to be finalized, but it will be during the afternoon, probably beginning at 2.30 p.m. or 3.00 p.m. But some people will arrive much earlier; some will bring picnics, I know, and they will give the day a holiday atmosphere, a form of celebration.'

'Good, well, Father, thank you for this advance notice. You'll keep in touch please, about the timing and other details?'

'Of course, and don't hesitate to contact me if there's anything more you need to know.'

Father Summerson left and Sergeant Bairstow came into the front office. 'You heard all that, Nick?' he asked.

I nodded. 'It looks like being a busy day.'

'You're telling me! There'll be lost children to consider; wandering old ladies; lost and found property; toilet facilities to provide; car and coach parking . . . There'll be other traffic in the valley, trying to squeeze past the pilgrims on those narrow lanes, and the local residents will play hell about it all. We'll have to ensure access for any emergency vehicles and there'll be litter; first aid facilities to think about; possible crimes like pickpockets or other thefts . . . '

'It'll keep us busy for weeks!' I laughed.

'And for that remark, young Rhea, consider yourself involved right from the start! Right now, in fact. Come along, we'll go and inspect the scene, shall we?'

In the Sergeant's official car, we drove the four miles or so across the hills and into the valley of Waindale. The lanes were peaceful, with the hedges just bursting into the fresh green leaf, while the fields and woodlands were changing into their spring colours. Flowers like wild daffodils and celandines adorned the verges and birds sang in marvellous harmony as we dropped down the steep incline into the lovely valley. To give the monks due praise, they certainly knew how to select an ideal site.

The tiny village with its cluster of yellow stone cottages, some thatched and others with red pantile roofs, reclined beneath the shadow of the hillside, while the magnificent Abbey occupied a huge, flat site deep in the valley.

'You know, Nick,' breathed Sergeant Bairstow, 'this view never ceases to thrill me. It really is incredible, those woods, the fields, the river down there – see? And the Abbey, silent and just a little mysterious . . . I've seen it with a mist around it at dawn; I've seen it at night in the light of a full moon, and at sunset too . . . '

I knew what he was trying to say. There was a magic about the place, an indefinable atmosphere rich with the scents of history and drama and it was something I'd experienced on the occasions I'd come here.

We eased our little police car into the car-park and emerged to breathe the crisp, fresh air of Waindale.

'And to think we get paid for this!' smiled Sergeant Bairstow. 'Come along, let's have a critical look at the interior.'

After explaining our purpose to the lady in the little wooden hut at the entrance, we walked around as we tried to envisage how the huge congregation would be accommodated; where the altar should be sited both for safety and for vision. We wondered whether crowd-barriers were needed and which was the best place to site the portable toilets, the first aid centre, the lost children tent and other essentials.

We had to ensure that the village was free to go about its normal business, and we must be equally sure that ambulances could gain access to any possible casualties in the crowd. Thoughts of this kind were part of any exploratory visit and Sergeant Bairstow was sufficiently experienced to be aware of the requirements. We both knew that an Operation Order would be needed to cope with all the problems of the day, and as a plan formed in his mind, he decided it was an ideal opportunity to make use of our band of local, dedicated Special Constables.

My next contact with Father Summerson came through a telephone call. I was in Ashfordly at the time and accepted the call.

'It's Father Summerson,' he said. 'I'm ringing about the Abbey celebrations.'

'It's PC Rhea, Father. I am familiar with the event so far.'

'Good, well I thought you'd better know that we have received some intelligence from our parishes. At this stage, we believe that the congregation will be in excess of 20,000 – it might even rise to 30,000. I thought you had better be aware of these numbers.'

I found it difficult to visualize such a crowd in Waindale Abbey, and expressed that point.

'Oh, the Abbey will accommodate them,' he said with some assurance. 'There is plenty of space. It is the traffic that worries me, Constable. From what I hear, most will be coming by coach but there will be many cars.'

I realized that the volume of incoming traffic would be similar to that which arrives at a popular race meeting, but this was no race track and there was a distinct lack of parking space. There were none of the facilities necessary for coping with such numbers. In short, we, and the church organizers, were to be faced with a car-parking problem of some magnitude. It could not be left to chance or ignored.

I thanked him for this advance information and wrote the details on a note for the attention of Sergent Bairstow. He contacted me a couple of days later and said, 'Nick, I'll pick you up at half past nine this morning. We'll have another look at Waindale Abbey – it's about the parking problems.'

We stood in the centre of the tiny official car-park and calculated that it would accommodate no more than twenty cars – and at an average of four persons per car, that was a mere eighty people.

'That'll just about cater for the official party,' Bairstow said. 'And there's nowhere else. They can't park in these lanes – they'd be blocked in no time. So young Nicholas, what are we to do?'

'We could organize parking elsewhere and bus them in here,' I suggested.

'Have you ever tried that? It causes chaos and delays. Besides, don't forget many of these folks will not be in organized parties. They'll drive to the dale in their own transport, and they'll come right here. We have no control over them.'

'There is a field about a hundred yards away,' I told him. 'Just beyond that cottage and small-holding.'

'Flat, is it? And dry?'

'I think so. We can inspect it now,' I suggested.

We walked along the lane towards an old stone cottage with smoke rising from its chimney. Hens clucked in the yard and there was a goat tethered among the apple trees in a small orchard. An elderly woman was sweeping the doorstep with a large stiff brush and Sergeant Bairstow addressed her.

'Excuse me,' he said. 'This field? Do you know whose it is?'

'Aye,' she said. 'Awd Arthur Craggs. Up yonder,' and she

pointed to a farmhouse almost hidden by trees. It overlooked the valley and the Abbey from its elevated site.

'Thanks.'

The field was ideal. There were two wide entrances, one at each end. Each was large enough to permit coaches and cars to turn off the lane as they entered the valley from both directions. It was a large, flat area of grass which had once been two fields, and the surface was solid. We tramped across it, testing the ground with our heels and trying to estimate how many vehicles it would contain.

'Even if it rains,' I said 'this surface will be sound enough. They won't get bogged down – it's solid enough to take the buses, isn't it?'

'I reckon it is, Nick. It's just what we need. But it won't rain,' chuckled Bairstow. 'I have it on good authority! Father Summerson says he's praying for a fine day. He assures me it will be fine and that there will be no rain and no weather problems. He's not even thinking of a wet weather programme or an awning for the altar!'

'That's faith for you!' I said. 'But God works in mysterious ways!'

'Then let's hope He approves of this field as a car-park!'

We decided not to take the car up to Arthur Craggs' farm, but walked up the steep, unmade track and found ourselves in an expansive and rather untidy farmyard. Other than a few bantams pecking for scraps, there was no sign of life, so we went to the house. The door was open so we knocked and shouted, and a woman called, 'T'dooer's oppen.'

We knew it was an invitation and so we stepped in. A farmer and his wife were sitting at a large, scrubbed kitchen table, each with a mug of tea and a huge slice of cake before them.

'Sit down,' she said without waiting for any introductions and went across to the kettle which was boiling on the Aga. Being familiar with the customary hospitality of the local farmers, we settled on chairs at the table, and she produced a mug of hot tea and a massive chunk of fruit cake for each of us. We weren't given the luxury of plates.

'Is it about me stock register?' said the man.

'No,' said Sergeant Bairstow. 'Are you Arthur Craggs?'

'There's neearbody else of that name lives here,' he said, grinning widely and showing a mouthful of stained and rotten teeth. He would be in his late sixties, I reckoned, a ruddy-faced man with a few days growth of beard around his jowls and chin. His eyes were light grey and clear and he wore rough working clothes, corduroy trousers with leather leggings and hob-nailed boots. We had arrived at 'lowance time', as they called their mid-morning break and even though this couple did not know us, we were expected to share their food. His wife, a plain and simple woman, now settled at the table but did not speak.

'Well,' said Sergeant Bairstow, 'this is lovely cake and a welcome cup of tea.'

'Thoo'll 'ave cum aboot summat else, though?' Those eyes flashed cheekily, playfully even. He knew we wanted some favour from him.

'Yes. You'll have heard that a service is planned in the Abbey, in August.'

'Aye,' he said, those sharp eyes watching us.

'Well,' said the sergeant, 'we are looking for somewhere to park the buses and cars. We understand that the field just this side of the Abbey belongs to you.'

'Aye,' he said, not volunteering anything.

'Well,' said Sergeant Bairstow, 'we wondered if you would permit the church authorities to use it as a car and coach-park, just for that one afternoon.'

'And dis thoo think they'd let me graze my cattle and sheep in yon Abbey, then? There's some nice grass in there. Or mebbe they might let me use yan o' their choches or chapils as a cattle shed, eh?' and he laughed at his own jokes. 'Christians share things, deearn't they?'

It was clear we were dealing with a difficult and stubborn old character, but Sergeant Bairstow plodded on.

'It would be needed all day, I reckon,' he said. 'On 24th August, it's a few months away yet, but we need to be finalizing our plans . . . '

'Well, Sergeant,' he said, sipping from his mug. 'Ah might 'ave sheep in yon field by then, or coos, or even some beeasts Ah might be aiming o' buying. There again, Ah might decide to put some poultry 'uts in there . . . thoo sees, Sergeant, Ah'm a busy farmer and my lands are needed all t'time, for summat or even for summat else. Ah's allus shifting things about . . . nivver stops . . . '

'It would be required only for that one day . . . '

'Yar day's t'same as onny other in my mind,' he said. 'It maks neea difference what day it is. Besides, Sergeant, Ah's nut a Catholic, and it's them lot that wants to come, isn't it?'

'I expect there'll be pilgrims of all faiths on the day,' Sergeant Bairstow said truthfully.

'Well,' said Craggs, 'Ah's nut gahin to say they can 'ave yon field. It's a lang while off yit, and Ah just might want to use it mesell.'

And he got up from the table.

With that note of finality, we made a move towards the door, and Sergeant Bairstow added, 'Thanks for the 'lowance. But can we ask you to think about it? For the good of the village, really, to keep all the traffic off the roads?'

'Aye,' said Arthur Craggs, with those eyes twinkling and almost mocking us. 'Thoo can ask me ti think aboot it.'

We said nothing to each other until we were clear of his premises, and then Bairstow sighed. 'By, Nick, there's some stubborn old mules around these parts. We need a decision from him – a "yes" decision I might add – before we can go ahead with the planning of this. Do you know him?'

I shook my head. I didn't. I'd never had cause to visit this farm, and so Sergeant Bairstow decided to ask someone else to make an approach to the farmer. Rather craftily, he discovered that Craggs had married in the Waindale Methodist Chapel and therefore asked the local Methodist minister to plead with Craggs. But this failed too. The cunning old farmer refused to commit himself one way or the other.

His indecision created an enormous problem for the organizers and for us. We began to look at several other alternatives for car and coach-parking, all grossly inconvenient but vitally necessary.

And then, in late June, Sergeant Bairstow received a very unexpected telephone call.

'It's Craggs,' said the voice. 'That field. Ah sha'n't be needing it on t'day of yon service. Thoo can 'ave it, Sergeant. Mak sure t'gates is shut when you've finished wiv it,' and he put down the telephone.

The relief was tremendous, and the arrangements went ahead with a new impetus. And then the big day dawned. It was fine and warm, a beautiful day as Father Summerson had predicted. During the previous week, the church authorities had fulfilled their role; the signs, toilets, first aid, lost children and lost property – everything had been fixed in readiness and the huge empty field bore enormous signs proclaiming it as the 'Car and Coach-Park'.

Until lunch-time, things went very smoothly. Then, as the time for the commencement of the service approached, the traffic intensified. With an hour to go, the tiny valley and its narrow lanes were congested with slow-moving vehicles, all heading for the car-park. Special constables and regular officers were guiding them along and ensuring none parked on the verges or roadside, but the queue grew longer and longer. There was clearly a delay of some kind at the head of the queue.

'Nick,' Sergeant Bairstow had come to investigate the problem. 'Pop along and see what the hold-up is.'

When I arrived at the field, I soon discovered the reason. Farmer Craggs had positioned himself at one entrance, and his wife was at the other; each was equipped with a card-table and a money-box and they had erected crude hand-painted notices which said, 'Parking, Coaches £3; cars 10/-; motor cycles 5/-; pedal cycles 1 shilling' and they were taking a fortune.

The queues, which extended in both directions from the gates, were the result of motorists and coach drivers pausing while having to pay. I had no idea whether this was part of the deal which had been struck over the use of this field, and knew I could not intervene. It was private premises. But the queue was lengthening and the delayed people would interrupt the Mass by their late arrival. I suggested to the passengers in several cars and coaches that they disembark now, before parking, and so they did. Others copied them, and soon we had a steady stream of pilgrims entering the ruins of this hallowed place as the drivers waited to park.

When I returned to the entrance, I found Sergeant Bairstow talking to Father Summerson.

'Well, Nick?'

I explained the cause of the hold-up, and Father Summerson grimaced. 'The crafty old character!' he said. 'He demanded a fee from us too and now he's charging the drivers!'

I could see it all; the cunning old farmer had withheld his permission until he knew the church would be willing to pay almost any price to have access to his field. I did not ask what price he had demanded, but then to ask parking fees as well . . .

'It's all cash too!' said Sergeant Bairstow. 'He'll make a fortune today!'

'But he has saved us a lot of problems,' said Father Summerson generously. 'We must not be too harsh about him; after all, it is his field and I'm sure we must have inconvenienced him somewhat.'

And so the day was a success. Craggs' field did accommodate most of the traffic and, as so often happens on these occasions, most of the vehicles were somehow parked before the service began. I went into the Mass and so did Sergeant Bairstow; it was a moving experience to see those ancient walls filled with people at prayer after so many centuries.

It would be some three weeks later when I saw Farmer Craggs again. He was crossing the market-place in Ashfordly and I hailed him.

'Thanks for helping us out that Sunday,' I said.

'Ah's done meself a load of harm,' he said, 'lettin' yon field off like that.'

'Harm?' I asked. 'What sort of harm?'

'Somebody's told t'taxman about it, and now he's been through my money like a dose o' salts, checking this, checking that, counting egg money, taty money. Gahin back years, he is . . . Ah shall be worse off than ivver now . . . '

And he skulked away towards the bank.

I never did know who had informed the Inland Revenue about Mr Craggs, but it was not a very Christian thing to do.

Tenants of life's middle state
Securely plac'd between the small and great.

William Cowper, 1731–1800

While serving the rural community which comprised my beat at
Aidensfield, it dawned upon me that Crampton rarely featured
in my duty commitments. But I did not neglect the village. I
paid regular visits to its telephone kiosk during my patrols and
from time to time, performed traffic duty outside the gates of
the Manor. Whenever His Lordship and Her Ladyship hosted
one of their frequent and glittering social functions, my role was
to prevent people in smart clothes and equally smart cars from
interrupting the routine of Crampton by indiscriminate
parking. A car thoughtlessly parked in a farm gateway can cause
untold havoc and delay in a rural timetable. Afterwards, I was
usually invited into the servants' quarters for a meal, an
acceptable reward.

It was the ordinary people of Crampton who seldom featured
in my work. Apart from the occasional firearms certificate to
renew or motoring offender to interview, there was rarely anything of greater moment. No serious crimes were committed;
there were no domestic rows or breaches of the peace of any
kind. There was no council estate and no pub either; these facts
might have been responsible for the happy absence of social
problems, but this was not the entire answer. It appeared to me
that the inhabitants of this peaceful place lived their quiet lives
in an oasis of blissful contentment.

It was almost as if they lived on an island of ancient peace in the midst of a turbulent modern world. Without doubt, Crampton was different from many other villages, including those on my patch and elsewhere, but I could not immediately identify the subtle points of difference. By local standards, it was a medium-sized place of perhaps 300 inhabitants with a Methodist chapel and an Anglican parish church complete with a very scholarly vicar. There was a shop-cum-Post Office, a village school, several farms and many cottages, while prominent on the outskirts was the Manor.

These factors placed it squarely on the same basis as many local villages, while its pleasant situation overlooking the gentle and meandering River Rye gave it an added scenic dimension. It was a place of remarkable calm and beauty, one which was well off the proverbial beaten track and which therefore avoided the plague of tourism and the subsidiary diseases it left in its wake.

The entire village was constructed of mature local stone which grew more charming with the slow passage of time. The gentle tan shades of the stone; the careless patchwork of red pantile roofs interspaced by the occasional thatched cottage; the tiny well-kept gardens which glowed rich with colourful flowers from spring until autumn and the whispering trees in the surrounding parkland, all combined to provide Crampton with a serenity that was the envy of many. Its way of life echoed of centuries past.

The pace was so unhurried; the inhabitants were shy and retiring and even the schoolchildren went about their business in a quiet, well-ordered fashion. The handful of teenagers who lived in the village never caused me any concern and I often wondered how they spent their free time. They, and everyone else, seemed very content with their lot, but I felt they were not subdued in any way. As time went by, Crampton became an object of some fascination and even curiosity; I wondered what made it so different and why it existed in such a quiet but distinctive way.

The first clue came one Sunday.

It was 10.15 a.m. on a bright, sunny morning in April and I was standing outside the village telephone kiosk, making one of my points. I had hoisted my motor cycle on to its stand and it was leaning at an awkward angle with my crash helmet perched on the fuel tank. Its radio burbled incomprehensibly in the peace of Crampton, but none of its messages was for me. This was the quiet scene as I waited in case the duty sergeant came to visit me, or in case someone from the office rang me on this public telephone.

All around, the birds were singing with the joys of spring and the village presented an idyllic picture of rustic calm. Its neat cottages nestled along each side of a trio of short streets; each of those streets clung to rising slopes of the valley as the morning sun glinted from their polished windows and fresh paintwork. Then I heard the sound of an expensive car engine.

Instinctively glancing in the direction of the noise, I saw a vintage Rolls-Royce emerge from the gates of Crampton Manor. It crawled sedately along the gravel road with uniformed chauffeur at the wheel, and I could see his Lordship and Her Ladyship in the rear seat. They were on their way to church. The splendid car, with every part shining after years of devoted care and constant polishing, cruised into the first street and stopped. The immaculately dressed Lord Crampton, a tall, slender man who oozed with the aristocratic breeding of his kind, climbed out and rapped on the door of a cottage with his silver-knobbed cane. Without waiting for a response, he moved to the adjoining cottage and repeated this action, then moved on to more cottages.

As he rapped successively on a sequence of doors, the car inched forward and then disappeared into Moor Street. I left my place near the kiosk and hurried in that direction, ostensibly upon a short patrol but in reality fascinated by this behaviour. I was in time to see His Lordship rap on a further four doors, then he climbed into his car which cruised up the street, turned right at the top and vanished from view.

But now, Moor Street was alive with people dressed in their Sunday finery. From all the houses visited by His Lordship, there emerged families in their Sunday best, and as they trooped up the street towards the parish church on the hilltop, they in turn knocked on all the doors they passed. More people emerged and in seconds, Moor Street was filled with smart people of every age, all heading towards their parish church.

Now the Rolls-Royce was cruising down Dale Street and it

halted at the top where a repeat performance was commenced. After his Lordship had rapped on four doors, the villagers emerged and knocked on others, and soon the populace of Dale Street was heading towards the church. As they walked and chattered happily, the Rolls turned into Middle Street which was where I happened to be. I had now returned to my kiosk and as the splendid vehicle turned towards me, Her Ladyship waved graciously and I responded with a polite salute, hatless though I was. I wondered if my action appeared to be the submissive touching of a forelock, but it was really a courteous acknowledgement.

The magnificent vehicle now stopped in this street. His Lordship, silver-topped cane in hand, thwacked more doors before ordering the car to continue. Off it went and by the time it halted at the lych-gate at the top of Middle Street, the entire Anglican population of Crampton, men, women and children, was marching towards the church. I've no idea how the Methodists, Catholics and other faiths fitted into this pattern and I did wonder, for just a fleeting moment, whether I was expected to attend. But I didn't make the gesture. I saw that His Lordship and Her Ladyship were first to enter the church, and noted that the early worshippers stood outside until the VIPs took their seats. Then everyone filed in. Only when the congregation was seated and the church full, did I hear the organist strike up the first hymn. It was precisely ten-thirty.

As I observed this quaint church-going arrangement, I realized I had witnessed a custom which had probably endured for centuries. I could imagine many past Lord Cramptons doing this self-same task from their ponies-and-traps, or from their coach-and-fours, and I now knew that I was working in a village whose ways had changed little since feudal times. The Rolls had replaced the horses; that was one visible sign of these modern times.

Few outsiders would be aware of this system of calling the faithful to church and I wondered whether the presence of individuals was monitored or checked in any way. Did His Lordship know when anyone had missed the service? And if so, what did he do? It was by pure chance that I had been in the village as this ritual was being executed, and it did give me a vital insight into the regulated mode of life in this charming, if somewhat old-fashioned village.

That Crampton continued to function along ancient feudal lines became more evident when I realized that the entire village was owned by Crampton Estate. It owned all the farms, the cottages and the shop; furthermore, most of the inhabitants worked on the estate. Some, however, were retired and continued to live in estate cottages for a meagre rent. I did learn, however, that one or two of the homes were now rented to younger village people who did not work for Crampton Estate, having secured work elsewhere. As time progressed, the number of estate workers was dwindling, but nonetheless, the estate had employed the parents and grandparents of these younger people, so the link remained.

From that time, as I toured the village on my periodic patrols, I did notice that several of the smaller cottages were unoccupied and sadly noted that some were falling into dereliction. Even if Crampton was clinging to its ancient ways, the Estate's power was being reduced simply because people were no longer working for it and occupying its cottages. Sooner or later, these would be sold, I guessed, perhaps to be revived as second homes for wealthy outsiders, or even to be turned into holiday cottages by the Estate.

One such cottage was occupied by eighty-two-year-old Emily Finley, widow of the late Archie Finley who had been one of the Estate's carpenters. After Archie's death six years ago, Emily had continued to live in their beautiful little home for the tiniest of rents. She was well looked after by the Estate from both the financial and welfare point of view, a fact which made her old age and widowhood as happy as possible. Then Emily died, and I received a telephone call from the Estate Manager, Alan Ridley.

'It's Ridley at the Estate Office,' said the voice one lunchtime. 'You've probably heard that old Mrs Finley's died?'

'Yes.' Word had reached me via the rural grapevine. 'I had heard. There's no problem, is there?'

I was thinking in terms of the coroner and whether the death was in any way mysterious or suspicious; if so, I'd have to arrange a postmortem, with all the resultant enquiries and maybe an inquest. A Sudden Death, as we termed this kind of happening, entailed a lot of police work.

'No, nothing like that, Mr Rhea. She died naturally, of old age I'd imagine. Her doctor's seen her and has issued the certificate. But it's her funeral on Wednesday in Crampton Parish Church. Eleven in the morning. The Estate is acting as undertaker. We do this for most of our employees and past employees and their spouses, free of charge, of course. There'll be a lot of cars and people about and we wondered if you would come along and keep an eye on things.'

'Of course.' I was only too pleased to oblige.

'I'd like to meet you on site to discuss the parking arrangements for the cortége, and of course, His Lordship's vehicle and those of the chief mourners.'

And so I agreed. We fixed a date and time, and this aspect presented no real problems. We could utilize the village street for parking the cars of any incomers, while the church had adequate space to accommodate and park the funeral procession including the vehicles used by His Lordship and the official party. Most of the mourners, being residents of Crampton, would be on foot anyway, for it seemed that Emily had no close family – no children, brothers or sisters.

The body would remain in the cottage until the day of the funeral, unlike some villages where it would be taken into the church the previous night. It was scheduled to depart from Holly Cottage at ten minutes to eleven and to arrive at the church in time for the eleven o'clock commencement of the service. I decided to arrive at Crampton, in my best uniform and white gloves, by no later than ten-thirty.

Before embarking on this duty, I consulted Force Standing Orders to see if there was anything I should know about my conduct at a funeral. I learned that the only specific instruction said, 'When passing a funeral cortége, members of the Force, of whatever rank, will salute the coffin.'

Just before ten-thirty that Wednesday, therefore, I presented myself outside Emily Finley's cottage in the full knowledge that there would be little to do. But I did know that the presence of a uniformed police officer at a village funeral meant a great deal to the relatives of the deceased – for one thing, it added a touch of local stature to the final journey of the dear departed.

As I approached, I discovered that the entire population of the village had arrived outside Holly Cottage. Old and young alike were there, and I learned that the Estate had given all its workers the morning off so that they could attend the funeral. Dressed in their dark mourning clothes, the villagers congregated around the tiny house, spilling onto the road and across the smooth grass which fronted these pretty little homes. Due to the numbers, I did find myself having to keep them in some sort of order as several pressed forward and obstructed the route the coffin would take. It did mean, of course, that Mrs Finley was assured of a fine send-off. I felt she would have been surprised at the turn-out, but on reflection accepted that this response was normal in this village.

Then the hearse arrived. But it wasn't a motor hearse, nor was it a horse-drawn vehicle. Some villages, I know, did make use of a black horse-drawn hearse with a smartly groomed black horse to draw it, but this was something entirely different. Between the ranks of assembled people, there appeared six young men smartly dressed in black suits, white shirts, black ties and bowler hats. I blinked as I saw them; they were all so like one another that they were difficult to tell apart. They resembled sextuplets, I thought, for they were like peas in the proverbial pod and they even moved in unison. In sombre silence, they were guiding something towards the cottage. It was a small four-wheeled trolley constructed of smart oak, with metal springs, spoked wheels and pneumatic tyres. Planks of oak formed two platforms, one above the other, the top one being about waist height. This polished and well-oiled vehicle, reminiscent of a pram without its cradle, moved silently and smoothly at the hands of its attendants. I noticed that Alan Ridley followed, now acting in his capacity as Estate undertaker. He was also clad in a black suit and bowler, and the little procession came to rest at the door of Mrs Finley's cottage.

Like everyone else, I stood in respectful silence to observe the proceedings and then the six men, preceded by Alan Ridley, moved indoors. They left the trolley outside. After a few minutes, the six emerged bearing the coffin on three strong slings which passed beneath it.

With obvious experience of similar small houses, they manoeuvred the coffin from the cramped space within and did so without dislodging the solitary wreath which lay on top. They hoisted the coffin on to the trolley, folded and stored the slings, then Alan Ridley approached with several more wreaths in his arms. These were carefully arranged on the lower level of the trolley hearse. When everything was in position, the funeral procession moved off. I walked ahead to halt any oncoming traffic that might arrive. To the sound of a tolling bell, the sombre procession filled the narrow confines of Middle Street as it climbed slowly towards the church; the six men did not have an easy task, guiding and pushing their precious load up the slope, but they succeeded.

They grew redder and redder in the face as the climb steepened and at the top, the vicar awaited beneath the lych-gate, the traditional resting place of corpses on their way to burial. His Lordship and Her Ladyship also waited at a discreet distance, standing close to the main door. Beneath the wooden cover of the lych-gate, the six bearers halted for just a moment to regain their breath and wipe the perspiration from their brows, and then the vicar began to recite the preliminary prayers. At this stage, the coffin, still on its wheels, was steered into the church. As it moved down the aisle, the accompanying mourners filed silently into their seats.

I saw Lord and Lady Crampton enter their pew as the coffin arrived at its position before the altar. I stayed at the back of the church.

At eleven o'clock prompt, the service began.

Even though I had never known Emily, I found both the service and the interment to be very moving. I gained the impression that the Estate and its workers were like a large and happy family; a true community which was being eradicated through the progress of time. Had Emily been buried by her few relatives, the church would not have been so full, nor would her funeral have been such an important event for the village. As things were, she was given a fitting farewell by those who knew and respected her. Following the interment, there was the traditional funeral lunch of ham in the Tenants' Room at the Hall. Everyone was invited, including myself.

There, I was privately thanked by Alan Ridley for the small part I had played, and I learned that the six bearers were three brothers and their three cousins. They all worked on the Estate as carpenters, stone masons, electricians and plumbers. Acting as bearers during Estate funerals was one of their regular additional commitments.

As I motor cycled home afterwards, I realized why this village did not feature greatly in any of my crime returns or in the Divisional Offence Report Register. It was due, I felt, to the family atmosphere of Crampton and the close relationship between everyone who lived and worked here. That closeness affected both their working and private lives.

I had no doubt that if a small crime did occur, a theft for example, it would be dealt with locally and I would never know about it. Perhaps the threat of dismissal from employment by the Estate caused everyone to be law-abiding, and I did know that the Estate dealt with any local disputes between neighbours. There were no domestic disputes in Crampton of the kind that officially concerned me, but I knew that this feudal type of existence was drawing to a close. And with its decline would come social problems and community strife.

As the deserted cottages were sold and occupied by outsiders, so this enduring family atmosphere would be diluted and the problems and difficulties of the outside world would afflict the village. The Estate would lose its paternal control for better or for worse, and I wondered if this would happen during my period as the village constable. After all, we were in the second half of the twentieth century, but it was pleasing to know that this kind of contented and untroubled life did continue in part of the English countryside.

But there was one occasion when I had to deal with a small outbreak of trouble in Crampton. Curiously, it arose as an indirect result of Emily Finley's death. Perhaps, to be more precise, it arose because of her empty cottage, but it did mean that I had to take out my notebook and begin the steps necessary to institute criminal proceedings.

To set the scene, it became the policy of Crampton Estate to sell off those empty cottages for which they had no foreseeable use. This applied especially to those which required a lot of renovation and modernization. As cottages became vacant, in the way that Emily's did, the Estate had to decide whether they were required for new workers, married staff, larger or smaller families or retiring employees. The work force was contracting; it was happening everywhere in the countryside and fewer cottages were needed. Nonetheless, Crampton Estate did occasionally take on new workers from outside.

Some of them required a house, and Emily's cottage had become vacant at the very time the Estate was considering the appointment of a trained accountant. Its increasingly complicated book-keeping now required those kind of skills and so Emily's little house was earmarked as a possible home for this new member of staff. Over the weeks following her death, I noticed that the house was renovated. Scaffolding appeared outside and pointing of the stonework was undertaken. New tiles were fitted to the roof and piles of stones, bricks and cement appeared in the garden as internal structural changes were made. A new bath was fitted and the kitchen was brought up to the standards of the period; the house was re-wired too and a partial damp-course installed.

Around this time, one day in May, I had to visit the Estate Office about some cattle movement licences and was offered a coffee by Alan Ridley.

'I see Mrs Finley's cottage is nearly finished,' I said after we had concluded our official business.

'Give it another week,' he said. 'It looks nice now. I wish she could have seen it, the work was long overdue. But we can't do that kind of job with folks living in them. Besides, old folks don't like upheaval or changes to their homes.'

'You've appointed an accountant, I hear?' I put to him.

'Yes, a woman. A Miss Rogers. Jean Rogers. She starts a week on Monday.'

'And she'll occupy that little house?' I was updating my local knowledge of the village.

Alan laughed. 'In theory, yes. In practice, no. You know,' he added almost as an afterthought, 'I think you ought to be in Crampton a week on Monday, say from eight o'clock in the morning.'

'Really, why?' I asked, slightly puzzled.

'That's the day we hand over the keys to Mrs Finley's cottage,' he said, and I detected a distinct twinkle in his eye. 'But we give them to the Maintenance Foreman; he arranges the housing moves. Might I suggest you are outside Mrs Finley's house just before eight?'

'You won't be expecting trouble, will you?' I asked, wondering what lay behind his suggestion.

'No,' he said, 'but I think you'll find it an interesting experience.'

So I arranged my duties to accommodate this unusual suggestion and on that Monday morning, I decided to perform one of my rare foot patrols around Crampton. I began at seven-thirty, and enjoyed the morning stroll; the village was full of rich blossom and in places, the clean, crisp air was heavy with varied scents. Birds were singing and the morning was dewy and bright, with the sun gaining in strength as it rose in the sky. It was a moment from a corner of heaven.

Just before eight o'clock, I made my way around to Middle Street, towards Mrs Finley's cottage, as everyone called it. Few people referred to it as Holly Cottage. I was surprised to see that a small crowd had gathered. It comprised men, women and children and I must admit that this baffled me. The sight made me wonder what was about to happen and why I was really here.

Then Alan Ridley arrived on foot. He acknowledged my presence with a brief nod and stood before the front door of the cottage, awaiting eight o'clock. As the church clock struck the hour, the Maintenance Foreman, a dour Yorkshireman called Charlie Atkinson, came forward. He was dressed in his overalls and ready for work.

As the clock was striking, Alan handed over to him the two keys of Mrs Finley's cottage, one for the back door and one for the front.

Charlie then called, 'Sidney and Alice Brent!'

A man came forward and accepted the keys. At the same time, Sidney Brent handed some keys to Charlie who announced, 'George and Ann Clifton.'

The Cliftons came forward, accepted the Brent keys, and then passed up some of their own.

'Alex Cooper,' and an elderly man emerged from the crowd to

accept the Cliftons' keys. He handed some back to Charlie, and so the process continued with about twelve families waiting to hand over their keys and accept others in return.

During this short ceremony, Alan Ridley moved to my side. 'Well?' he asked quizzically. 'Have you got it worked out?'

'No,' I admitted. 'What's going on?'

'We're re-housing,' he smiled. 'Or, to be exact, our tenants are rehousing themselves.'

'All these?'

He nodded; already, those who had been first in the queue, were disappearing hurriedly towards their homes.

'All of them,' he said. 'In a few minutes, all hell will break loose. The Brents will be coming here, to occupy Mrs Finley's cottage, and they'll want to be in right away. But that's Charlie's problem. Come along, let's go.'

He began to walk along the village towards his own office in the Hall and I fell into step at his side.

'So what's going on?' I asked as we distanced ourselves from the gathering.

'It's an old practice on this Estate,' he adopted a serious voice. 'When we appoint someone to our staff, we offer to house them. It happens everywhere – tied cottages, you know. And so we select one of our empty houses and modernize it. We clean and decorate it, as we did with Mrs Finley's.'

'But all those people handing in keys . . . ' I began.

'Yes,' he said. 'At some time in the past, long before my arrival here, this kind of thing caused an upset in the village. In appointing and housing newcomers in refurbished homes, we created the situation where workers of long standing were living in properties which were below the standard we offered to the newcomers. The newcomer's home was always refurbished and modernized, in the way you've just seen. So the tenants decided that whenever a house became vacant and was modernized, the longest serving tenant should move in, if he or she wanted to.'

I realized how things worked.

'So they all move up a notch?' I put to him.

'Yes, the whole village waits for an empty house like this. On the day, they're packed and ready, and so, in a few minutes, the

Brents will move into Mrs Finley's nice cottage, and then the
Cliftons will move into the Brents', old Alex Cooper will move
into the Cliftons' . . . '

'And your new accountant? Where does she fit into all this?' I
asked.

'It's not going to be easy, with her coming from outside the
village. I'll have to explain things to her. To be honest, some of
our manual workers, especially those born here, are quite happy
to accept a cottage which is, to be truthful, at the bottom of our
heap. In the past, they did so because they desperately needed
accommodation, and the rents we charged were affordable to
the poorest. But low rents meant we hadn't the funds to
modernize the homes. For a peppercorn rent, those folks were
happy to live in less-than-perfect accommodation. Their
"carrot" was to wait for the kind of movement you've seen today.
It enabled them to move up the scale and, let's face it, the Estate
benefits because it needs to modernize only one house every few
years. It saves us money and keeps rent down. Eventually,
everyone should get a chance to occupy such a place. But I fear
our new lady worker will not tolerate a house which is the last of
today's line – it's grotty, to say the least. We may sell it. She has
hinted she might buy a house locally. If we appoint more people
from outside, then our system of moving tenants is likely to die
out, I feel.'

'A strange system,' I commented.

'Now, if you go back into the village, you'll see that there is a
flurry of activity, with well over a dozen families moving house.
They're all moving today and all before ten o'clock!'

'You impose a deadline?'

'We must. Officially, they're not supposed to do it, but we
close our eyes and go along with the idea, up to a point. That's
why Charlie handles all the keys – it keeps some sort of order,
and it makes the tenants think it's got our formal blessing. So we
give them time off between eight and ten to make their moves.'

When I walked back through Crampton, an amazing sight
met my eyes. The village seemed full of carts, cars, lorries and
anything that would transport furniture. Already, many items
were on board – three-piece suites, wardrobes, beds and tea-
chests full of crockery. The gardens and grassy areas outside the

cottages were covered with household belongings and people were rushing in and out with arms full of objects. Helpers were flinging things on to the vehicles and it seemed there was a race to be first into another home. It was an amazing sight, a community house removal of the like I've never seen before nor since.

As I strolled about to observe this peculiar occurrence, I came across an argument, a rare event in Crampton. From a distance, I knew some kind of dispute was raging and that it involved a pile of furniture on a horse-drawn cart. The air was full of ripe language while angry arms were waving between the protagonists. Then one of them spotted me.

'Here's t'bobby,' I heard. 'Ask him!'

One of the men hailed me and I strode across.

'Yes?' I asked of anyone who might answer. There would be eight or nine people standing around the loaded cart. It was one of the old so-called market carts, a tipper with two wheels and a tailboard which lowered to facilitate loading and unloading. Already, it looked precariously overloaded with a tall wardrobe standing upright and a chest of drawers hanging over the tailboard. Every spare piece of space was filled with domestic odds and ends.

'Mr Rhea,' the man holding the horse's head addressed me. I knew him by sight, but did not know his name. 'Settle this for us, wilt thoo?'

They all began to shout at once, and I appealed for calm, then addressed the man with the horse.

'Ah'm t'owner of this cart,' he said, 'and Ah live out near t'bridge, on t'road to Brantsford. Hawkins is the name.'

'Go on,' I invited.

'This chap 'ere,' and he pointed to a young man close to the tail of the cart, 'well, 'e asked me to help him shift this stuff today. Hired me 'orse and cart to 'im, Ah did. Half a crown an hour.'

'Is this right?' I asked the man lurking at the tail.

He nodded, with a sly grin on his face, as the cart-owner continued.

'Two jobs to do,' he said, 'his mum and dad out of this house here, and into that 'un there,' and he pointed to a pair of houses almost opposite one another. 'Then, after that, Ah was asked to shift him and his missus and kids out of his spot and into that 'un what was occupied by his mum and dad.'

'Yes,' I followed it so far. Mum and dad into a smaller house, and son and growing family into their old house, which was slightly larger. Very sensible.

'Well,' said the cart man, 'him and his mates, all his brothers and what-have-you loaded me up with his dad and mum's furniture for t'first job and got me unloaded, all in seven minutes. Seven minutes to move house! When Ah got loaded up for t'second trip, from his house to his mum's spot, he said they'd do t'same all over again, load and unload in another seven minutes.'

'So?' I had not yet discovered the cause of the dispute.

'Well, they're saying that because Ah charges half a crown an hour, and it hasn't taken an hour, then they don't have to pay!'

'Did you tell them that the half-crown was the minimum charge for an hour or part of an hour?' I asked him.

'Nay, Ah didn't! There's no need for that sort of carry-on, Mr Rhea. Damn it, Ah thought two house jobs would take all morning, not fourteen minutes . . .'

This was not a police matter. It was what we called a business dispute, and so I told him that. I said it was nothing to do with the police; it was purely a business disagreement which must be sorted out between themselves.

'Then Ah shall keep this stuff on t'cart until t'hour's up,' he said, 'then Ah'll be in my rights to ask for t'money.'

'We'll unload it,' said the young man to his brothers and family. 'Howway, lads, get cracking. We can beat our last record for unloading, I reckon . . .'

But Hawkins had a different idea.

'Nay!' he shouted. 'Thoo can't touch this stuff! Not yet,' and he rapped the horse's flanks with a rein. It moved off quickly, but everyone followed, trying to grab items and carry them indoors. Some of the smaller stuff was lifted off, but the larger items were impossible to move. As the horse broke into a trot, its intrepid owner ran alongside and then jumped on to the front edge of his cart where the shafts met the body, and he sat there, reins in hand, as he whipped the horse into a gallop.

The furniture bounced and jolted along the street as the horse and cart left the family behind and then Hawkins halted. In a flash, he jumped off his cart and loosened the primitive tipping mechanism. With a jangling of metal, the bolts fell free and he slapped the horse.

It moved a short distance and the cart, now unbalanced, tipped backwards as all the furniture slid off the back and spread across the road. In a long, untidy line, furniture, clothes, pots and pans, clip rugs and a motley collection of things rolled into the street.

'If you're not paying, then Ah'm not moving it,' said Hawkins, folding his arms to observe the mayhem. At the moment the family ran towards their scattered belongings, a service bus, followed by an oil tanker, turned into the street. And at that same moment, I knew I had before me a clear case of 'Obstruction of the Highway'. The bus driver started to shout at Hawkins, but he only laughed as he managed to secure his cart to its chassis during the fuss. All this was happening as I approached the scene in the ponderous strides of the constabulary in action. Hawkins, however, was quickly mobile and trotted away his horse, chortling at his own astuteness.

'You'll have to move this stuff!' I ordered the owners. 'It's obstructing the road.'

'Not us!' snapped the brothers. 'Hawkins dumped it, Hawkins can shift it!'

'You'll all get fined for obstructing this road,' I shouted above the din. 'And it'll be far more than the cost of hiring that cart!'

'Nope,' said the family. 'It stays.'

Hawkins was already some distance away, and I would have to report him too; I knew where he lived.

The tanker driver leaned out of his cab. 'Are they going to shift that rubbish or shall I drive over it?' he shouted above the noise.

A stout, middle-aged woman wielding a broom came running to the scene, crying and saying, 'Our Harry, you stupid oaf! Get it shifted, now,' and she started to belabour him with the broom handle. Confronted by such positive persuasion, Harry and the other men of the family soon cleared a road through for the bus and the tanker, and then, as the heat of the moment evaporated, they began to manhandle their stuff to the side of the road. It took much longer than seven minutes.

So far as I know Hawkins never received any payment for that task, but he did eventually receive a summons after I had reported both him and the key members of that large family for 'Obstruction of the Highway'. When the Superintendent read my report, he laughed and formally cautioned each party, so there was no court case.

Never again, was I involved in the house-moving customs of Crampton, and sometimes I wonder if they still continue. And I'm also curious as to whether anyone has broken the Crampton record of seven minutes for moving the contents of one house into another.

6

The love of money is the root of all evil.

St Paul, d. *circa* AD 67

One of the less publicized aspects of constabulary work is the quiet assistance that police-officers give to members of the public; it would be possible to fill a book with glowing examples. This help comes in many forms, such as assisting in the repair of a broken down car; catching stray budgies; helping with the formalities of bureaucracy or coaxing worried souls through the maze of complex problems that life throws at them.

I recall one example which involved a colleague of mine. He was performing night duty on a main trunk road and came upon a family car which had broken down. It was a major defect and there was no overnight garage in the area. He learned that the occupants were heading for London; driving through the night to catch a morning flight for a long-overdue visit to an aged relative in Australia. Marooned as they were in the middle of the North Riding of Yorkshire, the constable promptly ended his shift by taking some time off duty. He was able to do this because of some overtime previously worked, and with no thought of being paid or even thanked, he drove the stranded family to London in his own car. It was a distance of 250 miles each way and they caught their flight.

Countless minor tasks are completed during a police-officer's daily round, each in itself a small thing, albeit of great value to the person who is helped. One feature of this work is that it provides a vivid insight into the private lives of others.

One example which occurred on my patch at Aidensfield involved Awd Eustace, whose real name was Eustace Wakefield.

His problem was that he could not light his fire, a fact which came to my notice early one winter morning. The house next door to his was empty for three months while the owners were overseas, and I was keeping an eye on it. This meant regular visits to ensure it hadn't been broken into or vandalized, and it was while examining the rear of this house that I noticed Eustace. He was chopping sticks just over the separating fence, so I said, 'Good morning.'

'Morning.' He was a slight man with long, unkempt grey hair and was stooped with age. Ragged old clothes, over which he wore a tattered cardigan, attempted to protect him against the icy winds of winter and he wore woollen gloves without any fingers. He was hacking away at some small logs and chopping them into kindling sticks.

'That'll warm you up,' I said, mindful of the Yorkshire notion that the act of chopping sticks warms you twice – once when chopping them and again when blazing on a fire.

'It would if Ah could get that bloody fire o' mine going,' said the little fellow. 'Damned thing, it won't draw. Them sticks is wet, mebbe.'

'They look OK to me,' I peered across the fence to examine them.

'Ah've tried and tried this morning,' he said. 'Damn thing won't blaze so Ah can't even boil me kettle.'

'I'll come round,' I heard myself make an offer of help.

There was no wonder his fire wouldn't ignite. It stood no chance. His grate was part of an old range of the Yorkist type. It had an oven at one side and a centrally positioned black leaded grate some two feet above floor level. At the opposite side of the oven was a hot water tank; this was built into the fireplace and fitted with a brass tap to draw off the heated water. A small can with a wire handle hung from that tap, and a kettle of cold water waited on a swivel hob.

But the grate was overflowing with ash. It was inches deep within the grate itself, but the tall space below was also full. The ash spilled and spread for a distance of about a yard into the dusty room. Directly on top of all this, he had tried to light his pathetic fire; the evidence was there in the form of charred newspapers and sticks, with odd lumps of coal uselessly placed.

'It'll never go with all that muck underneath,' I kicked the accumulated ash with my boot. 'It needs cleaning out, you need a draught for a fire to blaze. You've choked it to death!'

'Oh,' he said as if not fully understanding this elementary fact.

'Where's your shovel?' I asked and he produced a battered one from its place near the sink. I began to scoop shovelfuls from the huge pile of ash and soon had enough to fill his dustbin. After a few minutes of this dusty, hectic work, during which I removed my tunic and cap, I had his fireplace cleaned out and had added a layer of thick dust to that which coated all his belongings.

'Right,' I said. 'Paper and sticks next.'

He had a store of old newspapers in a wall cupboard and brought in some of the sticks he had been chopping.

'You ought to get some more chopped,' I suggested, 'and put them in this side oven to dry. But these aren't bad, they're dry enough.'

I laid his fire then went out to his coal-house. But it was almost bare. In one dark corner were a few lumps of coal, scarcely enough to last out this day. I managed to scrape sufficient for my task and laid it on the fire, applied a match and very soon it was blazing merrily.

'I'll tell the coalman to call,' I said to Eustace, taking his kettle and weighing it in my hands to see if it was full. It was, so I turned the swivel hob over the blaze so that the kettle would boil for his pot of tea. 'You're nearly out, you'll need some today.'

'Ah've no money,' he said. 'Ah've no money for coal . . . '

'Your pension's due on Thursday, isn't it?'

'Aye, well, t'coalman might wait a day or two then.'

As I stood before the welcoming blaze, I was well aware that this old man was poverty-stricken. The tiny back room, which served as lounge, living-room and kitchen, was dismal and virtually bare. The only furnishings were an old armchair with the stuffing protruding, a battered table and one old kitchen chair. There was a small, well-worn clip rug before the fire, but the stone floor was otherwise bare and in one corner there was a large brown earthenware sink with a cold water tap. The wooden draining-board contained all his crockery; it had been washed and stacked there until required. The bare walls had been distempered years ago and never cleaned or papered since.

The toilet, which was a WC, was outside next to the coal-shed and there was another room downstairs, but I did not go in, nor did I venture upstairs. It was plain to see that Awd Eustace lived in desperately poor accommodation with no money to spend on luxuries or even the basic necessities of life. I felt sorry for him and promised to look in from time to time.

When I left, he seemed happier and the kettle was beginning to sing. Later in the day, I came across the coalman as he was making some deliveries in Elsinby and asked him to drop a few sacks into Awd Eustace's shed. This he promised to do. I explained about Eustace's pension and the coalman was quite happy to wait for his payment.

From that time onwards, I made a practice of popping in to see old Eustace, but he never improved his ways. He never cleaned out his grate and always had trouble getting a fire going, so I became his regular grate-cleaner. Sometimes, I would stay and sample a cup of weak tea but he seldom chatted about himself. I did learn, however, that he had no family, except for a brother who lived somewhere in the Birmingham area. They'd never communicated for years. To earn a living, Eustace had worked on local farms all his life, labouring and doing odd jobs. He'd retired about twelve years ago, and had come to spend his final years in this tiny house.

Then one day I called and there was no sign of him. A bottle of milk stood on the doorstep and immediately I feared the worst. I knocked several times, then forced my way in and found him dead in bed. It is unnecessary to dwell upon the formalities that followed, except to say that he died of natural causes. A few days later, a solicitor contacted me. He asked me to be present as he searched Eustace's home for personal effects and documents. And the result was astounding.

We found twelve Building Society passbooks, each containing the maximum deposit of £5,000; there were bags of bank notes under the bed and stuffed in his cupboards; a sack half-full of gold sovereigns, and share certificates galore filed neatly in a battered suitcase. For a police constable, whose salary was then about £650 per annum, this was a fortune. The wealth in this hovel was staggering.

Awd Eustace had left a fortune and I expected it would go to his brother. Eustace had always existed on the smallest amount of money; putting all his savings away in stocks and shares, and in the building societies. The house was his own too, and so he could have lived a very comfortable and happy life. Why he chose to live in such lowly conditions, I do not know but there were many like him.

One old character always sat and read by the light of a candle, and once when I called to see if he was all right, he welcomed me into his room, settled me in a chair, and then blew out the candle.

'Thoo dissn't need t'light of a candle just ti chat,' he said, as if in explanation. 'There's neea point in wasting good money.' And I learned later that the same old man, who'd been left a lot of valuables by his well-to-do father, was quite content to barter a silk tie in return for a cabbage, or an exquisite piece of china for a few eggs. It was rumoured he could be seen in the light of his candle as he counted his piles of money, but I never witnesed this.

There were many similar instances of Yorkshire canniness in the handling of money; it has often been said that if a coin fell over the side of a ship with a Scotsman and a Yorkshireman on board, the Yorkshireman would be first into the water to retrieve it. There is no doubt that some Yorkshire folk are very careful and this trait was noticeable among police-officers and their wives.

There were, and still are, some very tight-fisted policemen and some equally careful wives. It must be said that the policeman's wage at that time was very poor and those with growing families did find it difficult to manage, myself included. Many made skilful economies but some went to extreme odds. I knew one lady who bought an electric washing-machine after months of careful saving, and then, in order to use it, sat up until after midnight so she could take advantage of cheap electricity. The burning lights probably cost more than she saved – unless she worked in the dark.

Another had a similar line of thought. Her parents bought her a washing-up machine, a fine piece of equipment which washed all her pots. But the woman worried about the cost of running it; the thought of massive electricity bills so horrified her that she decided to run it during the night. In this way, the cheaper electricity could be utilized to the full and the machine would be used only when it was completely full of dirty pots.

The snag was that the family had only one set of crockery. When all the pieces were dirty, they were placed into the machine and the family had to wait until next morning before they could be re-used. The mother would not hear of the machine being used during the daytime, so she bought a second set of crockery. But as one set was used at breakfast, another at lunch and some pieces casually during the day, two sets were not enough. So she bought a third set, with a few spare mugs and plates . . .

The result was that during the night hours, her washing-up machine, filled with three full sets of crockery from breakfast, lunch and tea, rumbled along on its cheap power. I don't know what it cost her in spare crockery and I often wonder if she thought she was being economical.

Inevitably, with circulating tales of such tightfistedness, (a state of mind which is very often regarded as common sense by its perpetrators) there are discussions as to which person, within our knowledge, is the meanest. All men know the fellow who will never buy his round in a pub; who coasts downhill in his car to save petrol or who always uses the office telephone to make his calls. Invariably, though, there is one person who becomes a legend in his own lifetime so far as tightfistedness is concerned. The police service is just as prone as any other profession and in our case, such a man was Police Constable Meredith Dryden.

Of middle service and approaching his forties, he sported a ruddy, moon-shaped face and a nice head of dark, curly hair. He'd been reared in a village on the Yorkshire Wolds, and was as careful as any man I know. He did free-wheel his private car down hills to save petrol, and did switch his house lights off each time he left a room, even for five minutes: what he saved on electricity was spent on replacing baffled bulbs. He grew his own vegetables which he sold to his wife at market prices; made all his family use the same bathwater to save on heating costs, and even cut his own hair.

When he first came to my notice, he was stationed on the coast, but was later transferred to Brantsford, just along the road from Aidensfield and Ashfordly. His reputation preceded him; long before Meredith arrived, we heard about his legendary meanness and wondered how he would get along with the happy-go-lucky members of Ashfordly section.

One of his habits quickly manifested itself. He got others to run errands for him on the grounds that it both saved his boot leather and obviated a lot of the aggravation that followed his miserly actions. I came across this one day when I was in the tiny police office of Brantsford. Meredith was sitting at the typewriter and a young probationer constable was at his side.

As I entered, midway through one of my motor cycle patrols, Meredith said to the youngster, 'Paul, nip down to the newsagents, will you? Get me a copy of the *Yorkshire Post* – I can read it over my coffee break.'

Eager to please, the lad put on his cap and off he went; I made some coffee as Meredith worked, and by the time the kettle had boiled, Paul had returned with the newspaper.

'Thanks,' said Meredith, not offering any payment to the youngster. We chatted over our coffee, and Meredith scanned the newspaper. Then, when we'd finished, he handed it back to the lad.

'Thanks, take it back to the shop. Tell 'em I'd gone when you got back.'

And so the young policeman was faced with the embarrassing choice of either taking back the paper, or keeping it himself. He kept it, but he learned not to run any more errands for Meredith the Miser, as we named him. In the office, he collected bits of string and old envelopes for use at home and on one occasion when a lady came collecting for the Red Cross, Meredith slipped a threepenny bit into her box, and then made an entry in his official notebook to the effect that he had done so. This was complete with the date, time and place of the transaction.

'You never know when folks are on the fiddle,' he said

earnestly. 'I'll check that the money has gone to the right place, just to be sure.' And he did.

We had heard that Meredith used his tea-bags several times before throwing them out and that he made his wife wait until the shops were on the point of closing before entering to make her purchases of perishable goods. That way, she often got the tail-end bargains of the day, such as cheap fruit and vegetables, or damaged tins of stuff. On the topic of housekeeping, word had reached us that his wife, Ruth, had to make a weekly request for the precise amount of cash she needed, whereupon Meredith would draw the cash from the bank.

Just how precisely his mind operated was revealed to me one Friday morning. On another of my motor cycle routes, I popped into Brantsford Police Station with some reports for signature, and Meredith was there.

I brewed some coffee and brought two cups into the front office. We sat and talked for a few minutes about our work, then I stood up and said, 'Well, Meredith, I must be off. I've work to do and people to see.'

'That'll be tuppence,' he said, 'for the coffee.'

'No,' I tried to correct him, 'we pay into a fund for the coffee, both here and at Ashfordly. Sergeant Bairstow collects it – I'm up to date with my payments.'

'I know, but we ran out of office coffee. This is my own – I brought it in for today, for myself. You owe me for one cup and some milk. Tuppence.'

For a moment, I thought he was joking, but the expression on that florid face told me he was serious. I handed over two pennies.

'Going far?' he asked, as I replaced my crash helmet, still smarting from his actions.

'Briggsby eventually,' I said, 'and then Thackerston.'

'You couldn't do a job for me, could you?' The request was pleasant enough. From an ordinary person, there would have been an instant and positive response, but as this was coming from Meredith the Miser, I had to consider all the likely consequences.

'What sort of a job?' I was wary of the things he had asked others to do.

'Cash a cheque for me at the bank before you leave town?'

After a moment's reflection, I agreed. I needed to cash one of my own for housekeeping, and so it would not be a hindrance. Meredith gave me a cheque for £6 13s 2d, and I said I would be happy to cash it.

It transpired that this was for his wife's housekeeping that week. I had no problem cashing it for him, but I now realized that it was true that Meredith did calculate the week's housekeeping allowance literally down to the last penny. Furthermore, he regularly went shopping with her when his duties permitted, his purpose being to ensure that she bought the cheapest goods without exceeding the tight budget he imposed. If possible, she had to save from her allowance. We began to feel sorry for poor Ruth Dryden.

Then Meredith had an apparent flush of generosity because he invited Alwyn Foxton and his wife for a day's outing on the moors. Alwyn had been at training-school with Meredith and was perhaps his closest companion.

'It's my birthday on Sunday,' Meredith had told him. 'I'm forty. Life begins at forty, so they say. I thought you and Betty, and me and Ruth, could have a day out on the moors to celebrate. I'm off duty that day. We'll use my car and we'll stop and have lunch at a pub, and then take things as they come.'

I do know that Alwyn was surprised by this invitation, as indeed everyone was, and he agreed to go on the outing. For the rest of us, as mere onlookers, it did seem that Meredith had mellowed and that the onset of forty had opened his mind and his wallet.

The historic outing was scheduled for the second Sunday in May and I recall that it was a beautiful day with clear skies and bright sunshine. The countryside was at its best, with fresh, new greenery along the hedgerows, colourful flowers in abundance both in the wild and in the rustic gardens, and a barrage of birdsong to complete the idyllic picture. The outing should be wonderful; I wished I was going (albeit not with Meredith), but I was performing a local duty that day.

It would be about a week afterwards when I next saw Alwyn, his grey hair perhaps a few shades whiter and his face drawn with anger. He had an envelope in his hand.

'Are you all right, Alwyn?' I asked. At that moment, I had

forgotten all about the moorland outing and was concerned for his health. He did look pale and sick, and I had a feeling it was connected with the letter in his hand.

'No I am not!' he fumed. 'The bloody man!'

I did not know what to say or how to react, but he said, 'You know that bloody man Meredith the Miser?'

'Yes,' I said tentatively.

'You were there, weren't you? When he invited me and Betty to have a day out with him? It was his birthday.'

'Yes,' I acknowledged. 'How did it go?'

'It cost me a bloody fortune!' Alwyn snapped, sitting down at the desk. 'Meredith turned up in his car, as promised, and in we jumped. We went up to Rosedale and Hutton-le-Hole and after a walk we all went to a cafe for some morning coffee.'

'That was nice of him,' I commented for want of something better to say.

'Nothing of the sort!' snapped Alwyn. 'By the time the bill came, he managed to disappear into the toilet. I paid, and I was happy to do so at that time. At that point, there was nothing to grumble about.'

It was evident that Meredith had been on top form that day, and so I settled down to hear more from Alwyn.

'We drove all over, stopping in villages, pausing to look at views and that sort of thing. In fact, Nick, it was a lovely outing. The moors were splendid and there's some magnificent scenery off the beaten track. Then we stopped at a pub which served bar snacks for lunch. Well, I paid for the first round of drinks and when the time came for the second, he went to make a telephone call. I paid for that round as well. Then Meredith told the landlord it was his birthday and ordered wine, and we had a smashing meal. And would you believe it, when the landlord brought the bill, Meredith vanished into the toilet again.'

'He did you again!' I grinned.

'Yes, I paid. I thought he'd square up with me later, so I paid up. I didn't want to cause any embarrassment in the pub. I thought he'd go halves at least, but he never offered a penny. Not a bloody penny! He just jumped into his car and came home, and thanked me for a lovely day out. I hadn't the heart to demand half-shares from him, not on his birthday.'

'Alwyn, old son,' I said, 'you know what the fellow's like, we all know what he's like. You should have been wary of him – and now you've given him a birthday treat, haven't you. I reckon he spends hours planning these campaigns.'

'That's not all.' Alwyn held up the envelope which had so clearly upset him. 'Seen this?' and he passed it to me.

It was a bill from Meredith. He was asking Alwyn to pay for half the petrol used on that outing.

In spite of our knowledge of Meredith and his methods, he continued to score against us in our off-guarded moments. At one time or another, most of us found ourselves at the expensive end of Meredith's guile. He managed on one occasion to get me to buy two raffle tickets for him; as the seller waited for Meredith to finish a telephone call, I paid her, but he never paid me. I don't think he won a prize but nor did I.

Then it was time for duty at York Races. The May meeting is always so pleasant, for the course is at its floral best and every one of us wanted to be selected as additional strength to aid York City Police. Extra officers were drafted in from all the neighbouring forces for duty at this busy course on race days. Such duties came around only once in a while, and it was so nice to be nominated. When I looked at the names of the colleagues who were to accompany me, I saw that Meredith was one of them. I made a vow to keep out of his way where money was involved.

In those days, we travelled by train and had to lodge overnight in York for the duration of the three-day meeting. Our digs were in some old terraced houses which overlooked the racecourse and for each of the three days we paraded at 11 a.m. for our duties. They included car-parking; security of the track, the horses and the jockeys; plus a watch for pickpockets, car thieves and the other unsavoury characters who prey on their fellows at race meetings, with a general brief to ensure that things progressed smoothly. It was a hard, but pleasant three days and we usually finished duty around six o'clock following dispersal of traffic after the last race. During our two evenings in digs, we went either to the cinema or to the local pubs for a drink or two, but if we were broke, we stayed in and played cards or dominoes.

Although we were not allowed to place bets while in uniform, we did manage to persuade CID officers or other acquaintances to put money on our selections. We enjoyed race meetings; they were a real tonic and a break from our more mundane duties.

Throughout that May meeting, Meredith's miserly reputation caused him to be frozen out of many social events; if drinks were bought, he was ignored unless he could be forced into buying a round. And that was a rare event. He was not allowed to play darts, dominoes or cards unless he put his money on the table first and in this cruel way the men, all of us, kept him at bay. Our actions did not make him alter his attitude; he remained as tightfisted and miserly as ever, and after the final day, as we travelled home by train, this character-trait shone through more strongly than ever.

Our train journey took us to Eltering where an official car would be waiting to take us home. The trip from York was through some delightful countryside but we were too tired and too broke to appreciate it; exhausted, broke and hungry, we were concerned only with getting home.

None of us had any money left; we'd either lost it on the horses or spent it on our enjoyment at the pubs or pictures, and so that long journey was pretty miserable. There were no refreshment cars on a trip of that kind – besides, none of us could have found the necessary cash to buy anything. There were eight of us in our carriage, all sitting quietly as we brooded over the past three days. Meredith was one and he was just as quiet as the others.

As the train chugged along, someone would say, 'By, I could just eat a round of fish and chips!' or 'I could do with a drink,' or 'I'm famished . . . oh, for summat to eat . . . ' But no one had anything to offer. We were skint.

And then, on the final miles into Eltering, our train entered a tunnel; it was about half a mile long, and in those days, the trains did not have lights on for such short trips in the darkness. We all sat there in silence, and when we emerged, Meredith was eating a toffee.

'Meredith, you sneaking sod!' snapped one of the men.

'Well, I did pass them around,' he said, chewing contentedly.

He made no offer to pass them around again, and from that point, I believed the story that Meredith could and indeed would peel an orange one-handed while it was in his pocket.

But with tales of such behaviour circulating among a group of men like police-officers, it was inevitable that they would make some effort to teach Meredith a lesson.

I'm not sure how or where the notion originated, or indeed who was the instigator, but gradually there arose a group feeling that Meredith was due to receive some kind of comeuppance, preferably of a financial nature. He had to be forced to pay for all his past transgressions, and we knew that this would be one of our most difficult achievements. Getting Meredith to pay for anything was rather like trying to climb Everest in a swimsuit.

As this germ of an idea floated around, it produced some good suggestions and some improbable ones; and it was by coincidence that Sergeant Bairstow said there ought to be a get-together for all members of the section. He proposed dinner at a local inn, one to which we could take our wives and meet one another socially and at leisure over a meal and a drink. Getting policemen together like this was nigh impossible due to their varied shifts and periods off duty, and even a determined effort like this would mean that someone was left out. We decided that special constables would man the market towns that evening so that the maximum attendance was assured.

Basically, it was a good idea. As the notion began to gain substance, it dawned upon us that this was the ideal opportunity to get our revenge on Meredith. We counted the likely numbers who would attend, and included our two sergeants, Charlie Bairstow and Oscar Blaketon. It was important that we discreetly tempted Meredith to attend; getting him there at all would be a difficult task because it meant he must be willing to pay his share. So we decided to invite the Inspector. Almost imperceptibly, the purpose of the occasion changed from a social function to a 'Get-Meredith-to-pay' event. We were well aware that he had promotion in mind and therefore regarded Inspectors as God-like figures who might help him on his way to the top; Meredith liked to grease around those in authority.

We reckoned we could make good use of that character-trait and accordingly spread the news that the Inspector was to attend. We also hinted that previous events had shown that promotion came to one of the officers who attended, sometimes within six months. That was enough for Meredith; he put his name down on the sheet.

By this time, Sergeant Bairstow was enjoying the situation and had entered the 'get-Meredith' field. Having achieved a suitable number of attenders, he rang the Boswell Arms at Brantsford and booked us in for a Friday night; then Bairstow stuck out his neck and told the landlord his name was Meredith Dryden and that he would be meeting the entire bill.

Word of this got around to everyone except Sergeant Blaketon, who lacked humour; we didn't inform the Inspector either, in case he objected to the subterfuge. To further our aims, we contrived a situation so that when all twenty-four of us were seated, Meredith was seated next to the Inspector's wife. We knew that would please him and that in such a position, he would be malleable.

Our plans made, we waited for the great night. True to form, Meredith scrounged a lift from a colleague at Brantsford and arrived to find a seating plan at the table. We enjoyed our preliminary drinks, during which Meredith's were paid for by someone who wished to ensure that he remained completely oblivious of our plans, and eventually we were asked to take our places at the table.

As it was a pre-arranged menu, there were no choices to be made, although the waitress did ask one of us which was Mr Dryden, whereupon she asked Meredith to choose the wines. He did this with pride, revealing a surprisingly good knowledge which impressed the Inspector. The meal was excellent, the companionship good and the night a huge success. After the meal, as we sat around the table completely sated and very content with our liqueurs and coffee. Finally, the landlady came to Sergeant Bairstow with the bill for twenty-four dinners and wine.

It was a discreet move, one which passed almost unobserved by the majority of the diners, but Charlie Bairstow pointed towards Meredith and said, 'That is Mr Dryden, he's paying.'

107

As she walked towards him bearing the bill on a silver tray, it dawned upon the assembled guests that a historic moment was nigh. The purpose of the night was about to be achieved. We observed the steady progression of the landlady's approach to Meredith's chair. He was engrossed in an animated conversation with the Inspector's wife and failed to notice the impending arrival of the bill.

As the landlady halted at his shoulder, we all watched, hearts beating with anticipation at the arrival of the supreme moment. Meredith Dryden was about to pay for something, for none of us would settle this bill.

'The bill, Mr Dryden,' she eased the tray before him. His face said everything. His brain, so finely attuned to the avoidance of paying, especially for anything which was for the consumption of others, must have told him that this was a set-up. He must have instantly realized that everyone – well, almost everyone – at that table, knew what was happening.

Meredith was fully aware that no one would come to his aid; he was on his own in this crisis. He had been well and truly cornered. Sergeant Blaketon was at the far end of the room beyond his reach, and the only person of substance close at hand was the Inspector. I'm sure Meredith realized that the Inspector knew nothing of this plot and so the Inspector was like an innocent babe as he faced the formidable financial skills of Meredith Dryden.

'Sir,' we heard Meredith say in a hoarse whisper, 'I've forgotten my cheque book – might I ask if you could pay the bill, and I will settle with you tomorrow when I come to the office?'

The Inspector, a leader of men and a man of substance who suddenly found himself being observed by almost every member of Ashfordly and Brantsford Sections, flushed a deep red, but he pulled out his wallet. It was he who had been skilfully cornered, and so he wrote out a cheque for the full amount. To give the fellow credit, he even gave a £1 tip to the staff.

None of us knew what to make of this, except that it was abundantly clear that Meredith had scored yet again.

'We'll have to make it up to the Inspector,' I heard Charlie Bairstow say later to Alwyn Foxton. 'We all know what it's about, so we'll have to have a whip-round. We'll have to pay our share. The bugger's beaten us again . . . '

'Meredith won't pay,' said Alwyn. 'The Inspector will finish up paying his share anyway!'

And so it was. We all paid our due amounts into a kitty which was passed over to the Inspector, but we knew that Meredith never paid his share. The Inspector had paid for Meredith's meal – Meredith the Miser had won yet again and had enjoyed another free meal.

But his success was short-lived. Less than three weeks later, he was transferred to a distant station.

With secret course, which no loud storms annoy
Glides the smooth current of domestic joy.

Samuel Johnson, 1709–84

For a large number of British workers, whether male or female,
there is a clear distinction between their work and their
domestic life. The home, with all its comforts and traumas,
is left firmly behind when a living has to be earned and throughout the working day, the pressures of the office or the working
environment supersede all but the most severe of domestic
worries or the blissful contentment of home. It is right that the
domestic life of an employee should rarely intrude into his or
her business or work, and so all but the closest of workmates
have no concept of a colleague's home life and circumstances.

But there are those who work either at home or from home;
rural doctors and vicars are popular examples, as are the local
postmasters or mistresses, shopkeepers, farmers, sales repre-
sentatives and many village businessfolk. To that incomplete
list can be added the village policeman.

For many rural bobbies, the village police house is both home
and office. And so it was with me. It was inevitable that there
were times when aspects of my domestic life became inextricably intertwined, albeit in the most pleasant of ways, with
my professional duties. Apart from being the police office of
Aidensfield, my house was also home to my wife and four tiny
children, along with all our hobbies and domestic activities.
Like all policemen in that situation, I did endeavour to keep

work and leisure completely separate, but at times this was impossible.

There is no doubt that the police house at Aidensfield ranks among the most beautifully located in Yorkshire, and possibly in England. Built in the 1960s on a superb elevated site, it is stoutly constructed of local yellow stone with a red pantile roof. It boasts a lounge with panoramic views, a dining-room and tiny kitchen, with three bedrooms and a bathroom. The garage adjoins and there is a through-passage which separates the house from the garage; off that passage there is an outside toilet and a wash-room. These outbuildings, small as they are, did help to accommodate that awesome range of bulky objects that young families accumulate, such as tricycles, prams and push-chairs. At the other end of the house, the west end, is the office. This is a spacious room with a solid wooden counter and separate entrance. In my time, it was furnished with an official desk, chair and telephone.

The hilltop site, which isolated us from the village below, was enhanced by a steep, mature and well-stocked garden. To the back and front of the house were panoramic views across the North York Moors, the Wolds and the valleys below. In the summer, it was a delight; in the winter, it could be a nightmare because, at times, the winds were so powerful that the garage doors could not be opened, while the carpets and rugs rippled like snakes as powerful draughts invaded our home and rattled the windows. At times, we were very prone to being snowed in; a fact which created frequent notes of disbelief among senior officers who sat in warm offices in distant, low-lying towns.

I must admit there were times when I was sure they thought I was inventing the snow to avoid a winter patrol on my motor cycle. On one occasion, it took me four hours to dig my way out of the garage, after which I was subjected to a telling-off for being late on patrol . . .

But, winter apart, it was a lovely place in which to live and to rear a family. By comparison with many other police houses, it was, and still is, a gem. At that time, of course, the privilege of having an officially-provided house was of immense value, especially on a constable's meagre salary with a growing family to support.

Perhaps, at this point, it would be of interest to learn how a young constable qualified for his very first police house. The Aidensfield house was not my first, but in order to progress through a range of police houses, one had to qualify for the first: once into the system, it was a simple matter of being transferred from one to another. The first hurdle was the most difficult.

In my own case, we had married some five years before we were posted to Aidensfield and we began our wedded bliss in a flat at Strensford. We rented this accommodation independently of the police but after three months in that second-floor flat I was summoned to the Superintendent's office.

'Rhea,' he said with a glow of benevolence on his face, 'a police house has become vacant in the town; it's an end-terrace house with three bedrooms and is not therefore, one of our standard houses. It's a modern house, by the way. But as our most recently married member, you might qualify to occupy it. Now, are you in a position to furnish a house?'

Quick as a flash, in spite of our solitary bed, our dining-table, two fireside chairs and clip rug, I said, 'Yes, sir.'

He wasn't to know that my scant furnishings would barely fill the kitchen, let alone a complete house, but I did not want this opportunity to evaporate. A modern three-bedroomed house, rent free, was a godsend.

'And do you intend remaining in the force as a career?' was his next question.

'Yes, sir,' I said with as much conviction as I could muster.

'And what about a family, Rhea? You have none, have you?'

'No, sir, not yet.'

'And your wife is working is she?'

'For the moment, sir, yes. She's a secretary at the council offices.'

He chatted about my future, and about the responsibilities of occupying a police house, and then he said it was mine. I could have the keys next week.

When I told Mary, she was delighted, for our new home was a modern, brick-built house with up-to-date kitchen fittings and beautiful decor. It had a small, pleasant garden and it overlooked the harbour at Strensford with magnificent views of the abbey and old town. It ought to be said, however, that the railway station and some sidings did lie between us and that water. But that was a minor blemish.

When the tide was high, the views across the wide, upper reaches of Strensford harbour were delightful, but when the water was low, it revealed a narrow channel among acres of shining black mud littered with junk which had been deposited over many years. But the house was lovely.

The fact that it was not a standard police house did not worry us. Standard houses were constructed so that when a police family moved from one to another (as they did with staggering frequency), their furnishings and carpets would fit. As a theory, it was fine, but some standard lounges were three inches shorter than others; some bedrooms were narrower or longer than others, and there were many minor variations which made nonsense of the system. Even in standard houses it was difficult to make the furniture fit, and another problem was that the decor which pleased some families was horrific and bizarre in the eyes of others. But it was nice to know that the authorities had our interests at heart.

Our house had been rented by the local police because of a shortage of standard houses in Strensford, but luxuries like fitted carpets or full bedroom suites did not concern us. We hadn't any. Happily, the decorations and exterior paintwork were in good repair.

At that early stage of marriage, we would have had difficulty filling a caravan with our belongings, let alone a semidetached mansion. Happy with our new home, we settled in and were very content. A few weeks later the Superintendent met me during a patrol.

'Rhea,' he said, 'I intend carrying out my house inspections and will be starting next week. I shall be calling on you. What is a convenient time?'

I performed some rapid mental gymnastics because I wanted him to come when the tide was full. I knew the harbour view would impress him, so I said, 'Next Wednesday, Sir? Would 3 p.m. be suitable?'

He checked his diary and agreed.

When I told Mary, she grew flustered. I had to explain that his visit was not to check upon our cleanliness or her housekeeping ability, but to ascertain whether any repairs or other work were required on the house, either externally or internally.

'If he looks in all the rooms, there's nothing . . . we've two empty bedrooms, nothing in the dining-room . . . ' She began to worry about our lack of furniture, and whether we would be asked to vacate it.

I must admit that this did bother me too, particularly as I'd recently assured him I could furnish a home. To cut a long story short, we borrowed from friends a dining suite, a three-piece suite, two single beds, two wardrobes, rugs, carpets and some sundry furnishings. The result was that on the day of the house inspection, our little home looked almost luxurious. All the young constables did this; we regularly borrowed each other's stuff on such occasions.

Because Mary was at work at the appointed hour I stayed to show him around. When the Superintendent arrived, I took him into the lounge, now fully furnished and smelling heavily of polish. A vase of flowers occupied the window ledge and pictures hung from the walls, but he was only interested in the lovely view. It was a fine sunny day and the full harbour glistened in the brilliant light. He rhapsodized over the scene which spread before him and chatted about the yachts and small boats on the water as he admired our superb maritime view.

Then he asked if any maintenance work was required and I said, 'No, sir, it's in good repair, inside and out.'

'Good, well, as you know, Rhea, we decorate internally every three years and externally every seven. That will be done automatically. If you need urgent work done, such as plumbing leaks, washers on taps and so on, submit Form 29.'

'Yes, sir.'

'Well, you keep a nice home, Rhea. Give my congratulations to your wife. It's nice to see things looking so well – and you've a nice taste in three-piece suites. PC Radcliffe has that design on his suite too, you know.'

Then he smiled and left. The Superintendent was very astute, I decided, and Mary was pleased that he did not venture any further than the lounge. Our impressive view had kept him in one room.

And so we started as occupants of several police houses. We bought more furniture when funds permitted and produced a brood of infants within surprisingly few years. By the time we arrived at Aidensfield, we had, of necessity, to furnish all the rooms to accommodate the six members of our family.

Once again, we were fortunate to be provided with a lovely house and a lounge with a view, even if it did mean regular house inspections. In addition, we had local government bureaucracy to contend with when maintenance or improvements were necessary. This led to several battles. My first concerned the outer passage and washing-room. The passage had a door at each end, and just off it was the room which housed the clothes washing facilities and which also acted as a storeroom. It sounds most convenient, but that neither the passage nor the washing-room had windows or lights. In the passageway, an open door would provide light during the daytime, but the wash-room could have served better as a photographer's dark-room.

So I made application, on Form 29, for a light to be fitted in the windowless washing-room. Then we would be able to use it for that purpose. The Superintendent rejected my request on the grounds that it was an 'improvement'; improvements to police authority houses needed special approval from on high, from bodies like the Standing Joint Committee and the County Architect. To reach them, my application would have to proceed via Headquarters' departments and the Chief Constable himself! For reasons he did not explain, the Superintendent refused to forward my report to them; our local 'official channels' terminated upon his desk. There seemed no way to by-pass that blockage.

I did try by explaining that it was impossible to work in that room and that, in its present form, it was useless for its intended purpose, or indeed any other. He continued to utter 'improvement' as his excuse for refusing to allow my report to reach other decision-makers. I grew more determined and renewed my campaign by tackling it from another angle.

My next Form 29 suggested that an outside light was necessary to eliminate possible danger to callers at the police house. I suggested that its best position would be above the passage's north-facing door. It would then shine along the passage at night (if the door was open), and would also shine along the entire frontage of the house. I thought it might even shine into the washing-room if two doors were left open!

That was rejected too, again by the Superintendent. Now even more determined. I re-applied for a light to be fitted outside the office door. This time, my Form 29 pointed out the possible danger to the public who might stumble over the steps and who might then sue the Standing Joint Committee for damages or compensation . . .

This time, I got an external light fitted – but it was over the door of the police office and its welcome light did not shine into the passage or the wash-room. When eventually I left the police house at Aidensfield, that washing-room and passage were still without a light. We had to squeeze our washing-machine into the tiny kitchen, no mean feat when it daily washed mountains of nappies.

Also under the heading of 'improvement' was my suggestion that some radiators be run off the little domestic coke boiler.

This tiny furnace was installed in the kitchen and its fierce heat filled the room and heated the water; even in summer, we had to keep it stoked up to cope with masses of baths, nappies and kiddy clothes. We lost gallons of perspiration and I reckoned it would keep two or three central heating radiators well supplied. But because this was an 'improvement', it was not permitted. My Form 29 was rejected.

Then the pipes of this boiler began to make frightening noises. Narrow pipes connected the boiler to the mains water supply and to the hot water tank upstairs, and they began to rattle and vibrate as the heat intensified. In time, I grew very alarmed and rang the Superintendent's office about it. He returned my call to say that such noises were normal in the plumbing world. He expressed this opinion without hearing the racket they made. I felt the noise was far from normal but realized that once again, I was battling against bureaucracy. I waited for a while and the noise grew worse; a friend said the pipes sounded as if they were blocked, a common occurrence in hot water pipes hereabouts because the lime deposits from the local water furred them.

Repeated requests via Form 29 met with nil response and this frustrated me. Being country born and bred, I was used to coping with my own domestic maintenance – we would never call in anyone to do jobs we could do ourselves such as painting, decorating, running repairs to machinery, tiling, pointing – in fact, anything and everything. But as occupants of a police house, we were instructed not to attempt any repairs or work, not even the replacement of a tap washer. I found these restrictions very frustrating.

The clattering grew worse. We reached the stage where we were frightened to light the fire because of the clamour coming from those pipes and this meant we had no hot water. Then came salvation. It came in the shape of a memo from the Superintendent which announced he was coming to conduct a house inspection.

I recognized the opportunity presented by his visit.

He was due at 11.30 a.m. one Friday, a busy day for nappies and infant washing, and so I arranged for the boiler to be well-stoked up and the flues opened wide to coincide with his visit. I was confident that the resultant noise from those pipes would terrify him. It didn't matter which part of the house he was visiting at the time, because I was sure the din could be heard throughout a building of castle proportions.

He came, inspected, had a coffee and asked about the pipes. After all, a succession of Forms 29 had made him aware of the problem. I said they were worse, upon which he ventured into the kitchen. It was now uncomfortably hot as the coke performed its heating role and he looked at the offending pipes. There was nothing to see – they were just two pipes running up the wall.

And then, almost as if they knew he was standing there, they performed on cue. It was just as if a giant with a big hammer was inside, banging and hammering to be let out and the whole house vibrated as the pipes visibly shuddered in their moment of triumph.

'My God!' he panted, rushing from the kitchen, white-faced and anxious . . .

Early next day, a plumber arrived. After an examination, he said the pipes were almost blocked; the hot water was trying to

117

rise through the cold pipe and had we not called him, there could have been a shocking explosion . . .

My final Form 29 confirmed that the pipes were working normally.

In such minor ways, my work and domestic life overlapped, although there were other instances. For example, at 4 a.m. one morning, a lorry driver knocked me out of bed and roused the entire family, simply to ask directions to Home Farm. On another occasion, at 6.30 a.m. one day when I was on holiday, a farmer came to the door to seek a pig licence. When I said I was on holiday and that he should go to Ashfordly Police Station, he said, 'Well, you're t'bobby, aren't you?'

I issued his licence.

In many ways, it was my young family which further involved me in this curious mixture of duty and home. One day, when I was enjoying time off during the week, I decided to do some gardening. I claim no green-fingered skills, but felt that if I dug enough holes and cut enough grass, I could believe I had achieved something positive. During this enterprise, Mary asked if I would look after the children while she went to Ashfordly to do some shopping. I agreed, so she jumped into our car and cheerfully vanished towards the market town.

The day was fine and warm, and I was thoroughly enjoying myself. The children were playing in the garden behind the house and I had fixed up a plastic bath half full of water which they were using as a paddling pool. After about an hour, I broke from my chores to make myself and the children a cool drink.

'Where's Charles?' I asked.

'Gone to the toilet,' said Elizabeth.

He was only three and I accepted her answer. I put his drink on the step and settled down to await his return. He did not come. I went indoors and looked at both toilets; he wasn't there. I went into his room and looked in the bed, the wardrobe and under the bed. He wasn't there either.

Knowing that children love to play hide and seek, I searched the whole house as only a policeman can, but found no sign of him. Now more than a little worried, I checked my office, the garage, the passage and the washing-room with its darkness. There was no Charles. I re-checked all the beds by pulling back the covers and looking underneath, then I searched the pram and finally tackled the garden. There were shrubs, trees and plants, a cold frame and plenty of long grass to conceal a little boy, but my frantic hunt failed to locate him.

By now, my concern was becoming genuine alarm and I made several more sorties into the house, the garage and the garden. And then I wondered if he'd jumped into the car to accompany Mary?

That seemed the only logical explanation, but the more I thought about it, the more I realized he hadn't. She'd have mentioned it, surely? She'd wanted a moment or two to herself . . . I'd seen her leave alone . . .

I stood in the middle of my garden, by this time a very worried man. Where on earth could he have gone? Even though the garden gates were shut, I went onto the main road and looked up and down. I was able to gaze along almost half a mile of highway, but there was no sign of the toddler. He'd vanished into thin air and I was in a dreadful dilemma. I could not leave the rest of them alone while I went to seek Charles, and I began to understand the problems of some parents. What could I do? Anyone else would have telephoned the police!

With this possibility rapidly gaining strength in my mind, I realized I couldn't remember what he was wearing. Of course, a three-year-old lad wandering about unaccompanied wouldn't be too difficult to locate . . .

I decided upon yet another thorough search of the premises. It drew a blank. Outside, the other children played happily, quite oblivious to my growing alarm, and at last I went into my office and dialled the Ashfordly Police Station number. It rang and rang; there was no reply. They're never there when they're wanted, I grumbled! I decided to ring the Divisional Police Station at Malton to ask if a car was patrolling in the Aidensfield area. That was quite possible because I was not on duty, and the area would not be left totally without a patrol. If there was a car nearby, it would be radio-equipped and the driver would keep his eyes open for any missing child.

I began to formulate my request; I would ask the driver to keep observations for a child aged three, with light brown hair, clothing unknown, who might be wandering . . .

As the phone began to ring, someone knocked on my office door. What a time to call! I was off duty anyway! Slamming down the phone, I opened the door. A lorry driver was standing there and he was holding Charles in his arms. His vehicle was parked outside.

'Found this kid,' he thrust the infant towards me. 'Wandering down t'hill . . . biggest wonder he didn't get killed . . . some parents . . . thought you'd know who belonged him . . .'

'Er, yes,' I didn't know how to respond. 'Er, come in . . . have a cup of tea . . .'

'No, got a schedule to keep. You know him then?'

'Yes,' I said, humbly.

'Good, thought you would. Give his mum a rocket, eh? For letting him get out like that . . . stupid bloody parents . . .'

And off he went.

I hugged Charles with relief, being unable to explain to the little fellow the problems he had created. I decided that my immediate priority was to fix child-proof locks on the garden gate, but also decided not to tell a soul about this. Not even Mary.

My latter plans went haywire too. A lady in the village had been present when the lorry driver collected the wandering child and had directed him to the police house. She told Mary . . .

The whole village knew too. I was suitably humbled, embarrassed and chastened. And little Charles never batted an eyelid, although I did fix child-proof locks to the gates. Ever since, I've had sympathy for parents whose children go wandering.

Another personal domestic crisis concerned Margaret, our two-year-old daughter. From the moment she could crawl, she could climb. She climbed the stairs and chairs, steps and trees, bookshelves and pantry shelves. She could climb on to the car bonnet, on to the motor cycle and on to the backs of settees and indeed upon almost any piece of domestic equipment or furniture. At times, I felt she had a wonderful future as a rock-climber or steeplejack and this was confirmed when she managed to climb out of her bedroom window on to the outer ledge.

She remained there as I pleaded with her not to move; with her safely indoors, I then secured the window, but soon she was climbing up the shelves of the wardrobe and sitting on top. On one occasion, she was marooned up an apple tree and on another managed to climb into a fireside chair and from there gain access to the mantelpiece. From these escapades, she was unscathed.

But, inevitably, an accident was bound to happen; one day she would fall and hurt herself.

One lunchtime, I returned from a motor-cycle patrol to find Mary holding little Margaret over the kitchen sink as blood poured from her tiny mouth. The accident had happened only seconds earlier. Without even removing my crash helmet, I took one look at the injury and found a gaping wound inside her mouth.

Without asking for an explanation, I rang the village doctor who, fortunately, was at home having his lunch. 'Bring her down,' he said. I packed some cotton wool over the wound to stem the flow and rushed Margaret to the doctor. Mary couldn't come – she had the other children to look after.

'No good,' the doctor said instantly. 'She needs hospital treatment, stitches. You take her there now, I'll ring to say you're on the way.'

With the tiny child sitting in the front seat of my car and holding her cheek against the wad of cotton wool, I furiously drove the seventeen miles into Malton to the hospital where a doctor met me. In moments, my little daughter was lying on an operating table, without anaesthetic, as the doctor examined the wound and prepared to stitch it.

'What happened to her?' he asked.

'I don't know,' I had to admit. 'I didn't ask . . . '

'It'll mend,' he said, producing a huge curved needle. I winced; I began to feel emotional at the thought of that tiny child suffering as I submitted her to this instant surgery. Margaret, God bless her, never cried and never complained. It was awful, watching her tiny frame being subjected to this treatment.

During this work, a nurse hovered around the theatre and as the doctor began to skilfully sew the wound, she came over to me.

'Some parents!' she said. 'Look at that poor child . . . and you'd think they'd bring her themselves . . . the police get all the rotten jobs to do . . . Fancy you having to do this . . . '

As she ranted, it became clear that she had no idea that this was *my* child; the fact that I was sitting there in full police motor cycling uniform had obviously led her into thinking I was doing my duty by protecting some neglected youngster . . .

She continued her verbal onslaught against callous and thoughtless parents as the doctor continued his work on the mouth wound. Then she produced a sheet of paper.

'Child's name?' she asked.

'Margaret Rhea, aged two,' I said.

'Father's name?'

'Nicholas Rhea,' I watched her write down these details.

'Address?'

'The Police House Aidensfield,' I said.

'No,' she threw me one of those withering glances that one expects from matrons, not nurses, 'the child's address, not yours!'

'That is the child's address,' I said. 'She's my child.'

'Oh,' she said. 'I had no idea . . . I thought . . .'

'She'll be fine now,' the doctor had finished. 'I've put three stitches in, they'll wither away in time and there'll be no mark. It's young, clean flesh, so it will quickly mend. There's no other injury.'

'Thanks, Doctor,' and I carried little Margaret out to my waiting car and drove home. Other than a puffy cheek, she seemed no worse and never once complained. When she arrived home, she sat in her high chair and ate her dinner. She behaved as if nothing had happened and the wound did not appear to give her pain.

I ate my lunch too, still upset by the trauma of seeing the doctor working so expertly and coolly upon her. 'Mary,' I asked, 'what happened to her?'

'She was climbing up the shelves of the bookcase,' Mary told me. 'I went into the lounge just as she got to the top – she fell off and her face hit the edge of the coal scuttle . . . '

Mary began to weep so I comforted her as, quite unabashed, Margaret continued with her meal.

In spite of our efforts to prevent her, she continued to climb for some years afterwards, but never with such dramatic effect.

Perhaps the funniest incident which involved both my work and my private life occurred one February morning. This is the sequence of events – my involvement came some time after the beginning of the saga, but is best to relate it from the start.

Around one o'clock on the morning in question, my mother and father were dragged from their bed by a telephone call from the CID at York. It came at a time when there was concern about letter bombs and the detective was calling from the GPO Sorting Office.

'Is that Mrs Rhea?' the detective asked my mother. He then provided the correct address to make sure he was speaking to the right person.

'Yes,' answered my mother, bleary-eyed and sleepy.

'This is York CID,' said the voice. 'I'm ringing from the GPO Sorting Office at York. This is a difficult enquiry, Mrs Rhea, and I don't want to alarm you, but are you expecting a parcel from anyone?'

'Well,' said my mother, not yet appreciating the problem, 'I might be, it's my birthday tomorrow . . . er today . . . '

'Ah!' There was some relief at this response. 'And you have no enemies? You, or your husband are not in sensitive work, are you? It's not the sort of work that would attract, well, a letter bomb?'

'No . . . well, I don't think so . . . '

'Well, the point is, there's a suspicious package here and it's addressed to you.'

The detective took immense pains to describe his problem without being too alarmist, but it seemed that as the GPO sorters were dealing with the night's influx of mail, one of them discovered a parcel which began to emit ticking sounds. As everyone dived for cover, the parcel was placed in a sand-filled bin designed to cope with exploding parcels. As it sat there, the entire staff of the sorting office took cover and waited for the bang. As they settled down behind whatever protection they could find, the police were called. And so the official procedures were set in motion.

The busy task of sorting the mail came to a halt and the district's mail was thus delayed until the CID arrived and the offending parcel was dealt with, probably by Bomb Disposal experts. One of the detectives, whom I shall call Gordon, arrived and looked at the offending object in the bin. It had now stopped ticking. Heads peeped above the counters and around walls as Gordon bravely scrutinized the parcel. Then he picked it up.

It promptly started ticking. Everyone dived for cover. He threw it back into the bin and vanished below a sturdy counter. Everyone waited for it to explode, but it did not. And so it lay at peace in its protective bin as the entire staff and the police hid behind their benches. They waited for a long, long time, but nothing happened. There was no bang and it had stopped ticking.

Gordon approached it again. The address on the parcel was legible; it bore my mother's name, hence the morning call to her.

'I've no idea what it might be,' she said. 'If it is a birthday present, it might have been sent by my daughter and son-in-law in London.'

'What do they do?' asked the detective.

'He's in the Metropolitan Police in London . . . '

'Then there could be risks . . . someone might be hitting back at him . . . '

Having elicited this information, Gordon rang Scotland Yard to check against the possibility of attacks against the police, and then rang my brother-in-law at his London home to explain the problem. But neither he nor my sister had sent the parcel. They were then asked if they knew anyone else who might have sent it; they suggested it could have come from my brother who lives in the Shetlands. He works for BP, and so there could have been some sinister links with a letter bomb.

As a consequence, he and his family were roused about 1.30 a.m. and the questions were repeated; they had not sent a parcel. Further checks were made with the security services, but there was no known campaign against our institutions.

My brother however, was asked if *he* knew who might have sent a parcel, if indeed it was a genuine parcel, then he said, 'My brother at Aidensfield might have sent it. He's a policeman too.'

With the intrigue growing stronger, the mystery growing deeper and the mail growing further delayed, Gordon now rang me. By this time, it was around two o'clock on a chill February morning. I staggered into my cold office to take his call. At that stage, I knew nothing of the drama.

'Nick,' he said. 'It's Gordon at York.'

We had been at training-school together and knew one another fairly well.

'York?' I muttered through a haze of sleepiness. 'What's happened? It's two o'clock in the morning.'

'We have a parcel addressed to your mother,' and he patiently related the story so far. 'Now, I had no idea the lady was *your* mother – I've been ringing Scotland Yard, the Shetlands, the Special Branch, GPO Security, MI5 . . . '

'Oh?' this sounded important.

'So, Nick,' he asked, with a hint of exhaustion, 'yesterday, did you post a parcel to your mother?'

'No,' I said. 'I sent her a card with a gift token inside. I didn't send a parcel . . . it's her birthday today, so I suppose someone . . . '

'Oh, bloody hell . . . ' There was a long silence at the other end of the telephone, then he said, 'Hang on, I'll have another look at it. We can't decipher the postmark you see, and we're worried about touching it . . . I'm sure it's your mother's name on it . . . '

But he did touch it. It was sitting in its secure bin, and he lifted it to check the postmark. It started to tick again. He dropped it back inside the bin and dived for cover as I waited on the line.

Everyone was still under cover, but eventually he returned to the telephone, breathless.

'God, this is awful,' he said. 'The bloody thing could go off at any minute . . . I'm safe behind a screen here . . . '

'You're a brave bloke to tackle it like you have,' I said.

'I'm not,' he said. 'I'm stupid. I've been to a night club for a few pints and don't know what I'm doing really . . . '

As this conversation continued, Mary appeared at my side. 'What's the matter?' she asked. 'Are you talking about your mother. Has something happened? Is she ill?'

'No,' I said, 'it's the CID. They think someone's sent her a bomb . . . '

Mary began to chuckle. 'A parcel? Brown paper, with white string? A sticky label on the front? The address written in black ballpoint ink?'

As she described her parcel, I relayed the words to Gordon.

'This is the one,' he growled. 'Bloody hell! What a night! The description fits. Did your wife send it, Nick? Has she sent a bomb to her mother-in-law or something?'

'Did you send it?' I asked Mary, my feet like ice-blocks on the cold office floor.

'Yes, why, what's wrong?'

I explained about the chaos in York and the terror she had inflicted upon the Post Office, the police and probably GPO Security. The whole of the region's mail would be delayed and several sorters were close to having heart attacks.

'It's a pair of scissors,' she said. 'A pair of electric scissors, for cutting material to make dresses.'

My heart sank.

'Is there a battery in?'

'Yes, I fitted it before we posted it . . . '

And so, when pressure was applied to that parcel in certain places, the scissors began to snip within their box . . . '

I apologized profusely to everyone and rang my mother to wish her a happy birthday.

The death of a dear friend would go near to make a man look sad.
                                    William Shakespeare, 1564–1616

Every autumn, the children of Aidensfield waited for the donkeys to return to Lingfield Farm. These were seaside donkeys. During the summer, they spent their time on the beach at Strensford where, day after day, they patiently carried laughing children backwards and forwards along the sands. Adorned in brightly-coloured bridles bearing their names, with ribboned top-knots on their heads and neat little saddles on their backs, they had been a part of the Strensford beach scene since Victorian times.

They worked very hard but were always models of tolerance and patience. Perhaps their gentleness was due to the fact that they were not overworked; during their working week, for example, they were subjected to conditions about their rest periods. They enjoyed one day off in every three, with three meals a day and an hour for lunch. Their working day did not exceed eight hours and they were inspected regularly by a veterinary surgeon. In some respects, their working conditions were better than those of police-officers!

During the winter, they came inland for their holidays where they were boarded out at selected farms. Jack Sedgewick at Lingfield Farm, Aidensfield, had for years taken five of the donkeys from Strensford. As a rule, they arrived by cattle truck at the end of the summer season and remained until the Whit-suntide bank holiday. They occupied a rough, hummocky paddock where they seemed to thrive on the wealth of thistles and other vegetation which had little appeal to other beasts.

They had a range of small outbuildings, some without doors, which served as stables. They contained plenty of hay as bedding and for food, and there was an outdoor water-trough adequately fed with spring water. Some shrub-like hawthorn trees added variety to the paddock's undulating landscape and provided slender shelter against the winter storms.

Jack Sedgewick, a large and kindly man, knew that his guests required regular exercise otherwise they would grow fat and lazy. This presented no problem because he encouraged local children to come along and play with his little group of donkeys. He taught the youngsters how to care for them; to make sure their feet were trimmed regularly; to coax them to their halters and to feed them with the right kind of things. Some children rode them, and a little girl even persuaded one donkey, called Lucy, to jump over a small artificial fence.

It was very clear that the donkeys loved the children and the children loved the donkeys; indeed, there is some kind of mysterious affinity between small children and donkeys. These gentle and calm animals, with their big, soft eyes and cuddly long ears – called 'errant wings' by G. K. Chesterton – are so lovable. It wasn't all smooth and jolly however. The occasional bout of stubbornness from a donkey who, for reasons best known to itself did not want to play, sometimes upset the youngsters, while a sudden session of braying made them jump with fright before dissolving into laughter. For the children, these minor upsets were lessons in themselves. For one thing, they taught the children they could not have all their own way, even with donkeys.

One winter, Lingfield Farm accepted its usual complement of five donkeys. They were Lucy, Linda, Betty, Bonny and Fred, and it was Fred who thought he was a human being. He loved to enter the house whenever possible; he loved to nose his way into small crowds and it was not unknown for him to poke his head through the open dining-room window of the farm whenever the family was having a meal. Calm, lovable and cuddly with his thick, grey coat and distinctive black cross on his back, he was a pet and a favourite.

Always popular with the children, he allowed them to ride him through the fields and lanes and when he got some distance from the farm, he would occasionally issue a blood-curdling braying noise, his way of checking whether any other donkey, male or female, was living nearby. The children used him in a Nativity Play at school where he stood as still as a rock and solemnly overlooked the model crib they had made. His acting was superb. From time to time, I saw Fred plodding along the lanes with his tiny charges making a fuss of him and I was pleased he provided the bairns with such pleasurable activity. These children would grow up to appreciate animals and their needs, and it was all due to their pal, Fred.

Then Fred disappeared.

It wasn't difficult to imagine the anguish and concern among the children and their parents. Indeed, poor old Jack Sedgewick was most upset too. He rang me just before ten o'clock one morning in April.

'Mr Rhea,' he said, with his voice showing traces of emotion. 'Ah've lost yan o' them donkeys. Fred, it is. Sometime since last night. Do you reckon 'e could 'ave been stolen?'

'I'll come down to the farm,' I assured him. To my knowledge, there had not been an outbreak of donkey thefts or moke-nappings and I couldn't imagine who would do such a thing. My own immediate view was that Fred had probably got through an insecure gate and wandered off. I felt he would turn up in due course.

When I arrived at Lingfield Farm, I found Jack Sedgewick and a small knot of children standing at the gate of the paddock which contained the other donkeys. The animals were standing together in a corner, watching us; if only they could talk, I thought. I halted my motor bike and parked it against a wall.

'Good of you to come down so quick, Mr Rhea,' he said.

'Fred's gone . . . ' 'He was there last night . . . ' 'I fed him, Mr Rhea . . . ' 'I took his bridle off . . . '

The children were all talking at once so I held up my hands to indicate silence.

'Just a minute!' I laughed. 'I can't hear anybody if you all talk at once. So, Jack. You first.'

'I found him gone,' one little girl couldn't contain her worry.

'Aye,' Jack confirmed. 'Young Denise here came down to t'field about half-eightish. She came to feed 'em all, and noticed Fred wasn't there.'

'Was the gate open or shut, Denise?' I asked her. She would be about eleven years old.

'Shut, Mr Rhea. It swings shut by itself.'

I tried it. It was fastened with a hunting sneck, a type of fastening which comprised a length of wood suspended from two chains. It had a carved notch and it slotted into a bracket on the gatepost. It was easy to open when on horseback; this was done by easing it back with a riding crop, hence its name. I eased back the sneck and let the gate stand wide open, but it swung slowly shut by its own weight and the sneck slid home. The gate was then secure. For this reason, it seemed unlikely that the gate could be accidentally left open. But I knew it was not impossible. If it had been opened only sufficiently wide for a child to emerge, it might not have had the impetus or weight to latch itself properly after only a small movement.

'Who saw him last?' was my next question.

'We did,' came a chorus of voices.

'Where?'

'In the village, last night,' they told me. I asked one girl, the tallest of the group, to explain. She said half a dozen of them had taken Fred into the village for a walk and a ride.

'Did anything happen, or did anyone say anything about him? Or to him? Can you remember?' I put to her.

'We all took turns riding,' she said seriously. 'He wasn't upset or anything.'

'Did anybody say anything to him? To you, maybe? About Fred? Was anyone angry or annoyed with him for anything?'

I was trying to establish whether anyone had threatened to take the animal away either as a joke or as a serious threat. The antics of the children and Fred could have upset someone.

'There was that man in the pub,' said one small girl.

'What man was that?' I asked.

'We got crisps and lemonade at the pub.'

'The Brewers' Arms?'

'Yes. We went to the door like we always do.'

'And what about the man? What did he do?'

'He smacked Fred on the nose,' said one of them. 'Just fun, though, he was just playing.'

'Maybe that's upset Fred!' I smiled. 'Maybe he's taken the huff and gone off to sulk! So what happened exactly, Denise?'

'We had Fred with us. We wanted some crisps and things, so we went to the pub. Fred followed us in. Or he tried to. He poked his nose over the counter and this man clonked him on the nose, just in fun it was. Fred backed away . . . that was all.'

'And after your walk with him, you put him back in the paddock with the others?'

'Yes, we gave him some hay, patted him for a minute or two and then we went home.'

'And did you shut that gate?'

They all swore that it was properly closed. Jack Sedgewick said he did his rounds after ten o'clock that night and noticed nothing amiss. I looked at the lanes which led away from the donkey paddock; if it had got out, it could have wandered into the village, or into the surrounding woods and hills, or even along the river bank. It could be anywhere.

'What about your buildings, Jack? Have they been searched?'

The children provided the answer; they had searched everywhere on the farm before calling me.

'I'll report him as missing,' I said. 'Now, how about organizing a hunt for him?'

And so I organized a small hunt around the likely places in and around Aidensfield; there were empty farm buildings, woods, copses, fields and so on. I allocated a safe place for groups of these children to search; each group comprised three for safety reasons.

Jack said he would walk his own land this morning to check ditches and other likely places, and I decided to ask questions around the village. After all, someone might have spotted a lone donkey trotting along the road. I told them I'd keep Mr Sedgewick informed of developments.

A couple of hours later, I was in the Post Office asking about Fred. Several people were there. They were asking for postal orders and stamps, and some were at the grocery counter. As I chatted and spread the news about Fred, a man in hiking gear walked in to buy some fruit and drinks. He noticed me, but he was not a local man. I didn't know him.

'Ah, Officer,' he said, his keen grey eyes showing bright in his weathered face. 'Just the fellow. I've just come through Plantation Wood,' and he showed me his route on a map clipped to his belt. 'And there's a dead donkey just off the footpath . . . '

'Dead donkey?' I almost shouted. 'Are you sure?'

'Well,' he seemed surprised at my reaction. 'Well, it was lying down . . . maybe it wasn't dead . . . '

I asked him to pinpoint the exact place, and noticed that everyone in the shop was listening. We identified the place as being about half-way along the bridleway between High Nab and Cross Plain, where it ran alongside Plantation Wood.

As I confirmed the details, the shop emptied rapidly and the customers scurried to their homes. They seemed to have been galvanized into action at the news. I decided to walk back to Jack Sedgewick's farm and break the news to him, then I would have to break the news to the children and decide whether or not to take them to the scene. I was sure Jack would help me to deal with the corpse.

'A dead donkey?' he gasped when I located him down his fields.

'So the man said,' I replied.

'Right, come wi' me, Mr Rhea, and be sharp,' and he led me to his implement shed. He started the engine of one of his tractors and bade me climb aboard. And off we rushed towards Plantation Wood, the tractor bouncing and bumping along the rough farm tracks. There was a definite note of urgency in his actions.

'What's the panic, Jack?' I shouted above the noise of the engine.

'A dead donkey!' he shouted back. 'I 'ope it's not poor awd Fred, but nobody's ever seen a dead donkey, Mr Rhea. Did tha know that? It's reckoned ti be good luck to see yan. An' we all need a spot o' good luck.'

He accelerated across the fields and from my uncomfortable perch beside his seat, I could now see a straggly line of local people. They were all rushing in the same direction, using a short cut from the village.

'Are they all going to see it?' I shouted at him.

'Aye, likely. Word soon gets about when summat like this 'appens. A dead donkey's a rare thing.'

As we drew nearer I could see the distinctive figure of the hiker leading the way. Several children had also joined the march. The news had spread with amazing speed. Jack's tractor pushed its way through the throng of people and we arrived, breathless almost, at the same time as the head of the procession. The hiker, baffled by this turn of events, was standing and pointing.

'It's gone,' he said, opening his arms wide in an expression of puzzlement. 'It was here, I saw it. And it's gone. It was lying right there!' and he stamped the ground with his boot.

And so the villagers never saw their dead donkey.

This is one of those peculiar legends which is supposed to have been started by Charles Dickens; it is said that no one has ever seen a dead donkey and if the news reached a village that a donkey was dying, everyone went to have a look. The legend has probably arisen from a belief that donkeys will wander off to seek a secret place to die.

We turned the tractor around and chugged back to Lingfield Farm.

'Could yon 'ave been Fred?' asked Jack.

'Who else?' I said. 'Mebbe he was just resting.'

'Aye,' said Jack. 'Mebbe. Mebbe he'll come back. Donkeys can live wild, tha knaws. Ah've 'eard of one living twelve years in a wood . . . Fred'll come back.'

The children were pleased it wasn't Fred who had died, but the mystery caused all sorts of rumours. People went back several times to see if the donkey reappeared but it never did. And Fred never returned to the farm. His companions showed no sign of distress at his continuing absence and the children did get over their sorrow. Later that spring, Lucy, Linda, Betty and Bonny went back to their beach without Fred, and no one ever saw him again.

To this day, I do not know what happened to him. In my

official report, I recorded him as 'Missing' because there was no evidence of theft.

But could that donkey have been Fred lying dead in the wood? Is there a mystery about dead donkeys that has never been revealed? Or did Fred find a new home somewhere?

I do not know. But I have never seen a dead donkey.

Among the lesser known duties of the village policeman are those connected with contagious diseases of animals. During our training-courses, we were told about anthrax, foot and mouth disease, sheep scab and sheep pox, swine fever, tuberculosis, cattle plague, fowl pest, rabies, atrophic rhinitis, epizootic lymphangitis, pleuro-pneumonia, bovine tuberculosis, sarcoptic parasitic mange, glanders and farcy and other exotic sounding plagues which produced devastating results and misery among farmers.

In the event of an outbreak, or even a suspected outbreak of any of these diseases, it was vital that immediate action was taken by the police, the Ministry of Agriculture, Fisheries and Food and the owner of the livestock. Police action involved the enforcement of a multitude of rules and regulations and the serving of a document called 'Form A'.

As many of our training-school instructors were city types, I'm sure they did not know the effect of, or the reason for, Form A. The result was that we emerged from training-school with the knowledge that if a cow frothed at the mouth or a pig was sick we served Form A. It all seemed very puzzling, and it was not until I worked in a rural area, where domestic livestock is so important to farmers and to the nation's economy, that the real purpose and importance of Form A registered in my mind.

Form A was a printed document which had to be completed by a police officer who suspected an outbreak of one of the diseases I have listed. He completed the form with the name and address of the farm, or even a portion of the farm in question such as a cattle-shed or pigsty, and formally delivered a copy to the farmer. For most diseases, copies were also sent to the Ministry of Agriculture, Fisheries and Food at local and national level, the local council, and to various police stations. The effect of this document was to bring to a standstill all movements of animals in and out of the suspect premises until a

Ministry vet had carried out his inspection. If he declared the animal(s) to be free from disease, the restrictions were lifted and life returned to normal. If he confirmed the disease, another set of procedures swung into action which could lead to the killing of a solitary pig on a small unit or the slaughter of a complete herd of pedigree cattle on a dairy farm. The precise action depended upon the disease in question; I have outlined the general procedures.

Form A was just one small part of the entire system, but as a whole, the impact of the rules and regulations did appear successful. For example, swine fever had practically been eliminated, sheep-dipping had virtually abolished sheep scab and strict import regulations kept rabies at bay. I never did know of a horse which caught epizootic lymphangitis and the last outbreak of pleuro-pneumonia was in 1898. We knew, therefore, that a major outbreak of a serious and contagious animal disease was very unlikely, and it's fair to say there were several false alarms, albeit with good intent. No chances were taken. Every suspicion was treated with the utmost care and attention.

In our county (the North Riding of Yorkshire), all police-officers were appointed Inspectors under the Diseases of Animals Act; in some counties, only sergeants and those with higher rank carried this responsibility and in some city areas, there might be just one such designated inspector within a police force. In a large rural area, it made sense for all officers to have the powers thus conferred upon him or her and this meant that in addition to normal criminal law and police procedures, we had to be fully conversant with the statutes and procedures relating to this huge and at times complex subject.

In some areas, members of the Ministry of Agriculture's staff carried out these duties and during my time at Aidensfield, there was a growing feeling that all such work should be carried out by civilian inspectors. The authorities felt that this aspect of police work should be gradually phased out. Both the police and the farmers greeted this possible change with mixed feelings. For the police, it gave them a marvellous insight into rural life and helped them perform their wide range of other duties, while the farmers welcomed a uniform presence rather than a plain-clothes person wandering about their premises, especially in times of strife.

It was during these slow but relentless changes that the country suffered a huge and devastating outbreak of foot and mouth disease. The awful effects of it filtered down to Reg Lumley's herd at West Gill Farm, Aidensfield.

I learned of the outbreak in October through the newspapers. A report said that foot and mouth disease had been confirmed at Oswestry in Shropshire, and that the police were faced with the task of tracing 2,500 animals which had been sold in the local market shortly before the disease had been discovered. It was a huge task; the cattle could be anywhere in the United Kingdom and every one of them could be carrying the virus. The problem was that the licensing system was not foolproof; bad writing on licences; missing ear-tag numbers which are so vital in the positive identification of a particular beast; and sheer carelessness in record keeping, meant that many cattle would never be traced. They could pass on the disease.

During an epidemic, a contact animal was often identified only when a new outbreak occurred many miles from the point of sale. Meanwhile, it had infected other animals, some of which had been moved away, and so the hunt continued. Foot and mouth disease spreads so rapidly that within five days of that original outbreak, fourteen English counties were declared Controlled Areas. Markets were prohibited and farmers guarded their farm entrances, allowing no one to enter unless their clothing and feet were disinfected.

This huge, fast spreading outbreak was one of the few occasions when members of the general public were inconvenienced. Its awful impact and consequences were such that it pricked the communal conscience of the public as never before. For probably the first time, the great British public knew something of the drama being played out on the farms of their countryside.

At Leeds and Bradford Airport, for example, passengers bound for Ireland had to walk over disinfected mats; the RAC Rally was cancelled; two hundred members of the Second Battalion of the Royal Anglican Regiment were drafted in to fight the outbreak near Shrewsbury; National Hunt racing was called off; the import of fruit, nuts and fresh meat was restricted on the Isle of Man; Christmas trees became scarce due to the restrictions imposed on movements to and from land, and farmers even had to get permission to vote in a by-election. All dogs within five miles of an infected place had to be confined and even poultry movements were restricted.

300 extra veterinary surgeons were drafted in, along with 2,500 ancillary workers; there were fourteen control centres in the country and everyone involved worked fifteen hours per day. All police leave was cancelled and the troops were called in to help with many of the heavy tasks. Burial of the slaughtered animals was one example where military hardware and skills proved most useful.

One paper summed it up like this: 'Two brothers came home to find a cow frothing at the mouth. They shut themselves and their families inside the house. Men from the Ministry came to slaughter and bury; the farm was quarantined and red and white "Keep Out" notices were erected around the boundaries. Policemen arrived and moved into a hut near the farm gate to stop visitors; the local market was cancelled and a pin was stuck in a map at the Foot and Mouth Control Headquarters.'

The fear generated by this outbreak can scarcely be imagined; the far-reaching consequences of the disease caused every farmer to barricade himself in his farm and to take every possible precaution to safeguard his own herd. And it was during this atmosphere that I got a call from Reg Lumley.

'Can thoo come, Mr Rhea?' he sounded almost in tears.

'What's up, Reg?' I felt that I needn't have asked.

'Yan o' my coos is frothing,' he said.

'Oh my God!'

My heart sank; it looked as if we had foot and mouth in this area, in Aidensfield. I could not comprehend the consequences.

'I'll call the Ministry,' I told him. 'I won't come down to the farm, I might pick up the disease on my feet. Can you arrange a system of disinfectant at the gate, Reg? A bath or summat will do for folks to walk through. Make folks paddle through it going in and out.'

'Aye,' he said slowly. 'Ah've been preparing, just in case. Ah've got a load of disinfectant and some waterproofs . . .

Ah'll see to t'gate; Ah'll chain it up to keep traffic out.'

Over the past weeks, as the disease had spread across the nation, I had been issued with some red and white 'Keep Out' posters and so, for the first time during my duties at Aidensfield, I found myself typing out Form A. It had Reg Lumley's name and address on it, and where it asked for the name of the suspected premises, I typed 'The whole of the premises of West Gill Farm, Aidensfield.'

As force procedure demanded, I compiled a telegram for transmission to the Ministry of Agriculture, Fisheries and Food (Animal Health Division) at Tolworth, Surbiton, Surrey. It said, in the jargon of the time, 'Important. Anhealth, Surbiton, Telex. Suspected foot and mouth disease. Reginald Lumley, West Gill Farm, Aidensfield, near York. N.R. Police, Aidensfield.'

Having despatched this, I next telephoned the local office of that organization and asked for the Divisional Veterinary Inspector. The Ministry now had vets working all over the county but I asked them to send one to Reg's farm; I then called the County Medical Officer's department and notified them, after which I rang my own Force Headquarters and finally Sergeant Blaketon at Ashfordly.

He asked me what I'd done and I told him; I assured him I'd done everything necessary and that Reg was already providing disinfectant at his farm entrance. I explained that I was on my way to the farm within the next few minutes with my 'Keep Out' notices and to serve Form A upon poor old Reg to isolate his premises. I knew he would have quarantined his own farm, but the official wheels must turn.

I then put on my rubber leggings, a long waterproof mackintosh and wellington boots. Dressed like this, I decided to walk the half-mile or so, for in this type of urgency we were no longer thinking in terms of minutes or seconds. Everything had come to a standstill and would remain so until the Ministry's vets had examined the suspect cow or cows. With my notices under my arm, and Reg's Form A in a buff envelope, I made my harrowing journey along the lane.

By the time I arrived at West Gill Farm, Reg was already in position at his gate. Dressed in oilskins and wellington boots, he was standing guard with a shotgun in his hand. A large zinc bath full of pale yellow fluid stood just inside the gate. A yard brush lay beside it and a tractor and trailer were parked nearby.

'Now, Reg,' I said.

'Noo then, Mr Rhea. Got all t'papers, hast tha?' His face was sad and drawn, and I knew I must be careful how I spoke to him. I must not be flippant at all, for farmers treat their cows like old friends. I knew he was on the verge of breaking into tears as he nodded towards the roll of notices under my arm.

' "Keep Out" signs,' I told him. 'I'll stick 'em up for you, on all your entrances. This makes all entrances forbidden areas, Reg. This is the only one that leads down to the house and buildings, isn't it?'

'Aye, t'others are just gates into my fields.'

'Good, well, I won't come through the gate. I'll do this job first – I've got some drawing-pins and string. I'll fix 'em on all the roadside trees and gateposts.'

'Thanks. Ah've already had two daft townies trying to walk their dog down my road. Ah told 'em it was an infected spot, but they didn't understand. They reckoned it was a public footpath down to t'pond, so Ah said it was out-o'-bounds now and anyrood anybody coming in would have to paddle through that bath o' stuff. They didn't like that, nut wi' their townie shoes on. That's why Ah fetched my gun – folks don't argue wi' that, Mr Rhea. That lot sharp cleared off then an' Ah told 'em foot and mouth was catching for humans, an' all. It mebbe is, is it?'

'I'm not sure,' I had to admit. 'I know anthrax can be caught by people . . . '

'Aye, well, it's matterless now. You go and stick them signs up and Ah'll stop folks tramping down my lane. You'll 'ave called in t'Ministry vets, have you?'

'I have, and they'll be here as soon as possible. It might be a while, they've other suspected outbreaks.' I could see moisture in his eyes. His banter had concealed his genuine feelings, I felt, but now he would be alone once again with his thoughts. Before I left, I handed him his Form A, and then turned away to post the notices on his various entrances, eight in total. He was a sad and lonely figure as he waited with his gun in his hands, guarding his gate against ordinary people and a virulent disease.

As I left, he opened my envelope, read the contents of the Form A and stuffed it into his pocket.

When I returned about forty minutes later, he was still there, pacing up and down as he looked out for the ominous approach of the vet's car.

'You go down to the house, Reg, I'll wait here,' I offered.

'Nay, lad,' he spoke softly. 'Ah couldn't. T'wife and our lad are so upset . . . they'd only upset me. Ah'd allus be wanting to look in on me cows . . . '

'It's not confirmed,' I tried to sound optimistic. 'It could be a false alarm.'

He shook his head. 'Nay, Ah doubt it. It's all around is that disease; somehow, yan o' my cows 'as picked it up . . . it's t'end, Mr Rhea . . . t'end . . . twenty years work . . . all for nowt . . . '

'Don't upset yourself,' I did not want to see this stalwart, tough farmer reduced to self-pity or tears, but he needed to talk to somebody. I happened to be that somebody; we were alone at the gate in our ungainly protective clothing, and we could look down the long straight track which led across his fields and into his compact clutch of farm buildings.

'Twenty years,' he repeated, almost to himself. I looked at him. A sturdy Yorkshireman, turned fifty I guessed; he had the round, weathered face of his profession, a face which had seen little else but long hours and hard work over those years. But that work had produced some pride, too, family pride I guessed.

'Twenty years, it's takken me to build that herd. Pedigree Friesians, they are. Eighty milkers, Ah've got. Eighty and Ah started wi' nowt.'

I glanced at the tall post which stood beside his main gate; it bore a small black and white sign which proclaimed that this was the home of the West Gill Farm Herd of Pedigree British Friesians.

'Ah did it for t'lad, for our Ted. Ah needed summat to pass on, Mr Rhea. He's grown up wi' them Friesians and knows 'em like they was bairns, Mr Rhea. We all do, every one on 'em. Me an' all, and t'wife. Seen 'em come along from calves, most of 'em. Bought some and bred some; fussed over 'em, made sure they were just right. Bedded 'em down at night, seen to 'em when they were badly . . . best Friesians for miles, they are.'

He was staring into the distance as he talked, not looking at me and not looking down upon his farm in the shallow valley. He was gazing beyond all that, reminiscing and pouring out his heart in his own simple way.

'And now it's all gone . . . they'll be killed, all of 'em . . . put down like rats. Ah've been so careful, Mr Rhea, with foot and mouth about, taking care, watching where Ah bought things, where Ah went, disinfecting . . . '

'Don't,' I said uselessly. 'You're only making things worse. It might be a false alarm . . . '

I tried to give him a little hope.

'Nay, Ah knows foot and mouth when Ah sees it. Yon awd cow 'as it, there's nowt so sure . . . '

He went on to say how, as a young farmer, he had recognized the potential in a herd of Friesians; he'd seen them as ideal cattle for his plans, cattle which would produce first-class milk. They were useful beef animals too. So years ago, he decided to build himself a pedigree dairy herd, his own very special effort. And his idea was to introduce his only son, Ted, to the skills of dairy farming so that he, in turn, would continue with this herd. He wanted Ted to improve and expand it.

'Ah'd got all soorts of ideas in me head, Mr Rhea. Ah was gahin ti keep better records of 'em all, go for bigger milk yields an' that . . . '

It was good to hear him talking and I allowed him to ramble on, sometimes asking what I thought was a sensible question. I learned a good deal about Friesians that afternoon, but it also taught me enough about foot and mouth disease to make me realize the end had come. I didn't hold out much hope for his herd now, not after listening to his knowledgeable description of the disease and its drastic effects.

It would be over an hour later when a small car eased to a halt on the verge near the gate. A tall young man in a smart lovat green suit climbed out and announced that he was Alan Porrit, a vet from the Ministry of Agriculture. After shaking hands and expressing his sorrow at the awful news, he announced his approval of our immediate actions and donned his own waterproofs.

After swilling himself in the disinfectant, he said, 'Come along, Mr Lumley. Show me where to go.'

'Nay,' said Reg. 'Ah can't. Ah just can't go down there. Not now . . . you go and get it ovvered with.'

Tears welled in his eyes and he rubbed them roughly with his fist.

'Ah'm being right daft and sentimental, but you go. Ah can't . . . '

'I think you should Reg,' I said. 'You'll be needed down there. I'll stay here.'

After some gentle persuasion from us both, Reg joined the vet and I watched them walk into the distance. Their sorry figures seemed to diminish as they approached the farm, and then, as they reached the paths which divided one towards the byre and the other to the house, they halted.

From my vantage point on the lane, I could see them in deep conversation, then Reg began to shake his head. I saw him turn and walk towards his house. He left the vet standing alone. The vet turned on his heels and strode purposefully towards the byre which contained the suspect cattle.

As Reg approached the back door of his house, his hands were over his face. He was sobbing like a child. Someone inside opened the door; he went in and the door closed behind him.

That epidemic of foot and mouth disease cost the country over £200 million. No one knows how much it cost Reg Lumley.

9

Is it, in heav'n, a crime to love too well?

Alexander Pope, 1688–1744

In the great and pleasant rural landscape which surrounded Aidensfield during my time there, serious crime was practically unknown. Certainly, there were many minor thefts, most of which were never officially reported, and I'm sure there were motoring offences which never came to my notice. Other breaches of the law, such as drinking late in the country pubs or petty acts of damage or vandalism were dealt with in the spirit of the law rather than by the letter of the law. A quiet word in the right ear usually prevented further trouble.

It would be wrong to claim that Aidensfield and district was totally free from crime. It was not; every so often, an outbreak of criminal activity would occur, usually of the kind described as petty damage, theft or the unauthorized borrowing of cars. There were some house-breakings, shop-breakings and poaching, and if we suffered three crimes in the district during a month, the local papers described it as a crime wave.

These waves were very tiny, therefore, more like ripples on a village pond than the kind of waves that swamp ocean liners. Nonetheless, they did cause distress to the victims and this in turn caused anxiety among the villagers. From my point of view, these crimes, minor though they were, did involve my colleagues and me with extra duties. There were observations, report writing and court appearances, but I did not mind. In fact, I enjoyed the experiences they provided, albeit with deep concern for the victims, for the investigation of crime is fascinating. To investigate and detect crime is probably one of the major reasons for anyone joining the Police Service.

As time passed, and as each minor breach of the criminal law was dealt with, I did begin to wonder if a major crime or series of crimes would ever occur on my patch. I began to feel that this period of peace was too good to be true, and then, in the spring of one year, I was faced with an outbreak of arson.

Arson was, and still is, one of the most serious of crimes and the legal definition then said that arson involved the unlawful and malicious setting fire to buildings, including churches, warehouses, railway stations, shops and sheds, as well as crops, vegetable produce, coal-mines and ships. It was then categorized as a felony both at common law and by statue. The common law crime was confined to houses and their outhouses, while the statutory crime, featured in the Malicious Damage Act of 1861, involved a detailed list of the objects of the kind listed in the above definition. I remember that in those days, it was not legally possible to charge anyone with arson to a motor vehicle or television set because new fangled contraptions of that sort were not mentioned in that 1861 Act – other possible charges such as malicious damage to personal property had to be considered.

In the weeks following that first act of arson there developed a series of troublesome fires, all of which involved either haystacks or hay in barns. I could discern no pattern, except that the attacked barns or stacks were usually in isolated locations. Some, however, were in the centre of our market towns and as time went by, I began to despair of ever catching the fire-raiser. Some of the fires were on my beat, and although all the local officers were involved in the investigation, I felt it was my duty to arrest the culprit. The battle both to halt and deal with the villain became a personal challenge.

News of the first fire came in the early hours of a Saturday morning in April. Just after 1 a.m. a passing motorist noticed flames licking the asbestos roof of a Dutch barn. He roused the farmer and his wife, who called the fire brigade by dialling 999. As a matter of routine, I was informed by our Control Room and clambered from my warm bed around quarter past one.

Rather than waste time climbing into my motor cycling outfit, I used my own car to rush to the fire. It was at Low Dale Farm, Briggsby, less than ten minutes' drive from Aidensfield. The farm, a small concern with livestock, poultry and arable land, was owned by Arthur Stead and his wife, Helen. When I arrived, the Fire Brigade was already there. Hoses were spraying hissing water into the fierce centre of the fire which had a very secure hold. Men were working in the heat of the flames as the bales of hay glowed in the night. The flames cast frightening shadows upon the house and nearby buildings and showered dangerous sparks across the dark countryside. Most of the flames licked the exterior surface of the hay, while a stiff night breeze carried sparks and more flames into the interior of the barn. Small new fires were breaking out all over the place; it looked like a lost battle.

With old raincoats over their nightclothes and wellingtons on their feet, Arthur and Helen, both in their late fifties, were using hayforks in an attempt to pull untouched bales clear of the inferno.

Helpers had arrived from neighbouring farms and cottages. Men and women were working around the barn, removing bales by hand. After announcing my arrival to the Fire Brigade, I used the Steads' telephone to relay a situation report to Control Room, and then joined the rescue effort. I began to haul bales from the barn and throw them clear of the spreading blaze.

One problem lay in a stiff easterly breeze which made the hay glow deep within the stack as the intense heat consumed the dry material. We tried to hoist some burning bits well away from the barn, but the speed of the fire's consumption beat us. Gallons and gallons of water were sprayed into the depths and we did manage to remove a considerable amount of uncharred hay.

During a lull, I spoke to Arthur.

'We've got a fair amount out, Arthur,' I commented, wiping my dirty hands across my face. We were all black from the smoke and sweating profusely in spite of the chill night air.

'T'cows won't eat it, Mr Rhea, even if it 'as been saved. It'll smell o' smoke, you see . . . might mak bedding or summat. . . '

'You'll be insured, are you?' I asked.

'Aye, but cows can't eat insurance money; they need fodder. It's a while yet before we can turn 'em out to fresh grass.'

I knew that the local farmers would rally to help poor Arthur with his forthcoming feeding problems; they always did when anyone suffered a loss of this kind. But we had fought a losing battle. As fast as we removed bales, others burst into flames; it seemed as if the blaze had crept deep inside the stacked hay and I wondered if our removal of the bales loosened the packed hay and permitted the air to enter. This would fan the flames. As things were, it wasn't long before the entire contents of the barn were a mixture of searing heat, smoke and untidy charred hay.

We kept an eye on the drifting sparks but they disappeared across the fields and missed the buildings. As dawn came to Low Dale Farm we could see the full extent of the devastation. The barn was burnt to a shell, some roof portions having collapsed when the supports gave way in the fire. It contained a jumbled mass of charred and useless hay which was still smouldering. It would continue to smoulder and smoke for days. All around were piles of hay which had been saved by the volunteers, hay which the cattle would not now touch because it was tainted by smoke. The entire area was saturated with dirty water and we stood in a sea of mud and straggly strands of hay.

Arthur and Helen gave us all a breakfast of ham and eggs with copious quantities of hot tea. As we stood outside and I gathered the information necessary for my Fire Report, one of the senior fire officers took me to one side.

'Constable,' he said, 'we feel this is a suspicious fire. We can almost certainly rule out spontaneous combustion which, I'm sure you know, causes a good many stacks and barn fires. That usually occurs within three months of a stack being built – this one is eight months old. Fire from spontaneous combustion works from the inside and moves to the exterior. This started on the outside walls of hay, so it looks deliberate. The seat of the blaze was on the outside of the hay, at the east end of the barn, low down upon the stacked hay but just off ground level. There was a platform of hay left where some upper bales had been removed, and the blaze was creeping up the outside walls of hay when our men got here. I am confident that spontaneous combustion is not the cause and that an outside agent is responsible.

It could be an accident, but I'm calling in our experts for their opinions.'

This meant I must now inform the CID who would liaise with the Fire Brigade and a formal investigation would commence. It would be backed by statements from witnesses plus any scientific evidence salvaged from the scene. Inevitably, poor old Arthur and his wife would be under suspicion of having deliberately set fire to their hay for insurance purposes, and I knew the investigation had to be thorough, if only to exonerate them. I was sure they would never resort to this kind of evil. My witnesses were Arthur and Helen themselves, several fire officers and the motorist who had noticed the blaze, but none could provide any real evidence to show how the blaze had started. It remained a matter of opinion and speculation, but continued to be 'suspicious'.

A week later, there was a second blaze. Although this one did not occur on my beat, it was only four miles away at Seavham and the circumstances were very similar. Around two o'clock in the morning, Ronald Thornton and his wife Alice, who farmed at Home Farm, were roused by barking dogs. Wary of intruders, they had peered out of their bedroom window to see one of their haystacks ablaze. It was in the corner of a field, away from the buildings, but was valuable for livestock feeding.

I noted the date and time, and although I did not attend this one I did later contact the Fire Brigade to ascertain whether it could be linked to the blaze at Low Dale Farm. Other than to say the cause was not spontaneous combustion, the Fire Brigade would not commit themselves. Nonetheless, the similarities included an isolated haystack, an outbreak in the early hours of a Saturday morning, and the suspicious nature of the blaze. The Thorntons were not insured, I learned, which somewhat added to the mystery.

If they had not done it deliberately which seemed most unlikely, and if it was not an accident (there were no chimneys or exposed flames nearby), and if it was not spontaneous combustion, then who had done it and why? These were the questions we had to answer.

I tried to find links or more similarities with the Stead fire, but failed. My avenues of investigation included bad business deals; possible fraud; family feuds; jealousy, petty spitefulness or malice; the work of a pyromaniac and a host of other domestic and business likelihoods. To my knowledge, no known arsonist lived in the area.

The next blaze was three weeks later, on a Wednesday night at Crampton. It was discovered earlier than the others, around eleven o'clock. A neighbour had smelled smoke and had investigated the cause only to discover bales of hay well ablaze in the barn of Throstle Nest Farm. This barn was close to the centre of the village and happily, there was no strong breeze to fan the flames or to disperse the dangerous sparks among the houses.

Mr and Mrs Bill Owens farmed Throstle Nest; their splendid farmhouse occupied an elevated site surrounded by its spacious land, and a pair of Dutch barns stood at the bottom of a lane. This lane formed a junction with the road which led into the village, and their neighbour, Jack Winfield, lived in a cottage near that junction.

Jack's swift action and the rapid response by the Fire Brigade kept damage to a minimum, but the familiar story emerged. It was another suspicious fire, so like the earlier ones. As the Brigade fought the fire and helpful villagers removed bales of unburnt hay, the drifting smoke penetrated many nearby homes. The smell would linger for days afterwards. During a lull, I spoke to Jack Winfield, a retired farm worker.

'Now, Jack, did you hear or see anything? We've had a few of these fires now.'

'There was a motor bike about the village tonight,' he said without hesitation. 'I grumbled, 'cos it made my television picture go funny. Motor bikes do that, you know, sometimes.'

'What time?' I asked.

'Nine o'clockish,' he said. 'First time, that was. Then again later, before t'fire broke out. Not long before, but I couldn't be sure of t'time really. Same bike, I could tell by t'noise.'

'Has it been before?'

'Can't say I've noticed it. Mind, if I hadn't had my set on, mebbe I wouldn't have noticed.'

'Did you see it then? Do you know who it was?'

'Sorry, lad, no.'

After quizzing him at length, I took a written witness statement from him. For the first time, we had a hint of a suspect, slender though it was, and before the Fire Brigade left, one of their officers came to me.

'We found this,' he said, opening the palm of his hand to reveal a spent match.

'Where, precisely?' I asked, accepting this new piece of evidence.

'About five feet from where we believe the blaze started,' he said, pointing to a piece of muddy land. 'We think it started low down this side, where some bales have been removed . . . '

'Like the Low Dale fire?' I interrupted.

'Yes, in a similar position. The flames crept up the outside wall of hay before gaining a strong hold. This match, which is clean and new as you can see, was lying on the ground.'

'Thrown away, you think?'

'Its position suggests that.'

I pinpointed the precise location of this match and drew a little sketch in my notebook so that it would be committed to paper for future records. It was an ordinary match, not from a book of paper matches or a short-stemmed Swan Vestas. Its unweathered appearance said a lot; there was a distinct possibility that it was associated with the blaze.

I reported these new facts to Sergeant Blaketon at Ashfordly, and he decided to institute a series of nightly police patrols. Their purpose was to trace the motor cyclist and/or the fire-raiser. At this stage, we felt there was little point stopping all motor cyclists, but did decide to record the registration number of every bike seen during our patrols. I was aware, too, that the fuel tank of a motor cycle contains petrol and what better method is there for a fire-raiser to carry this incendiary aid?

If and when another fire broke out, we could consult our records and check the movements of all recorded bikes. It would be possible to see if they tallied with the date, time and place of the fire. Even so, with such massive rural area to patrol, the chances of a police vehicle crossing the path of the fire-raiser were remote to say the least. But we had to try.

For the next couple of weeks there were no reported stack fires. We began to feel that our presence on the roads and the fact that our purpose was enhanced by local gossip, had deterred the arsonist. But we were wrong.

The next fire broke out in the centre of Ashfordly. Tucked into one of the side streets was a farmhouse and behind it was a square stackyard and a motley collection of implement sheds. The fields belonging to this farm were some distance away on the outskirts of the town, but this curious town centre farm, known as Town Farm, was a thriving enterprise.

I was on night duty one Friday and was patrolling the surrounding moors and hills when I spotted a bright blaze in the centre of Ashfordly. It was 1 a.m. For a moment, I thought it was a bonfire in a garden, one which had been lit earlier and whose flames had been revived by a sudden night breeze; but in seconds, I knew it was too large for that and I feared the worst.

From my vantage point on the hills, it was impossible to say precisely where it was. All I could determine was a bright, flickering flame somewhere among a dark collection of houses and other buildings. I accelerated the little motor bike down towards the town and it was then that I recalled the tumble of farm buildings and sheds just off Field Lane. As I entered the town, I knew the worst. I roared towards the blaze. It was now showing as a bright orange and red glow against the sky above the houses, and I could see a pall of thick, black smoke. This was no garden bonfire and I feared another arson attack.

The moment I turned the corner and identified the precise location, I halted and radioed my Control Room. Through its radio network, the Fire Brigade was summoned and I asked Control Room sergeant to awake Sergeant Blaketon. Then I began to rouse the sleeping occupants of the farmhouse and several nearby homes. The horrified farmer said there were horses in some of the buildings and so I helped him to evacuate his animals.

Two tractors were in the Dutch barn; they were already covered with blazing hay which had tumbled from the stacked bales and so began another battle to save his equipment and machinery. The farmer's wife was in tears; neighbours were terrified for their homes and the horses were snorting and frisky in their fright.

We did not save the barn, the hay or the tractors but no

human or animal life was lost. With Sergeant Blaketon at my side, I began a meticulous search of the scene. We were seeking that spent match which could be some distance from the barn. He found it. Lying 5 or 6 feet away from where the wall of the hay had been, he located a clean spent match, miraculously having avoided the trampling feet and gallons of rushing water. He preserved it for evidence. It was another important indication that the same person was responsible for all the fires.

The Fire Officer in charge said he believed the blaze had not been due to an electrical fault or to spontaneous combustion; he expressed an opinion that the tractors might, in some way, have been responsible. The possibility of a short circuit from a battery couldn't be ignored.

A more detailed investigation would follow and the charred remains would be examined. When we told the firemen about the match, he said, 'That figures. We think it might have started on that outer wall of hay, not far from there . . . that's the second match you've found, eh?'

We began to ask about the motor cycle noises in the night and one of the neighbours, a retired bank manager, did tell us he had heard a motor bike. It was not mine because the timing was different. I hadn't been near the place until just after 1 a.m. He had heard one about midnight, he said, but could not say whether it was coming towards Town Farm or leaving it.

But it was enough for us, after that, we intensified our nightly patrols for the motor-cycling fire-raiser. At the same time, we renewed our enquiries from earlier victims. We asked them whether they had antagonized anyone who owned a motor bike and we continued our efforts to establish a link, any link, between all the scenes of the fires.

But we did not find any connection.

Then I had a stroke of luck. It was one of those moments of good fortune that all detectives require and with which some are blessed throughout their careers. In my case, it happened while I was off duty. I recognized the clue for what it was and became excited when I realized I might have found the arsonist.

It was a Friday, which was market day in Ashfordly. I went to market with Mary to help with the shopping and to look after the children. For me, it was a trying but enjoyable chore. I was wandering among the stalls in my off duty casual clothes, pleased that it was a fine spring day and that there were books and antiques to examine. I ran into friends and acquaintances to chat with and the entire experience generated a pleasing air of rustic contentment. It was a welcome break from my routine.

Then, as I poked among some junk on a stall, seeking old inkwells (which I collect as a hobby) I noticed the motor cyclist. He was sitting astride a green BSA Bantam in front of one of the pubs which overlooked the market place. He was laughing and chatting to a pretty girl. I watched and, because motor cycles were very much on my official mind, began to observe them.

I was in an ideal position. As I watched, I saw the youth dig into his trousers pocket, pull out a cigarette and light it. Then, having done so, he flicked the spent match over his shoulder and drew heavily on the cigarette. My heart thumped; I found a pen in my pocket and jotted the make and registration number on a piece of paper and followed with a description of him and his girl. Then, I ambled across to find that match. I had to have it for comparison with the others.

It was easy; it was the only one lying nearby. The youth was engrossed in his chat with the girl and didn't even glance at my approach. The match lay about 5 feet behind him.

Not wishing to draw his attention, or indeed anyone else's, to my curious behaviour, I 'accidentally' dropped my car keys close to the match then stooped to retrieve them and my valuable piece of evidence. Now, the match would be scientifically compared with those already in our possession, and discreet enquiries would be made into the owner of that BSA. The chain of evidence was growing stronger. I went straight to Ashfordly Police Station with the match, and Sergeant Blaketon said he would have it taken immediately to the Forensic Laboratory at Harrogate.

Prompt enquiries from the Vehicle Taxation Office at Northallerton told us that the youth lived at Malton; we learned he was called Ian Clayton. And so, at last, we had a very likely suspect.

The problem was whether to interview him immediately, in which case he could deny being near the fires, or to make some discreet enquiries and observations with a view to gathering more evidence and facts about his life and background. We decided we needed more evidence if we were to link him with the fires; after all, we had no proof yet, merely surmise, and so we circulated to all police officers, his description and details of his motor cycle. We would find out about his work and how he spent his leisure hours and if necessary, his movements would be monitored as he went out at night. We might even catch him in the act of lighting a fire.

Two days later, we received a telephone call from the Forensic Science Lab at Harrogate. Their experts had examined all three matches and said that, in their opinion, they were similar.

Scientific evidence confirmed they had come from the same manufacturer and even the same batch of timber, but the lab experts would not commit themselves to anything more positive. A written report would follow. As evidence of arson, this was, in itself, far too flimsy. Our suspect remained a mere suspect.

Two weeks later, the little BSA Bantam was seen heading towards Ashfordly. It was discreetly followed and Ian Clayton collected his girl friend from a house at 45 Stafford Road, Ashfordly. With each perched astride the tiny bike, it motored towards Waindale. It was about ten-thirty and it was dark. Having shadowed them into Waindale in his patrol car, PC Gregson radioed for me because Waindale was on my beat. He said they had driven along Green Lane. I received the call and set off for that hamlet. There was a feeling of excitement in my bones.

I used my own car because I felt this would be wiser than using the police motor cycle. A police motor cycle was far too prominent for this task. I parked in Waindale, making sure the car was out of sight, and began to walk along Green Lane, seeking haystacks and Dutch barns. I knew the location of most, and then, as I silently moved along the lane, I arrived at Green Farm. In the darkness, I could distinguish the tall supports of the Dutch barn, and then, as I padded silently into the complex, I came across the BSA Bantam. I could smell the heat of its engine as it leaned against a dry stone wall, and a quick examination of its number plate proved it was the one we sought. My heart was thumping now; I had to find him before he fired this stack, but I also needed evidence of his crimes.

Other than the sounds of the night, including some furtive scuttlings from rats and mice, I could not see or hear anything. But he was here. Had he seen me? Was he watching me? If I wasn't careful, he might escape on his bike . . . perhaps I should have disconnected the plug lead?

All kinds of worries and plans crossed my mind, and then, as I stood in the shelter of a tractor shed, my eyes became accustomed to the gloom. Aided by a low light from the curtained farmhouse windows, I saw the flicker of a match. It burnt a hole in the gloom; it flickered for a few seconds and then flew in an arc to splutter into darkness. This was it!

I sped towards that place. The match had died now. It had not set fire to anything. But there was another tiny glow of red. And I smelt smoke. Cigarette smoke. Not burning hay.

I shone my torch. A pool of light burst upon the young couple, boy and girl, each partly dressed, each acutely embarrassed after their love-making in the hay. And in those moments, the youth's smouldering cigarette was cast away to land somewhere in the dry hay . . .

I found it before it ignited the hay, kept it as evidence and took them both to Ashfordly Police Station in my car. To cut a long story short, after a protracted investigation about their movements, Ian Clayton and Susan Longfield did admit visiting all the burnt barns and stacks. They identified them only when we took them to each one in turn. Susan, being new to the area, and Ian, living fifteen miles away, had seen the reports in the newspapers, but had never realized the fires had occurred in barns they had used. Names of villages and isolated farms meant nothing to them.

They had not known the names of the farms they had visited; they had simply jumped on the little bike and toured the lanes until they came to a warm and cosy barn or haystack. There they stopped and made love in the hay.

And afterwards, Ian always lit a cigarette which he discarded without thought . . .

He was charged with arson of each of those stacks and barns and appeared before the magistrates in committal proceedings.

After considering all the facts, they found no case to answer because the fires were accidental. In their considered opinion, there was no malice in his actions and they accepted he had not unlawfully and maliciously set fire to the hay.

Another of my rare major criminal investigations concerned a case of housebreaking which even today remains unsolved.

Tucked discreetly behind the village street in Aidensfield is St Cuthbert's Cottage, a delightful small house which dates to the eighteenth century. With two bedrooms, a living-room and kitchen, it has beamed ceilings, pretty windows and roses growing around a rustic porch. When its elderly occupant died, it was bought by a Mr Lawrence Porteous of Leicester who wanted it as a holiday home. He retained most of the old lady's antique furniture, but modernized and decorated the little house until it was a veritable gem. It was the kind of home for which any romantic young couple would have yearned.

At this time, it so happened that one young couple from Aidensfield desperately needed a home. In their estimation, St Cuthbert's Cottage was ideal. They lacked the funds to buy it, but after the sale they did write to Mr Porteous to ask if he would rent them the cottage even for a short period, until they found somewhere of their own. He refused.

They wrote again a week or two later, pointing out that it was empty for most of the year, and that they had no home . . . but again he refused.

The situation had arisen like this. Jill Knight, née Crane, was the youngest daughter of Mrs Brenda Crane, widow. Mrs Crane and Jill had lived in another Aidensfield cottage which was owned by a property company. When Jill married young Paul Knight, he moved into the same cottage and, with his new bride, shared the accommodation and its running expenses. Then Jill became pregnant. Through one of those awful quirks of fate, poor Mrs Crane suffered a heart attack and died about the same time.

The house had been in her name; consequently upon her death, the property company wanted to repossess it for another tenant, a retiring employee of theirs. Because Jill and Paul were not holders of the rent book, they were told to vacate the house.

If they refused, then the due processes of civil law would be implemented to evict them. They were given three months notice. This put them in a terrible dilemma. Paul worked for an agricultural implement dealer in Ashfordly and needed another home in the area, so that he was near enough to cycle to work. He couldn't afford a car and the buses were too infrequent.

Wisely, he applied for a council house but was told there was a waiting-list; his name would be placed on that list and in the meantime, he must find alternative accommodation. Not surprisingly, he got his eye on St Cuthbert's Cottage as an ideal short-term solution and that was how he came to write to Mr Porteous.

Repeated refusals from Lawrence Porteous put the youngsters in a real dilemma. I knew them both and liked them, but I could see the strain beginning to have its effect, especially upon the heavily pregnant Jill. The worry made her pale and constantly tired, and she began to neglect her appearance. Her mother's death, her own pregnancy and the housing problems were more than any young girl should have to tolerate.

'No luck?' I met her in the shop one day.

She shook her tousled head.

'Paul's been asking all over,' she said, her pretty face drawn with anxiety. 'We got chance of a council house over at Scalby, but it was too far for Paul to get to work. If you see anything, Mr Rhea, you'll let us know? They can't put us on the street, can they? Me being pregnant and that?'

'No, I'm sure they can't and I'm also sure something will turn up . . .'

'We only need something till we get a council house near here,' she said. 'There's bound to be one soon, isn't there? The council said they come up fairly often.'

I did feel concerned for them. There were lots of suitable cottages in the surrounding villages, but this was the period when rich folks were buying them for holiday homes. Some were purchased as personal holiday homes or weekend cottages, and others were bought as investments to be rented weekly or for mere weekends to holiday-makers.

There is little doubt that the merits of this upsurge in buying country cottages did have a dual value; it did prevent many old cottages from falling into ruin and it did bring some welcome business into the village stores and inns. But on the other hand, it denied many young people a village home, either for rent or for purchase, because it made fewer local homes available.

This was brought home to me by the case of Jill and Paul Knight. I felt sure the council would never allow them to be thrown on to the street or taken into a hostel of some kind, but the wheels of official departments turn so very slowly and with such a lamentable lack of feeling or compassion. The officials would have no concept of the heartache involved in the long periods of waiting and hoping.

As I worried about the future for Jill and Paul, I received a visit from the postman.

'Mr Rhea,' he said as he knocked with my morning mail, 'somebody's broken into that little cottage down the village, St Cuthbert's.'

My heart sank.

'Much gone?' I asked.

'Dunno,' he shook his head. 'They got in by smashing a window at the back, in the kitchen. It's still open.'

'Right, thanks,' I said. 'I'll go and have a look.'

As he'd said, entry was by smashing a pane at the back. The burglars, or housebreakers, had opened the kitchen window and climbed through. Once inside, exit had been through the kitchen door by unlocking the Yale catch. I could not tell whether anything was missing for I had never previously been in the cottage, and the intruder(s) had not made a mess.

I now had a crime in Aidensfield. If the breaking and entry had occurred after 9 p.m. and before 6 a.m. it would be classified as a burglary. Outside those times, it would be recorded as a housebreaking. Since 1968, due to a change in the law, all such breakings have been categorized as burglary.

I contacted the key-holder, Miss Cox, who lived two doors away and together we made a brief examination. I asked her not to touch anything, but to look around and tell me what was not in its usual place.

'Oh dear, oh dear,' she muttered as she surveyed each room

at my side. 'Oh, dear, oh dear, how awful.'

She was a fussy little woman of indeterminate age, probably in her sixties.

'Can you tell me what's been taken?' I asked, notebook at the ready.

'The television,' she said, pointing to an empty corner.

I quizzed her and found out it was a black and white Murphy set, with a 12″ screen.

'The radio,' she said in the kitchen. This was a Bush portable in a red and cream case, with a plastic carrying handle. 'And a vase, a nice old vase in green glass.'

'Thanks.'

We searched the entire cottage, but nothing else seemed to have been stolen. She checked it regularly, but could not say it was secure at 9 o'clock last night. So we recorded it as house-breaking, a lesser crime than burglary. I thanked her, and obtained the telephone number of Mr Porteous; then called in our CID and Scenes of Crime experts; they would examine the cottage for fingerprints and other clues.

My next task, apart from completing the formal written Crime Report, was to make house-to-house enquiries around Aidensfield in the hope that someone had either heard or seen something. The CID would do their skilled work after obtaining a key from Miss Cox and I asked the local plumber to reglaze the broken window.

From my office, I rang Mr Porteous to break the bad news. After assuring him that all possible had been done, and that his cottage would be secure before nightfall, he decided not to drive up from Leicester. I said it was not necessary.

Funnily enough, another two cottages in a deep moorland village were raided about a fortnight later, but in each case, the MO was different from the Aidensfield crime. I was sure the Aidensfield housebreaker had not broken into the others but those crimes did prompt a telephone call from Mr Porteous.

'Ah, Mr Rhea,' he said. 'I've just seen the paper – two cottages have been burgled on the moors. Is this a regular happening in your area?'

'It's becoming more commonplace,' I had to admit. 'Some of these holiday homes, with expensive furnishings, are easy meat you know. They're empty for long periods and it doesn't take a genius to realize they've got things like TVs and radios inside; all easily disposable.'

He paused. 'We're going abroad for the summer,' he said, 'so we won't be using St Cuthbert's Cottage for our fortnight's holiday. It'll be empty from now until October; that's six months. Miss Cox will pop in from time to time, but you'll keep an eye on it for me, will you?'

'Of course,' I said, 'but it's always at risk, you know that.'

'I know. I've heard about these people who live in houses for you, house-sitters or something. Have you anyone in your area who would do that? For a fee, of course.'

I was about to say I knew of no one, when I remembered Jill and Paul Knight.

'I know a young couple who would do a good job for you,' I said. 'They'd be willing to house-sit for you, for six months or whatever it takes.'

I told him all about Jill and Paul, and how they were now waiting for allocation of a council house. He recalled their pleading letters.

'I didn't commit myself before,' he said. 'After all, I don't know them and at that time I did intend using my cottage most weekends . . . but, well, for a gap of six months . . . '

'They are on the council waiting-list,' I stressed, 'but this would be useful to both you and them.'

'Ask them to ring me,' he said, 'I'll discuss terms; I was willing to pay someone, so I may decide to allow them the cottage rent free or possibly a nominal rent, for legal purposes . . . '

Three days later, they moved in.

Five days afterwards, the stolen goods were found in an old van which was rotting in a quarry. They were quite undamaged and after successfully testing them for fingerprints, they were restored to St Cuthbert's Cottage. It was good news for Mr Porteous.

My enquiries into the crime drew a complete blank but it was a remark I overheard from a drinker in the Brewer's Arms which caused me to think.

'By gum,' said the man over his pint one night, (he was

chatting confidentially to a pal. but I heard him,) 'it's a rum sort of a do when you've got to burgle a house to get folks to take notice of you. Still, yon lad's got a roof over his head now.'

From time to time, I still reflect upon that unsolved crime.

CONSTABLE
THROUGH THE
MEADOW

1

'Meadows trim with daisies pied,
Shallow brooks and rivers wide.'

L'Allegro, John Milton, 1608-74

For the rural police constable going about his daily routine, this is more than a poetic image; sights of this kind are a pleasant part of country life and the constable's patrols take him through a whole galaxy of meadows, sometimes along major roads, sometimes along narrow lanes and occasionally by little-used bridleways, green lanes or tortuous footpaths with centuries of history beneath them.

On the edge of the moors where I used to patrol, some of the fields are divided by rippling brooks which we call becks or gills, other boundaries are marked by the sturdy dry-stone walls of the region, and some make use of hedgerows or even timber-and-wire fencing. There are spacious flat fields used for the growth of cereals or the nourishment of herds of milk-producing cows, and tiny patches of grass which have the appearance of being artificially created from the heather or bracken of a wild moorland hillside.

Some of the meadows adjacent to the moorland are almost too small to be considered fields or meadows, perhaps being better described as paddocks. One local name is intake because they have been cultivated after being securely walled from the wilderness of pervading heather, but they continue to provide a refuge for a few hens or moorland sheep, even a cow or horse.

Those on the edge of the moors usually contain a patch of smooth, short grass with very few flowers because the black-

5

faced sheep of this region continually nibble at it until they produce a surface which is as smooth as a prize lawn. In the dales below, however, the meadows are more lush; on the fertile earth, they thrive upon the natural goodness which has accumulated over the years. They feature as parts of a beautiful green carpet decorated with profuse and colourful vegetation; in the spring and summer they are a delight, and in the winter they sleep unmolested.

There were times when I patrolled beside meadows filled with butterflies and bees busily exploring a bewildering range of blossoming wild flowers. Clovers and vetches patterned the greenery with tiny dots of colour and in the changing seasons I noted celandines, red poppies, sorrel, a variety of thistles, pretty red campions, cow parsley, buttercups, daisies and more besides, sometimes with a charming border of wild roses or honeysuckle along the carefully trimmed hedgerows.

In the late spring or early summer, before haytime, the meadows are rich with a multitude of pretty grasses and I learnt there are about a hundred and fifty varieties in this country, our farmers knowing which will produce the best nourishment for their grazing livestock, or which are most suited for transformation into hay and silage. I discovered that after the grass has been cut for haymaking, the coarse grass which follows is called fog by some Yorkshire farmers.

'By yon fog's leeaking well,' a moorland farmer noted one morning. I looked for the familiar wispy clouds in the valley and wondered why he had made this comment on a clear sunny morning, but was later to learn he was speaking of the grass in a recently mown hayfield. I believe there was an old Scandinavian word 'fogg' meaning a limp type of grass.

In addition to this form of fog, there is a variety of grass called Yorkshire Fog which is most attractive and very widespread throughout Britain and Europe. Growing up to two feet in height, it has a soft green/grey stem and when it flowers in the summer, it produces a most delightful pink and white hue which turns to purple as the long days of summer edge towards another autumn.

Whatever their functions, these meadows and the highways and byways that knit them together like a huge patchwork quilt are an echo of history. Many of the fields which today support livestock or produce crops have been fulfilling this role for centuries, altering their functions and appearance to keep pace with the requirements of good husbandry. The changing techniques of farming and the increasing use of large agricultural machines mean that the size, shape and uses of our fields must alter to keep pace.

Some of us grumble about the removal of hedges with all the consequent upheaval among the wild life that depends upon them, but we may not appreciate that this results from the desperate need to feed the expanding human race by making the best use of modern machinery.

We grumble about the disappearance of footpaths or the use of chemicals, the removal of small copses or the way new roads and buildings encroach upon the natural landscape. We may not like these changes, but they are part of the moving pattern of the landscape which has been occurring since man first cultivated the land and made the countryside his home.

History has noted the fields existed more than 3,500 years ago; there were fields in medieval times, fields born from the enclosures of the eighteenth and nineteenth centuries, and the extensive but controversial fields of modern times.

Throughout history, the countryman has loved the fields which surround his home, so much so that they have been given names. For the village policeman going about his daily business, it was necessary to know these names because they cropped up in his work. They were just as important as other place-names in and around the village and I was soon familiar with names like Hundred Acre, Highside, Beckside, Rough Edge, Stoney Heights, Back Lane, Maypole Hill, The Bottoms, Low Leys, Croft End, The Carrs, Hagg End, Manor Intake, Hob Hole, Castle Lands, Hawthorn Leys, Lucy Ings and others.

Some of these names are self-explanatory, and others are widely used to describe the nature of a field. For example, a carr or The Carrs refers to an area of heavy, rough marshy ground which is not close to the moors, often being used in connection with a low-lying area.

Ings is another word for a pasture with these features – many

7

local ings are covered with water and there is a fine example at Fairburn Ings, a modern haven for wild life close to the A1 near Ferrybridge in West Yorkshire. A ley is a rich arable field which has been put down to grass, while an intake of the kind mentioned earlier is generally a patch of land which has been reclaimed from the moor. In our local dialect the word is often abbreviated to intak. Of some curiosity interest is the prefix Lucy, as in Lucy Ings mentioned above. This word is spoken and written in different ways such as Lousey Lane, Lowsey Ings, Lucy Field and so forth. It is nothing to do with a girl called Lucy nor does it mean lousy (as in awful); it comes from an old word meaning pig-sty, one derivation of which is loosey. So Lousey Lane, Lowsey Ings or Lucy Field refer to places where pigs were once kept.

Another interesting word is neuk; it means the corner or angle of a field and is perhaps more widely known as nook, as in nooks and crannies. This also appears in some locations such as Cocquet Nook or Blew Neuk, both being place-names on the North York Moors.

During my patrols, I was frequently traversing the heights of the moors from which magnificent vantage points were available. Time and time again, it was possible to park my police motor-cycle and sit astride it as I gazed across the panoramic landscape below.

The fields and meadows decorated the countryside in a manner which has become so much a part of the English country scene, and from these lofty positions I could only wonder at the range of colours, shapes and locations. From a distance and from a height, those meadows were truly a gigantic patchwork quilt, but in the course of their history, they had witnessed a thousand stories, ancient and modern. They had seen more changes and innovations than we might hope to recall, and many of then remained stubbornly silent about their experiences. Some, however, did contain relics of earthworks, old tumuli, bygone settlements and even Roman remains, and from these sources the history of our district could be told.

Sometimes, at the crack of dawn, I would sit upon my police motor-cycle and gaze in wonder at the illusion of history before me and, later, I came to realise that my own duty was somehow reflected by changing circumstances of those meadows. Just as they appeared in many shapes and sizes, so did the duties I was bound to perform. Large tasks and little tasks, major incidents and minor jobs all came my way, and just as the meadows changed during the year, so did my work. It was altering all the time, with constant innovations forcing changes upon the entire police service, changes which eventually filtered down to my level. In a lifetime, those meadows would evolve beyond all present recognition but in spite of that, they would remain English meadows.

My work would be transformed too, but an underlying feature was that it would always be police work, albeit of a very special kind. Whatever variations were wrought upon society and upon the police service, the vital ground-level work of the constable would continue. With an air of permanence that can be under-estimated, those meadows and the British police constable will modify and be modified to accommodate society's needs.

I had arrived at Aidensfield just as the era of the pedal-cycling village constable was ending; I enjoyed the swift transportation offered by a little Francis Barnett two-stroke motor-cycle, even if that transportation was tainted with the need to cater for the British climate. To perform a patrol, however short, I had to smother myself in oily waterproofs and if I visited anyone's house, I had to stand outside lest the oil from the bike or water from the road caused damage to the home. Carrying papers and documents was fraught with danger and there were immense difficulties in conducting a roadside interview in pouring rain.

But, in many ways, I did enjoy my motor-cycle patrols. The power of freedom and the rush of fresh air combined to give a tremendous feeling of elation and I like to think this open air life kept me healthy and free from colds. But change was on the horizon.

One day in early summer, I was informed that I was to be issued with a mini-van.

It would replace the motor-cycle I used for my patrol work and at first I welcomed the news. A four-wheeled vehicle with a roof and comfortable seats would be so much better for my duties; I'd be able to carry equipment, forms and circulars and it would in all respects be a great improvement upon the motor-bike. But there was one snag. I had to share the van with the constable on the neighbouring beat whose house was seven miles away. If the authorities could not appreciate the problems this would create, then I could. The chief snag would be the possibility that the little van would be miles away when I required it urgently. I might be marooned with no official transport. When a constable lives on official premises as I did, he must be expected to cope with any emergency that occurs, even during off-duty periods. And there would be complications in making the change-over at the end or the beginning of each shift whether it was then in my possession or the possession of a colleague. On paper, it seemed a feasible idea; in practice, I knew it would generate problems. But the police service, always a Cinderella when it comes to local authority expenditure, could not afford to supply every rural constable with a van.

Its arrival, however, signalled another change in the methods of patrolling a policeman's rural patch. Instead of being on duty twenty-four hours a day, the village bobby would now work in shifts of eight hours, sharing his beat with other constables and performing duties away from his own beat.

It meant that I must now patrol an expanded area, albeit for only eight hours a day, but my work would thus become more formalised and regimented. I would have to work shifts to accommodate the changing work pattern because, in order to ensure a full twenty-four hour cover every day of the year, the system requires about five officers. Three are needed every day to span the twenty-four hours in eight-hour shifts; to cater for days off, sickness, courses, holidays, court appearances and other absences, expected or unexpected, extra officers must be available. And so, with the stroke of a pen and the gift of a van, the policing of Aidensfield changed. I would be expected to patrol other parts of the district, while constables from afar would be invading my patch.

I did not welcome this; I would far rather have been fully responsible for the Aidensfield beat for twenty-four hours a day, and allowed to work at my own discretion. But it was not to be; progress had arrived and it could not be halted.

On the day the van was to be issued, I had to drive my little motor-cycle over the hills to Police Headquarters. This was its last trip as a police motor-cycle and it was rather sad; quite unexpectedly, I felt a twinge of sorrow at its departure and was tempted to try and buy it. But official wheels had already started to turn, and the Francis Barnett was to be sold, along with other redundant motor-cycles, to the dealer who had won the contract to supply the vans. The outdated bikes were therefore part-exchanged for up-to-date transport in the shape of little grey vans.

Having said a rather emotional farewell to my bike, I relinquished my protective clothing, crash helmet and gauntlets and handed over the bike's log-book to the admin. department of our Road Traffic Division. Thus I severed all links with my motor-cycle. I was shown to my new van which stood among rows of others awaiting their drivers; each was gleaming in the morning sunshine and they were all alike. There seemed to be hundreds of them, all in symmetrical rows with their bonnets facing east, but there were probably about fifty! Each was a brand-new Morris mini-van clad in a pleasing grey livery; this surprised me. I had expected black or navy blue, but it seemed the service was moving away from its past stereotype colours. Furthermore, none of the vans bore police signs, the only visible link with the service being the blue lamp perched in the centre of each roof. Inside the cab, however, there was a police radio set plus an official log-book for recording dates, times and distances of journeys, petrol issues, oil consumption and the name of each driver. There was a tool kit, a spare wheel and nothing else.

The rear of each little van was completely bare and empty; the ridged metal floor had no covering and there were no shelves or compartments for storage or for conveying the paraphernalia of constabulary duty. In truth, that empty rear compartment was of very limited value; no one (except a child) could sit there although I did note the huge battery strapped down near one of the rear-wheel arches.

This had replaced the original car battery because of the additional power required for the radio which would be functioning virtually round the clock, and for activating the flashing blue light should it ever be required. After a short course of instruction about operating the mini-van, the radio and the blue light, and a lecture about the need to regularly clean the vehicle inside and out, to rigidly abide by servicing dates and oil changes, to enter details in the log immediately upon completion of each journey and to report any fault however minor, I was allowed to leave.

It was at this point that another problem faced me and countless other constables. It was a simple problem – police officers are among the largest of people and mini-vans are among the smallest of motor vehicles. Getting some officers into those driving-seats was rather like a size 6 foot being squeezed into a size 4½ shoe. Not being as tall or as broad as some, I found that I could get into the driving-seat and, with the seat pushed back to its maximum, I could operate the foot pedals and hand controls. But I could not wear a cap while driving. Even though we wore peaked caps and not helmets, I now knew the purpose of that empty rear part – it was to carry the caps of constables at the wheel, even if they were liable to rattle around in that empty bare area. Once inside, however, I started the engine, listened to the crackle of the tiny exhaust and switched on the official radio. Having booked on the air, I found first gear, noted the fuel tank was full and set a course for Aidensfield.

On the journey home, I gained impressions of my cap bouncing around in the rear, of me bouncing around in the front and the little van *et al* bouncing across the moors. I was later to learn that passengers in mini cars are nervously aware of this bouncing motion because their rumps hover dangerously near to the road surface while the suspension of the vehicle gives the overall feeling of riding in a high-speed motorised trampoline. But we made it.

During that half-hour trip, I learned to drive with my head slightly bowed to avoid crowning myself on the roof, and managed to manipulate the miniature pedals by judicious use of my police boots. Sometimes, however, the expanse which formed the soles of my boots made me strike two pedals at the same time, but protests from the mini rapidly corrected that fault. The simultaneous operation of a brake, clutch or accelerator is enough to confuse the cleverest of transmission systems and the mini had the sense to protest loudly and actively at this abuse.

Once at home, the children were delighted. Tiny as they were, they thought it was my personal van and so I let them sit in the back; for them, the experience was wonderful and they squeaked with delight as they tumbled and rolled about the bare metal floor. Lots of little faces peered out of the rear windows like miniature prisoners in a miniature Black Maria, and more squeals of delight occurred when one of them tweaked the switch of the rotating blue light which flashed and reflected brightly in the windows of the house.

They spent a few minutes playing in the van, sometimes listening to the burble of voices that muttered eternally from the official radio and sometimes pretending to drive it to an accompaniment of suitable brum-brums and pip-pips. It was a moment of fun in a vehicle that had a very official function to perform. After a coffee, I rang Sergeant Blaketon to announce my return to Aidensfield with the van and he ordered me to drive to Ashfordly Police Station so that he could formally inspect this newest of acquisitions. Before leaving, I made sure the children hadn't left anything in the van, because Oscar Blaketon was not the sort of person to appreciate a child's desperate need to play 'going to Nanna's' in Daddy's new police car.

I parked it outside the square brick-built police station at Ashfordly and entered; Sergeant Blaketon was writing something at the front desk and actually smiled at my arrival.

'All correct, Rhea?' he asked; this was his way of saying 'Hello.'

'All correct, Sergeant,' I chanted the ritual response.

'The section's new vehicle functioning all right, is it?' he continued. 'No breakdowns, mechanical defects, malfunctioning of equipment, unnecessary rattles, squeaks or groans? Damage or wear and tear? Punctures or oil leaks?'

'No, it seems to go very well,' I said. 'Good acceleration, the braking seems OK and it corners very well. I didn't hit anything on the way here either,' I added.

'You're to share it with other beat men, Rhea,' his face never

13

cracked at my veiled sarcasm, for his smile was now stored away for use at a future time. 'That van does not belong to Aidensfield beat, you appreciate?'

'Yes, I know that, Sergeant.' I was now behind the counter and had removed my cap. I had some report writing to complete, and this seemed the ideal opportunity to do it on the office typewriter. 'You wanted to see the van?'

'In a moment, Rhea. I'm busy compiling a set of instructions right now,' he said, 'You'll have to familiarise yourself with them, so you might as well type them out for me. Copies to all users of the van, copy for the office notice-board, copy for Divisional HQ, and a copy to be stuck inside the van's log-book. All to note and sign as having read and digested the said instructions.'

I knew Blaketon's obsession for detail and his practice of committing his orders to writing; I could visualise the contents of his order. I was not disappointed when he presented his neat handwritten work for me to type. After identifying the vehicle by its registration number and the call sign of the radio set, he listed a host of 'dos' and 'don'ts.'

These included the following:

'Members will, repeat will, maintain the vehicle in a roadworthy condition. Under no circumstances will road traffic laws and regulations be infringed. Members will therefore inspect the van before and after each journey.

'Members will, repeat will, inspect for defects such as faulty lights, worn tyres, defective windscreen wipers, brakes and steering, and any other fault, mechanical or otherwise, which might infringe either the Road Traffic Acts or the Construction and Use Regulations. The van will not, repeat not, be driven upon a road if it is in such a condition that statutory provisions are infringed.

'It will be the responsibility of drivers to thoroughly check the roadworthiness of the van; responsibility will be deemed to devolve upon the person driving it when such a fault develops. It will therefore be in the interests of all members to check the vehicle meticulously before taking it on the road. Any defects or damage then discovered will, repeat will, be reported immediately.

'Members will, repeat will, ensure that the vehicle is filled with petrol at the conclusion of every tour of duty, and that the oil, water and tyre pressures are checked, and if necessary, replenished. Details will, repeat will, be entered in the log book, and in the pocket books of the officers concerned. It is imperative that this instruction is obeyed. Failure will be considered a disciplinary offence.

'Members will, repeat will, ensure that the vehicle is driven courteously at all times and that drivers set an example to the public by the high standard of their driving.

'Members will not, repeat not, consume food or drink within the vehicle.

'Members will, repeat will, at all times be correctly dressed when using the vehicle. Caps will, repeat will, be worn, tunics will be fastened correctly and ties will be knotted. When meeting a senior officer of or above the rank of Inspector, members will emerge from the vehicle before saluting.

'Members will not, repeat not, carry unauthorised members of the public, friends or family in the vehicle, unless their presence is necessary in the performance of their duty, eg upon arrest or other emergency.

'Members will, repeat will, ensure that ashtrays are emptied regularly and that the vehicle is thoroughly cleansed inside and out at the conclusion of every tour of duty, unless the exigencies of the service prevent otherwise. In these circumstances, a report will be submitted to explain those exigencies.'

Having written out his instructions, he handed them to me and as I began transferring them to paper, he went outside to examine the van. He spent some minutes and I saw him stooping to examine the tyres and to seek evidence of any damage, however minor, that might be present. He looked inside, checked the radio for its effectiveness and the ashtray for residue, looking into the log-book and then lifted the bonnet. He dipped the oil and spent some minutes tugging at plug leads and checking internal engine matters. Next he tested all the lights, the flashing indicators, the windscreen wipers and washers and even the interior light.

Then he took it for a brief drive around the block, and, satisfied that it was absolutely correct, took out his own pocket-book and made a note to that effect. Woe betide an officer who might suggest the vehicle had been delivered with a fault. Blaketon's record showed that it was in perfect order upon arrival, therefore any faults which developed would be the responsibility of the driver at the time. I knew that we must all treat the van as if it were our very own and I also knew that some officers, upon damaging an official vehicle (even accidentally) would not mention the matter, hoping that a subsequent driver would be careless enough not to check the vehicle before taking it out. Thus blame or responsibility could be avoided and the unwary innocent saddled with another's sins. We all knew the value of being ultra-cautious in such matters.

I completed Blaketon's piece of typing and made no comment as I passed it to him for signature. By the time I had finished my own work, copies had been signed and one was prominent upon the office notice-board.

'So the van's yours for today and tomorrow, Rhea?' he said.

'Yes, Sergeant.' After studying the duty sheets, I understood the arrangements.

'So when you knock off duty tomorrow night, at ten, you will deliver it to Falconbridge beat?'

'Yes, Sergeant.'

'Make sure it's filled with petrol,' he said. I nodded.

'Shall I book off duty late then, or will PC Clough come on duty early?' I asked.

'I don't follow your logic, Rhea.'

Knowing his attitude for precise timing, I said, 'If I arrive at PC Clough's house at 10pm to hand over the van, and he then drives me home, I will not be able to book off duty until 10.20pm or thereabouts. I will be in uniform, in an official vehicle, with an officer who is on duty. So I will be on duty, won't I? And this will happen every time the van is handed over. One of us will have to work extra time either before our shift or after it. Shall we all claim overtime for the hand-overs, Sergeant?'

He looked at me steadily, his dark eyes never showing any emotion . . . . .

'Rhea,' he said, 'a constable is never off duty.'

'So if the van is involved in a traffic accident as I am being taken home, and I am injured, will I be able to claim that I was injured on duty? It makes a huge difference if there is a question of compensation or an entitlement to an ill-health pension, Sergeant.'

He knew I was right, and I guessed this aspect had never occurred to him, or to those who had dreamed up the system of change-overs in this way. He was thinking rapidly, mentally assessing the enormous legal complications which could accrue from any incident which might happen within those disputed few minutes.

'I will ask the Superintendent to authorise half an hour's extra duty for at least one of the officers involved in every change-over,' he said. 'I will ask for it to be included on your overtime card and to be taken off when duty commitments allow.'

'Thank you, Sergeant,' he knew, and I knew, that this matter had to be determined right from the outset; minor though it appeared on the surface, there could be immense ramifications which might affect the officer or his family if something went wrong during those contentious few minutes. For an officer to be killed or injured when on duty differed hugely from one killed or injured when off duty.

The next problem, unforeseen by Sergeant Blaketon, occurred when the Superintendent visited me at the beginning of one of my tours of duty. The little van was parked on the hard-standing in front of my police house and the Super-intendent parked behind it, awaiting my emergence from the house. He did not come to the office which adjoined, but preferred to wait outside to see if I was late on duty; that's how some senior officers operated. But I had seen the arrival of his black car and went outside prompt on the stroke of two o'clock. I was to perform an afternoon shift from 2pm until 10pm, and had custody of the van because PC Clough of Falconbridge was enjoying a rest-day.

As I emerged, therefore, I slung up a smart salute and smiled as the Superintendent clambered from his car.

'Now, Rhea,' he said. 'Anything to report?'

I updated him on events which had occurred on my beat over the past few days and he nodded approval at the way I had dealt with them. Then he turned his attention to the mini-van and asked my opinion upon its suitability.

I enthused over it, but refrained from mentioning the hand-over complications. Sergeant Blaketon would have seen to that – it was a matter of internal politics.

Then the Superintendent began, 'I came past your house last night, Rhea, around midnight.'

'I finished at ten last night, sir. Same hours as today.'

'Yes, I know. And when I drove past, I saw the van standing there, on the hard-standing.'

'Yes, sir.'

'It was not in the garage, Rhea. There is a garage at your police house and I would have expected you to garage the van there, for security and safety.'

'It's a private garage, sir, my car's using it.'

'The official motor-cycle used it, Rhea.'

'There was plenty of room for both, sir, I could park the bike alongside the car. That garage was added to the house long before official cars and motor-bikes were issued. Garages adjoining rural-beat houses have always been used for the officer's private car.'

'Then I feel the practice must cease, Rhea. Now that you have the official use of a van, the van must surely take precedence over your private vehicle.'

I noticed that he did not directly order me to garage the van nor was I ordered to remove my car. I felt there was scope for manoeuvre which in turn suggested there was some official doubt about the rights of the occupants of police houses. After all, the police house was my home but unlike some civilian tenancies, there was no rental agreement. A police officer simply moved in and out when instructed and obeyed orders if there was a dispute. I knew of no order which dealt with the current matter and the only condition of occupancy that came to mind was that I could not take in lodgers without permission!

As I pondered the Superintendent's remarks, I realised that if I was unreasonable in my attitude, he might post me to a less-than-pleasant urban area, and I felt sure there was scope for discussion or flexibility.

'You are responsible for the care of the van while it is in your possession,' he reminded me. 'It is a police vehicle and it does contain valuable police equipment, such as a radio. The van and

18

contents are your responsibility, Rhea.'

'Yes, sir,' was all I said. I understood the import of his remarks.

'It will not be resting at your house every night,' he reasoned and I saw a twinkle in his eye. 'Others will be making regular use of it and it will be used for night shifts, so I think a little common sense will sort out this dilemma, don't you, Rhea?'

'Yes, sir,' I agreed.

And so it was. My private car continued to occupy the garage at my police house, and from time to time, I would give the mini a treat by placing it inside for the night. Then I discovered that if I parked the mini on the front lawn, it was obscured from the road by the privet hedge. Neither the Superintendent nor Sergeant Blaketon was in the habit of coming into the house or office, preferring to wait outside at the other side of that tall, thick hedge. And if they could not see into my garden, then neither could potential breakers-in of police vans . . .

Common sense did prevail and no one grumbled about the van's open-air life.

The van, its other drivers and I soon settled into a trouble-free working routine and we had no problems; indeed, the little vehicle proved its worth over and over again. Its tiny engine and small size coped with the large constables it had to carry, and the steep hills of this dramatic part of Yorkshire. It was most useful for carrying assorted objects and for protecting us from the English weather, thus enabling constabulary duties to be performed with far greater ease than hitherto. But on one occasion when I was surreptitiously carrying a load of rather doubtful legality, I found myself face to face with the redoubtable Sergeant Blaketon.

It happened around 10 o'clock one Wednesday morning.

I was working a day shift from 9am until 5pm, a rare treat. Such routines are few in a police officer's life and I was looking forward to the evening off. At 9am, therefore, I began work in the office which adjoined the house and by 9.45am was ready to begin my patrol.

Just as I was leaving, my wife, Mary, rushed in.

'Oh, thank heaven I caught you!' she panted. 'The car won't start.'

An immediate problem was presented, for it was Mary's turn to convey seven or eight children to the village play school. Elizabeth, our eldest, had started play school and thoroughly enjoyed it, and the mums worked on a rota system, each taking their turn to tour the nearby farms and cottages to collect pre-school-age youngsters. It was an important part of village life, a bonus for the children and a welcome tonic for the mums.

I had a quick look at our car and decided the battery was flat; it had been causing problems in recent weeks and I had never got around to replacing it. Now I had no choice and would obtain a battery today, but first, we had pressing commitments to keep. Those youngsters and their mums would be awaiting collection at farm gates, isolated spots and remote cottages.

'I'm going out on patrol,' I said. 'I'll collect them. Give me a list.'

And so, armed with a list of children's names and addresses, I set about this mission. Most of the mums saw nothing odd in their local constable collecting their offspring in a police van, while the children thought it was marvellous. Squatting on the cold, hard metal floor, they pretended they were chasing robbers as they listened to the dour voice from the police radio. They blew the horn and Elizabeth showed them how to flash the blue light, as a result of which we flashed the light at every halt to announce our arrival. By the time I returned to Aidensfield, the rear of the van, and the front passenger seat, were full of small, noisy but excited children. I had lost count of the number on board, but they seemed so happy at this change in their routine.

They babbled and chattered, made police siren noises, caught robbers, arrested thieves, chased speeders, battered my brain with questions, and generally created something of a party atmosphere in the back of the little van. The bouncing didn't seem to bother them, for in their minds, they were keen police officers engaged upon a matter of grave importance. I've no idea how many villains we arrested on that trip, but I reckon each child caught several and tonight they would recount their experiences to their dads. As a public relations exercise it was marvellous and as a means of getting those children to school it was a success.

But the noise they generated within the confines of the van

was colossal and I was pleased I was not a play-school teacher having to tolerate it for longer periods. On the last lap, I turned into Aidensfield and was about to drive down the lane to the house which hosted the school, when I saw the tall, severe figure of Sergeant Blaketon standing on the corner of the road. My heart sank. Of all the people to meet this morning of all mornings . . . I thought of his instructions about using the van, about unauthorised passengers, about disciplinary proceedings, about the law on overloading, about insecure loads . . .

I had probably broken several laws on my goodwill mission.

I could not avoid him. I eased to a halt before him, flushing furiously as I anticipated his wrath. I switched off the engine and climbed out, my mind full of excuses, reasons, apologies . . .

'It was urgent . . . ' I began.

But he ignored me and thrust his head inside the van and I heard him say, 'Now then, what's going on in there?'

There was an instant babble of juvenile response; I heard tiny voices shouting at him about catching robbers and poachers and making people drive better and then, after asking more questions and generally joining in the chit-chat, he emerged.

'Is this the village bus service, Rhea?' he asked me.

'Er, no, Sergeant, you see . . . well . . . they're going to play school . . . er . . .the car taking them wouldn't start, you see, so they were stuck . . . I . . . well . . . '

'Got a Public Service Vehicle operator's licence, have you?' was his next question. 'Know about seating requirements in vehicles, do you? Safety of passengers?'

'Er, well, Sergeant,' I started. 'It was an emergency . . . . '

'So all you lot have been arrested, have you?' he poked his head inside again.

'Ye . . . e . . . e . . . e . . . s . . . ' came the sing-song response. He emerged, smiling with joy.

'Nice one, Rhea. Creating goodwill with the public and making the kids happy, eh? All right, carry on.'

And so I did.

I learned afterwards that the play-school teacher had asked them to draw a police van and, without exception, they had included Sergeant's Blaketon's big smiling face.

2

'Our deeds still travel with us from afar.
And what we have been makes us what we are.'

George Eliot, 1819-80

Patrolling in the warmth and comfort of the mini-van was heavenly after the inconvenience of the motor-cycle and I think it is fair to say that one adverse effect was to make us rather lazy. When using the motor-cycle, particularly during chilly weather, it was sensible to walk as much as possible, if only to keep warm. But that exercise was unnecessary with the mini-van. We were cosseted in an all-embracing warmth from which, especially in the chill of a long night, we were unwilling to emerge. This tended to make us drive where we should have walked; we took the van around all manner of unlikely places, roaming behind buildings, through factory premises, into farm-yards, along narrow alleys and over fields, all of which were the kind of places we should have walked in our efforts to prevent and detect crime.

Our supervisory officers and our own consciences told us it was not a good thing to spend so much time sitting in a van, that exercise was necessary for continuing good health and that foot patrols were a vital part of the constable's crime-preventing and public relations repertoire. Each of us appreciated such precepts and although we began our patrols with those aims uppermost in our minds, they soon evaporated once we settled into the cosy routine of heated and motorised patrolling.

We learned, for example, the best places to park in order to shine either the van's headlights or our own torch beams upon vulnerable windows and doors; we located places in which the van could be concealed for a short nap, a tasty but forbidden sandwich or sip of coffee from a flask. We knew where to hide from Sergeant Blaketon or which unmapped track offered the best short-cut through the lush and scented meadows of Ryedale.

It was a bout of idleness of this kind which led me into a spot of bother one night. It happened like this. Tucked in the centre of my beat, well away from urban civilisation, was a derelict airfield. The nearest village was Stovensby, a tiny collection of pretty stone houses on a gently rising street, and everyone knew this patch of cracked concrete and unsightly old huts as Stovensby Airfield even though no aircraft had used it since the end of World War II. Leading from the village into one corner of the airfield was a narrow, unmade lane, across which someone had, years ago, erected a gate.

As time passed, however, that gate had fallen into disrepair which meant that courting couples, trespassers and all manner of other inquisitive folk ventured on to the airfield from time to time, perhaps to steal bits and pieces from the derelict buildings or perhaps to conceal themselves in the old ruins so that their love-making was kept a secret from prying eyes, as well as from suspicious husbands, wives and neighbours.

Squatters, tramps, down-and-outs and persons on the run from life, from HM Forces, from the police or from their families would sometimes hide here too.

The area covered by the old airfield was huge; remnants of the Air Traffic Control Tower remained, as did buildings which had been Station Headquarters, Squadron offices, hangars, sleeping accommodation, etc. Many of them were windowless, some were roofless and none had been officially occupied or used for almost a quarter of a century. In the broad light of day, the airfield reeked of dereliction and decay, although the old runways themselves were in fairly good order. They were like huge modern highways which crossed and re-crossed this patch of Ryedale and they had survived surprisingly well without any formal maintenance. The area between them comprised overgrown grass, weeds and scrubland, although some of the fertile areas had been leased to a local farmer who managed to grow wheat there.

No one seemed quite sure who owned the airfield; perhaps the Air Ministry had forgotten it was there, perhaps someone had purchased it years ago and had no idea what to do with it . . . . I never knew. What I did know, however, was that the deserted runways were regularly used by learner drivers, by young men who fancied themselves as racing motorists, by teenage motor-cyclists who roared about the place doing crazy things with their moving machines such as wheelies or head-stands on the saddles, and even by pedal-cyclists who organised time trials and races around the perimeter track.

The old notices saying 'Trespassers will be Prosecuted' or 'Air Ministry Property - Keep Off' had fallen down and although there could have been a question of illegal use, it was not the job of the civilian police to enforce any such rules. We knew that the public, rightly or wrongly, made use of the old airfield and we did not raise any formal objection because we knew where many of the youngsters got to. They were safe here, far better using this enclosed area for racing or showing off than attempting their doubtful skills on the open road.

So we closed our 'official' eyes to the many trespassers although, at night, we did make routine patrols through the airfield, checking for possible lawbreakers who might dump stolen cars here, steal bits from the buildings, cause damage or perform a host of other illegal acts. Children on the run from school or home were another aspect of our searches, as were depressed folks who wanted to be left alone with their thoughts, or even to commit suicide.

One night in early May, I was performing an all-night duty, having started at 10pm. I booked myself on duty from home by ringing Eltering Police Station at 10pm and asked for any routine messages. I was given a list of unsolved crimes committed locally during the day, plus details of a car which had been stolen from Scarborough. It was a Ford Consul, five years old and a dark green colour, and it had been stolen from outside the Spa before eight that evening.

According to the police at Eltering, a villager from Stovensby had telephoned at quarter to ten to report a car with blazing lights repeatedly circling the old airfield at high speed. There was just a possibility that it was the missing vehicle in the hands of joy-riders, as other cars stolen from the coast had been found abandoned here.

I was therefore asked to check out this report.

It was a foul night with pouring rain and lingering mist as I arrived in Stovensby village. The time would be around 10.20pm and the late spring dusk had matured into a heavy darkness due to the weather. I drove the little van down to the fallen gate which marked the entrance to the airfield, the windscreen wipers having trouble coping with the teeming rain. I extinguished the van lights as I peered through the gloom, hoping to catch sight of roving car lights somewhere in that vast expanse of misery and darkness. I saw none, so maybe my own approaching lights had alerted the thieves? Perhaps they'd gone? Perhaps it was just a local lad having a fling around the place in his own car? Maybe it was thieves who had run for shelter and were hiding in one of the many disused buildings? The lights could have been anything or anyone, harmless or potentially harmful.

I waited for five or ten minutes; there was no sign of activity on that airfield, not a hint, not a light. But if a car had been seen earlier – and not all that much earlier – then a full search would have to be made.

To make a proper search, I should really walk; I should take a torch although, strictly speaking, I should make a search in complete darkness so as to surprise the villains in possession of the stolen property. In the darkness, I could creep up on them . . . . But, I reasoned, if they were in a car, they could escape simply by driving off and I would be marooned in the middle of the airfield with no car, no radio and no chance of catching them. I reckoned that if I circled the airfield in the mini-van, shining my lights into and behind all the old buildings, I might flush out the thieves. Then I could give chase, and my radio would allow me to summon any necessary aid. That seemed a far better idea.

So I switched on my lights, crossed through that tumbledown gate and found myself driving along the glistening wet concrete of an old wartime runway. The rain, the mist and the darkness made driving very difficult, and without a detailed knowledge of the layout of the airfield, I really had no idea where I was heading. My only hope was to pick out the buildings one by one and then scan them in my headlights. If I did detect anything or anyone suspicious, then a more detailed search could follow.

With the excitement of the chase making my heart pound just a little faster, I located the first of the buildings and drove towards it; it was an old hangar, vast and empty in the darkness so I drove right inside, did a sweeping turn in the mini and watched as the beams explored every corner.

Old oil drums littered the floor, a few rats scuttled off at my intrusion and there was an old settee against the far wall, but it was otherwise deserted. I moved to the next location, another hangar similarly deserted. As I searched each building, the radio in the van burbled into life and I recognised my own call sign.

'Echo Seven,' it said. 'Location please.'

Every half-hour, our Control Room sought our location in this manner, then plotted our movements on a map so the most conveniently-positioned vehicle could be directed to any incident. It was also a means of checking our individual safety; if we failed to respond, we might be in trouble.

'Echo Seven' I spoke into the mouthpiece. 'Stovensby Air-field.'

'Received. Echo Nine?' the next car was requested.

As locations were sought from every mobile on duty, I continued my search. Sometimes, I walked in the light of those headlamps, sometimes I drove around a block or behind the more remote buildings, but I did make sure that every possible hiding place was examined. As I progressed, I found it was becoming more difficult to see the buildings ahead; the rain and mist obscured them and so I found myself having to drive at a crawling pace in the gloom. From time to time I'd leave the van with its engine running and lights blazing as I fought my way through the thickening mist to a building with a difficult access.

I must have searched every conceivable nook and cranny without finding anything remotely suspicious, by which time I had decided that no stolen car was hidden there. There was nothing and no one lurking on that deserted airfield. Of that, I was positive.

I radioed Control. 'Echo Seven,' I announced. 'Have completed search of Stovensby Airfield for reported stolen vehicle from Scarborough. No trace. Am resuming patrol. Over.'

'Received Echo 7. Control out.'

With the windscreen wipers assailing the tumbling rain, and the dense fog now blanketing the entire airfield, I screwed my eyes against the white screen outside. While I had been busily searching the buildings, the fog had dramatically intensified and now I could barely see the runway ahead of me. I could not determine the edges of the concrete . . . . I moved to one side, swerving to catch a glimpse of the runway's extremities. I failed. The twin beams cut into the fog like two long shafts of solid light, but they did not penetrate it. The light simply reflected back at me. I was moving at less than walking pace now, my head out of the window hoping to see where I was heading . . .

But I was hopelessly lost. I'd lost all contact with the buildings which had, to some extent, broken the fog's density and I was encircled by a thick white blanket of dripping clinging mist. I was somewhere inside a dark fog-bound wilderness and had lost all sense of direction.

I found myself fighting the onset of panic; I knew that I was only a few miles from home and from civilisation, but at the same time, could not find the route which led off this old airfield. It was almost like being trapped, like driving through a black, unlit tunnel and into a massive blockade of cotton wool; the mist was so thick that it had become a wall of brilliant white through which nothing could apparently pass. Although I was still driving, I had no impression of movement or distance for I could see nothing but the reflected glow of my headlights. I was upon a featureless plain and the headlights would not even pick out the surface of the runway. I had no idea whether I was in the middle, on the edge, doing a circuit of the perimeter track or simply driving around in circles on an expanse of featureless concrete. I have never been so helpless. It was like one of those nightmarish dreams that childhood worries can cause and there seemed no immediate relief.

I knew it would become easier in daylight, but dawn was hours away, and I felt such an idiot. I was lost within such a small patch of England . . . but I could not stay here all night. I had to find a way off, and so I kept moving. Once or twice, I ran off the edge of the runway, but fortunately the ground was solid enough to carry the weight of the mini-van, and after each mishap I managed to regain the solid surface. I had no idea how long I'd been looking for the exit until my call-sign sounded from the radio.

'Echo Seven, location please,' asked the voice.

I must have been chugging around for nearly half an hour! I did a rapid mental calculation. If I failed to reply to this request, Control would think I was missing or injured, and a search would be established. And in this fog, more officers could get lost as they hunted for me! Furthermore, at the last 'locations' I'd already said that I was resuming patrol and if I now announced that I was lost in the airfield, I'd look a real idiot in the eyes of our Control Room staff.

Surely I would soon find the exit? I'd been going round in circles for ages, and must have covered miles, however slowly I'd been driving.

'Echo Seven, not receiving. Echo Seven, location please,' repeated the voice.

'Echo Seven,' I decided to pretend I was patrolling normally and made a guess about where I might have been if I'd emerged from the airfield. 'Echo Seven. A170, travelling east and approaching Brantsford. Over.'

'Received, Echo Seven. Echo Nine, your location please,' all cars were now being asked this question.

As the half-hourly ritual continued, I renewed my efforts to drive off the runway. Travelling at less than walking speed in the darkness, often with my head out of the window for better vision, I continued to search. But it was hopeless. By the time of the next 'locations' call, I was still on the airfield. But I daren't admit it.

When Control Room next asked Echo Seven for its location, I said, 'Echo Seven. Eltering towards Cattleby.'

'Received Echo Seven,' responded the voice. 'Echo Nine?'

And so it continued. I daren't halt the vehicle for any length of time in the fog to search on foot in case the battery could not cope with the demands upon it from the combined effects of the heater, radio and the lights; I did not feel inclined to switch off the lights in this ghastly silent world. So I continued to drive around; in any case, I wanted to find my way out! For each half-hour, therefore, I provided a fictitious location when asked, and when the time came for my refreshment break at 2am, I took a gamble.

We were supposed to take our refreshment breaks at police stations and not in our vehicles; I knew Ashfordly was un-manned at night and hoped no one would attempt to contact me there by telephone. So, when I would normally have broken my tour of duty for refreshments, I radioed to Control 'Echo Seven, refreshments Ashfordly. Over.'

'Received, Echo Seven.'

I halted in the gloom and had my break at the wheel, in contravention of Sergeant Blaketon's rule about not eating or drinking in the mini-van. I kept the engine running and the equipment and lights operating, for I needed light and heat, and then, after enjoying my sandwiches and flask of coffee, I decided to risk a brief exploration on foot. I'd leave the lights on and the engine running so that I could re-trace the van. Perhaps this would help me find the exit?

With my hand torch, I tried to determine my whereabouts but failed. In whatever direction I walked, I found nothing but more featureless expanse of runway and the thickest fog I'd ever encountered. I daren't stray too far from the car either, in case I failed to re-locate it. And so, at 2.45am at the official termi-nation of my break, I had no alternative but to recommence my circuits of the airfield.

'Echo Seven,' I introduced myself. 'Resuming patrol at Ash-fordly, towards Gelderslack.'

'Received, Echo Seven,' acknowledged Control.

And so the second half of my shift began. The rain had ceased now, but the fog had not lifted and the darkness was just as intense, but I knew that before my knocking-off time at six o'clock, daylight would arrive. This would help me find a route off this awful place.

For the next two and a half hours or so, I continued to provide fictitious locations, listing places I would have visited during a normal night patrol. Happily, it was a very quiet night and I was never directed to any incident. And then, soon after I'd given my final location at 5.30am, the fog lifted. A gently breeze had risen as dawn was pushing the darkness aside, and I saw the distinct movement of the thick fog. Wisps began to float away and then, with remarkable speed, it began to disperse. In the daylight, I could now see the outline of some buildings and hazy roofs of the village on the edge of the airfield.

And I was less than a hundred yards from the exit!

I need hardly express the cheer that I felt as I drove out of that old gate, and with considerable relief, I made for home. According to the log-book which I had to complete, I had covered nearly forty miles around that airfield, a useful distance for a night patrol. My eyes were red-rimmed and sore with the strain of staring into that wall of fog, and I was mentally shattered.

I arrived home at six o'clock to find Sergeant Blaketon and PC Clough waiting for me. They were in Sergeant Blaketon's official car. Clough was to take the van out from 6am until 2pm, and on this occasion, Sergeant Blaketon had decided upon an early visit to both Ken Clough and myself. And he had undertaken to ferry my colleague to Aidensfield Police House to collect the van.

'Morning Rhea,' he said as I emerged, bleary-eyed and very anxious to get some sleep. 'All correct?'

'All correct, Sergeant,' I managed to say.

'The duty chap at Eltering said something about you searching for a stolen car on the old airfield?'

'Yes, Sergeant. I searched for it just after commencing my shift. It wasn't there.'

'You sure?'

'Yes, Sergeant!' I snapped the answer. 'I searched every possible place. The airfield was deserted.'

'Good, I thought you'd have done a thorough job.'

'Is there a problem?' I asked.

'It's just that Eltering Police Station got one or two calls during the night from residents at Stovensby. They reckoned cars were running round the airfield all night. They reported seeing lights and hearing engines in the fog. Eltering's sending a car to have a look in daylight – apparently, a road-traffic car attempted to investigate last night, but turned back because of dense fog.'

'I've just come from there, Sergeant,' I decided to tell him. 'I did a final search myself, in daylight with the fog thinning. I saw nothing – that was only half an hour ago.'

'They must have imagined it, Rhea. So, nothing else to report, eh?'

'No, Sergeant,' I said with determination.

'Good, then sleep well,' and they left me.

It was a long, long time before I returned to Stovensby Airfield and I never ventured there during a fog!

Mind, there were times when I wondered how those wartime pilots had coped with these Stovensby pea-soupers. Perhaps they had never become airborne, pretending instead to fly upon long circuitous missions into enemy territory?

There was another occasion when a duty trip in the little van caused something of a headache, and again it involved a journey which would certainly have caused Sergeant Blaketon to consult his book of rules. Happily, he never learned of this particular mishap.

Like so many memorable incidents, this one happened through a chance conversation. I was on patrol in the mini-van with instructions to deliver a package to a member of the Police Committee who lived on the edge of my beat. The package had come from the Chief Constable via our internal mail system and I was the final courier in this postal routine. I think it contained a selection of local statistics and pamphlets required for a crime prevention seminar in which she was to be involved. She was out when I arrived, but I spotted a gardener at work in the grounds of her spacious home and he told me to leave the mail in the conservatory. She'd find it there, he assured me. He pointed me towards the door and then, eager for a moment's respite, asked me how my family and I were settling in. I did not know the man, but saw this as yet another example of how the public knows the affairs of their village constable!

As I'd been at Aidensfield for a year or two by this time, I was able to say we were very happy and enjoying both the area and the work.

'Got the garden straight, have you?' he asked with real interest, and perhaps a little professional curiosity.

'Not really,' I had to admit. I love a well tended garden which comprises vegetables, flowers and shrubs, but I never seemed to have the time to create the garden of my dreams. Mary, however, in spite of coping with four tiny children and a hectic domestic routine, did manage to spend some time tending the garden.

I told him all this and he smiled.

'Tell her not to be frightened to ask if she needs owt,' he offered. 'Cuttings, seeds, bedding plants, that sort o' thing.'

'Thanks, it's good of you,' I responded.

'Well, we've often a lot o' spare stuff and t'missus is happy to give bits and pieces to t'locals.' By 't'missus' he meant his employer. 'You've only to ask.'

It was at this point that I remembered Mary asking me to keep an eye open for horse manure during my patrols; she'd mentioned it some days ago and it had slipped my mind until now.

'That reminds me,' I said half apologetically, 'she did ask me to look out for some horse manure. That was ages ago.'

'Ah, we don't have any o' that,' he said. 'But there's plenty at Keldhead Stables. They can't get rid of it fast enough. It's free to take away. Just go along and help yourself.'

'They're the racing stables, aren't they?' I asked.

'Aye, they get some good winners from there if you're a betting man. Grand National, Cheltenham, Lincoln, Derby – they've won some big races. You can't go far wrong if you follow them – they've often winners at Stockton, Thirsk, Ripon, Beverley and Wetherby an' all. I don't mind admitting I've won a bob or two on 'em.'

'So their manure should make our rambling roses gallop along, eh?' I laughed. 'Thanks, if I'm ever out that way, I'll pop in.'

We chatted about other trivia then I moved on. Keldhead Stables was off my beat in another section and it was highly unlikely that I would be able to pop in during a duty patrol, so I made a mental note to tell Mary. Perhaps we'd make a special trip there on my day off.

Then, through one of those flukes of circumstance, I was directed there within a week of learning about their manure offer. It was a Saturday evening in late May and I was making a patrol from 5pm until 1am, being responsible for the entire section in my little van. Shortly after 7pm, I received instructions over my radio to proceed immediately to Keldhead Stables where a prowler had been sighted – by chance, I was the nearest mobile.

This was not uncommon – people did trespass upon the stables' premises, sometimes just out of curiosity or to see a famous winning horse in its home surrounds. The motives of some, however, were a little more suspect because, at some other stables, there had been attempts to dope horses which were favourites to win. Scares of this kind had led to increased security at all racing-stables (and many existed in our area), consequently reports of such trespassers were fairly frequent.

I rushed towards Keldhead and drove into the stable yard. Waiting for me was J.J. Stern, the noted trainer, and his face bore clear signs of relief at my arrival. After a very brief chat, he pointed towards the stable block and said a lad had seen a man creeping furtively about. By now, something around half an hour had passed and I felt sure any visitor would have left, but I made a thorough initial search of the premises. Stern had already examined his horses without finding a fault and nothing appeared to have been damaged or stolen. With a stable lad in tow to guide me through the complex of buildings, I made a second very detailed examination. It took some time, but I found no one.

Afterwards, I detailed my actions to J.J. Stern and advised him that if other uninvited guests trespassed on his premises, he should take care to record a detailed description of the visitors, and to obtain the registration number of any suspect cars that were around. So many people fail to do this when they see a suspect car – a car number in these circumstances is vital to an investigation and can very swiftly help to trace the culprits.

He thanked me and said he would issue instructions to his staff to follow my advice. Then he asked if I'd like a coffee. It was at this point that I remembered Mary's wish for some manure – and at this very moment I was surrounded by a huge amount of surplus horse muck.

I hesitated to ask, but he had guessed I was about to make a request of some kind. He must be plagued with people asking for winning tips, but I was not seeking this kind of information . . .

He smiled as if not to discourage me.

'Er,' I began. 'While I'm here, I was told you had some horse manure to get rid of.'

'Manure? Tons of it! Want some, Mr Rhea?'

'I wouldn't mind some, not a lot . . . I'll pay,' I offered. 'I can help myself . . . '

'Nonsense. It's free to any good home! We just want shot of it. Look, you've earned a coffee for your advice, so come into the office and I'll get young Christine to pop some in your van. Are the rear doors open?'

'I'll unlock them,' I said, and I did, leaving them standing open.

In the office, he picked up the intercom telephone, dialled an extension and a girl answered.

'Christine,' he said. 'There's a police van in the yard. Pop some manure in the back, will you? The doors are open.'

She agreed and he replaced the phone. 'She's new here,' he said. 'Only sixteen, but she's mad on horses. It's only her first week, so it'll do her good to see what goes on.'

He organised a cup of coffee, asking if I would like a touch of Scotch with it, but as I was on duty and driving, I declined the latter offer. The coffee would be fine.

We chatted for about quarter of an hour, he telling me about his life in horse racing, and me trying to explain a little about the work of a rural constable. He was a charming man, I decided.

Just as I stood up to depart, his telephone rang so I excused myself and left him to deal with his caller. When I got outside, the van doors were closed and there was no sign of Christine; I had never even seen the girl and could not even thank her for her trouble.

But when I opened the driver's door, I was horrified. The stench that met me was appalling, and as I stared into the rear compartment, I saw that it was full of hot, fresh horse manure. It was neatly spread across the width and along the length of the back of the van.

She had filled every space, but she had not bagged it; she had

34

simply shovelled muck into the back of the van, as a farmer would have shovelled muck into a cart. I could have died on the spot. What on earth could I do?

I thought fast, closing the door to shut off some of the stink; if I returned to complain to J.J. Stern, he'd probably fire the girl . . . and it would look as if I was rejecting his generosity . . . I decided to drive away.

Gingerly, therefore, I climbed into the malodorous interior, already feeling itchy as flies were buzzing around, and began the trip home. The weight in the rear was enormous and it affected the steering, making it dangerously light as I took to the winding lanes to avoid being seen.

I opened all the windows and found that the flow of fresh air did keep some of the powerful pong at bay, but it was a terrible journey. My uniform and hair would reek of the stuff when I emerged.

After radioing Control to say I had searched Keldhead Stables but had found no intruder, I decided to sneak home and remove the muck. But on the way, I got a call to a road traffic accident about two miles from Aidensfield. Groaning, I could not avoid this duty; happily, it was not serious and no one was hurt. A farm lorry and an old Ford Cortina had collided on a junction near Briggsby, but the lorry had been carrying farm manure too, several tons of it. Due to the accident, it had been catapulted from the lorry and had almost smothered the car and peppered both drivers.

The Cortina, a battered old vehicle, had been carrying a drum of waste oil on the back seat. The oil drum had overturned inside the car, resulting in a terrible mess to both the car and its driver. The fulsome smell surrounding this scenario was dreadful, so much so that the contribution made by my uniform and van was of no consequence. After dealing with the accident and arranging for the load, the vehicles and the mess to be removed, I chugged home.

There is no need to explain the effects of this combination of events upon my person and upon the little van, save to say that Mary and I spent the next three hours frantically trying to remove the muck and then attempting to rid the van of the lingering effluvium.

But the manure had filtered into every possible crevice; try as we might, we never did remove it all.

I bathed and changed my uniform for the second half of my patrol, but the miasma remained; I cleaned the rear several times afterwards, using all kinds of disinfectants and smelly things, but it seemed that for ever afterwards, the mini-van smelled of horse muck. Some of the other drivers, including Sergeant Blaketon, did from time to time refer to the redolence; I said it had come from dealing with the accident to the muck-carrying lorry, some of which had penetrated our official vehicle. I'm sure he did not believe me, but he never questioned me further. After all, it was I who had to live with the unwholesome results of my manure venture.

In spite of everything, we should not criticise that young girl – after all, she had obeyed her boss's instructions to the very letter. However, the incident did teach me that orders must be precisely and clearly given if they are to be properly obeyed. And so Mary got her muck and the garden did benefit from it.

On another occasion, another car landed me in trouble, but it was not a police car this time. It was my own.

Even though we had been issued with our little van, the faceless powers-that-be felt it was prudent that, from time to time, we patrolled on foot.

I think this idea came to them because there were, inevitably, occasions when two rural beat constables were on duty at the same time, when both simultaneously required the official van.

Clearly, we could not patrol together, consequently when our duties overlapped in this way, one of us was scheduled to work a foot patrol, perhaps for four hours or even for eight. Now, in a city or town, this is a splendid idea and there is no finer way for a constable to meet the public and for them to meet him. But it does not quite operate the same way in rural North Yorkshire.

For one thing, villages or centres of population are several miles apart. Another thing is that such centres may contain only six or eight houses and a telephone kiosk, added to which many of the farms which created our work were located some distance away from these little villages. Furthermore, our patrols were governed by the location of telephone kiosks because we had to stand beside a nominated kiosk every hour on the hour in case our superiors wished to contact us, or in case there was an emergency.

How we would have travelled to any emergency was never discussed, but this system meant that we spent about an hour walking along deserted country lanes between villages, following which we stood beside a telephone kiosk for five minutes. After that, it was time to walk to the next village which meant we never had time to meet people or time to perform any duty of more than a minute or two's duration.

To my simple mind, it seemed very silly to spend periods of almost one whole hour beyond communication with the public. Virtually the only companions I had upon those long country walks were the beasts, birds and insects of the fields and hedgerows. Cars carrying people did flash past and occasionally one would halt to ask whether I required a lift anywhere, but such occurrences were rare. More often than not, I simply left one village telephone kiosk and walked to the next without meeting a solitary person.

From a purely selfish point of view, it was marvellous. It meant I was getting paid for regularly taking a most enjoyable walk through some of England's most beautiful countryside, a pleasure for which many were prepared to pay considerable sums or to travel long distances. But from a police efficiency point of view, it was ridiculous. The amount of official time wasted was considerable and besides, what aspects of police work could I engage upon in such circumstances? The answer was nil, other than a spot of musing upon aspects of the profession.

I had a word with the Inspector about this ludicrous situation, but his response was simply. 'If it says foot patrol on the duty sheets, then that's what you must do.'

I attempted to defend my logic by saying that an hour spent in every village *en route* would be far more beneficial than an hour spent plodding along an empty road; if I spent time in a village, I could meet the people and undertake the traditional role of a village constable.

There were always enquiries to complete about local crimes or happenings, investigations to be made and contacts to be established. But my reasoning fell on deaf ears. Foot patrols were foot patrols and there must be no arguments against the system. Try as I might, I could not persuade anyone to change the useless ritual. Then, one foul and rainy day, I hit upon a solution.

Rather than endure many hours walking to nowhere in the pouring rain, I decided to use my own private car to transport myself between the villages. I would not claim anything by way of expenses from the police authority; I would quietly drive between points for my own convenience and peace of mind. This would enable me to spend the best part of an hour in each of the villages upon my route, so giving me a greater opportunity for solving crimes, meeting people, getting acquainted with the locality, absorbing knowledge about the area and its personalities and, in fact, doing all those varied jobs a police officer should do.

None of my superiors knew about this little scheme, and so when I was next detailed to undertake a foot patrol of this kind, I decided I would once again use my own car to transport me between points. Upon arrival in each of the villages, I would conceal it well away from the telephone kiosk, just in case the Sergeant, the Inspector or the Superintendent called on me and objected to my enterprise. So far as they were concerned, I was still spending all my time on foot.

I almost fell foul of the Superintendent on one occasion because I arrived in Elsinby by car, only to find him standing at the telephone kiosk, awaiting me. And he was a witness to my arrival in this very unofficial transport.

With some apprehension, I parked and walked towards him, throwing up a smart salute upon my approach. He chatted amiably for a while and then threw in the barbed question,

'Why are you using your private car, PC Rhea?'

'I've a firearms certificate to renew, sir, at Toft Hill Farm. It expires this week. It's a mile and a half out of the village, and I wouldn't have had the time to do that, and then walk to my next point on time.'

It was true, as it happened, and he accepted my excuse.

'Well, so long as you don't do this regularly, PC Rhea. Remember this system is designed as a foot patrol.'

'Yes, sir.' I had become too wise to argue and quietly determined that I would studiously ignore this instruction, albeit with the knowledge that he would inform the Inspector of my transgression. But I could easily conceal the car in countless hiding places at every village I visited. And so that is how I conducted my foot patrols.

Then, on a damp, cold and foggy evening one November, I was performing yet another of these marathon patrols. This one, whether by accident or design I am not sure, took me to the more remote corners of my patch. I had started at 5pm, and was due to patrol, on foot, through those remote lanes until 1am with a refreshment break around mid-way.

In my view, to patrol on foot along unlit roads in the foggy darkness was rank stupidity. It was both dangerous and futile, and so I decided to use my own car. Things went well until I arrived at my 8pm point in Ploatby; in that time, I had managed to call at local inns, to chat to residents and to conduct a miscellany of minor enquiries. And then, as I stood beside the lonely kiosk in the thickening fog, the Inspector arrived in his official car.

'Ah, Rhea,' he smiled, 'Nasty night. Anything to report?'

I detailed some of the duties I had performed since starting work at five and he expressed his satisfaction. Then, after signing my pocket-book to record this conference, he appeared to have an attack of benevolence.

'Shocking night, Rhea.' He regarded the deepening fog. 'Where's your next point?'

'Nine o'clock, sir, at Waindale, then I'm off duty at ten o'clock at home for my refreshment break.'

'With a long wet walk in between, eh? In that case jump in. I'll give you a lift to Aidensfield, you can make your nine o'clock point there instead of Waindale. Then you can patrol your own village until refreshment time. I'll inform Control of the change. It's silly tramping these lanes in this fog.'

For a moment, I wondered if some of my earlier protestations had had an impact, then I realised with horror that it would mean leaving my own car abandoned out here.

And if I left my car here, it would mean a long walk back for it! Or, I might cadge a lift . . . As I dithered in my momentary indecision, he unlocked the passenger door and waved me in.

'Come on, Rhea, I haven't got all night.'

As he issued his order in those curt words, all thoughts of refusing his offer evaporated and so, with my heart sinking at the thought of a long trek back here, I settled in the warm and comfortable front seat of his fine vehicle. He drove confidently and smoothly away and within quarter of an hour was dropping me in the splash of light outside the Brewers' Arms in Aidensfield.

'Goodnight, Rhea,' he said, and vanished into the misty darkness.

He left me standing in the pool of warmth outside the pub, so I went in, half deciding to regard this as an official visit when I might chase out of the premises any stray under-age drinkers, and half to see whether any of the Ploatby farmers were in. Maybe I could persuade one of them to give me a lift back to my car? But I was out of luck. The pub contained no one from that part of the dale and I had no wish to intrude upon the drinking-time of anyone else.

By the time I'd chatted to some of the locals about crimes reported in the national papers, to others about the state of the weather, refused several offers of a drink and checked two youngsters for their ages, it was nine-thirty.

A quick peramble around the village took the time around to ten o'clock and then I knocked off for supper. I had a grumble to Mary about the Inspector's actions, but she didn't offer much sympathy.

'If they say foot patrol they mean foot patrol,' she said with feminine simplicity. 'You haven't forgotten I need the car early tomorrow, have you?' she added. 'I'm going to see my mother and I must get some shoes for Elizabeth. She's got a hole in hers.'

I decided not to pursue the matter; I would endeavour to retrieve my car sometime during the remainder of this tour of duty. After all, when I resumed my work at 10.45pm, there would be a couple of hours left before 1am, and I might still beg a lift from some of the pub regulars. But when I looked at my points and predetermined route, I saw it took me well away from the local pubs. The short second half of my patrol took me through some lonely poachers' territory, not villages.

At the end of this marathon shift, therefore, I still had not recovered my car. Tired and footsore at 1am, I trudged into my little office beside the house and rang Eltering Police Station to book off duty. The duty PC wished me goodnight. Mary was in bed and had left a mug and biscuit on a tray; I would make myself a cocoa. But she needed the car first thing tomorrow . . .

And there was no local officer performing night shift who might come to my aid . . . I daren't ring Kit Clough at Falconbridge who was in possession of the official van. He'd completed a 2pm–10pm shift and was due out at 6am so he'd be fast asleep; I couldn't rouse him for this and did consider rising early myself, to beg a lift from him as he began his tour. But I couldn't guarantee he'd be free to do the trip – the Inspector might go out early to meet him or there might be some other commitment.

It was my very own problem, so I crept out of the house and started the long, weary, wet and dark walk back to Ploatby to collect my car. I've never known such a long, foot-weary trail. In the pitch darkness and in thickening fog, I slowly made my way to Ploatby, the time ticking away and my energy being sapped at every step.

But I made it. Somehow, I managed to reach it and with a sigh of relief, opened the door and sank into the driving seat. For an awful moment, I thought it might not start due to the damp atmosphere, but it burst into life and carried me safely home.

As I sank into bed just after two o'clock, trying desperately not to rouse Mary, she muttered, 'Busy night? Working late?'

'Yes,' I said, drifting into a blissful slumber against the warmth of her resting body.

That night, I dreamt I was trekking to the North Pole in my sore, bare feet.

3

'Aye, marry, is't; crowner's-quest law.'
Hamlet William Shakespeare, 1564-1616

The romance and excitement of finding buried treasure was something fairly common in the countryside around Aidensfield. It happened to residents and visitors alike, and I become involved in many of these occurrences because of the fascinating and ancient law surrounding treasure trove.

The reason for so many discoveries is that the district around Aidensfield is rich in historic ruins. They include castles, abbeys, churches and even battlefields and, over many centuries, these have attracted pilgrims and travellers both from our country and from foreign lands. Because those ancient visitors were careless like the rest of us, lots of them mislaid things like coins, swords, jewellery and other personal valuables, then through the passage of time these became buried in the earth. Many years later, due to the use of modern technology in the form of metal detectors, deep ploughs or sheer good fortune, these were found amid scenes of great excitement.

One source of discovery was the humble footpath. Linking these establishments, and indeed linking the tiny villages between them, were footpaths and bridleways through woodland and along the banks of our streams and rivers. Those villages also boast origins which can be traced across the centuries, and in more than one case, evidence can be found in the

42

village churches, some of which date as far back as the seventh century.

For example, modern visitors can examine two tiny minsters; one can be seen at Kirkdale (*circa* AD 654) over whose doorway is a Saxon sundial, the most complete in the world, which bears the longest-known inscription from Anglo-Saxon times. The other is at Stonegrave (*circa* AD 757) and each gives some indication of the immense span of English heritage which is present in this beautiful area of Ryedale in North Yorkshire.

This sense of history continues with abbeys founded some five hundred years later, such as those at Rievaulx and Byland, whose grandeur was reduced to ruin by the Reformation, while some four hundred years after their destruction more abbey-building took place at Ampleforth.

Castles like those at Ashfordly, Eltering, Elsinby, Helmsley, Pickering and Gilling East add to the majesty of the locality, and it was to these places via remote villages and hamlets that travellers came. They have travelled these byways for many centuries, rich and poor, royal, noble and common, British and foreign. And in many cases, they lost their personal belongings, perhaps the odd coin or jewel, or even a goblet or defensive weapon.

In the case of places liable to be raided either by villains or tax-gatherers, however, the people concealed their hard-earned wealth. They hid coins in the walls of castles and abbeys, up the chimneys of cottages and mansions, or buried them in earthen-ware jars in the gardens or fields. And, of course, many local folks lost the occasional coin.

The result of all this is that the fields, woods, paths and gardens of Ryedale, and indeed the whole of England, are rich with buried treasure. Every year, thousands of pounds worth is discovered, some by accident, some by the use of metal detectors, some during road works or building construction and some by sheer good luck. There are many recorded instances when ordinary people have suddenly found themselves in pos-session of a fortune – one example occurred when workmen were excavating the site of a new building at York University. They uncovered 2,880 Roman coins, while in 1966, a hoard of twelfth-century coins then worth £30,000 was found near Newstead Abbey in Nottinghamshire. Twenty years later, treasure-hunters at Middleham in North Yorkshire found a unique fifteenth-century jewel of gold with a sapphire inset. It was sold for £1,430,000. In cases of this kind, the rule is not 'finders keepers', because when certain treasure is found the law of England, with its curious provisions for dealing with treasure trove, steps in. And this is how the police and the coroner become involved.

The coroner generally concerns himself with sudden or violent deaths, so why does he supervise the laws on found treasure? The answer lies far back in our history and a little explanation is now called for: in dealing with several cases of this nature and to satisfy my own curiosity, I delved into the reason for this odd aspect of our legal system and discovered a fascinating trail of legal history.

The first thing to remember is that treasure trove is defined as gold or silver, whether in the form of plate, coin or bullion, which has been deliberately hidden in the earth or in a house or in any other private place. This immediately rules out other valuables such as precious gems, bronze, pottery and glassware etc, unless these are set in either gold or silver. It also rules out gold or silver coins, plate or bullion which have been *lost*. The law on treasure trove does not concern itself with lost articles, but merely those which were hidden, however long ago.

If the owner is not known, treasure trove belongs to the Crown, i.e. the State, but before being handed over, a decision must be made as to whether a particular item is or is not 'treasure trove', i.e. *hidden* treasure which has been found. This is the duty of the coroner who must hold an inquest (that is an enquiry) to determine whether or not the gold or silver object in question was lost or hidden. This can often be determined by the circumstances of its discovery. In very simple terms, a gold coin found under two inches of earth beside a well used footpath was probably lost. There is no clear evidence that it had been concealed, therefore it would not be declared treasure trove, and would probably belong to the finder or perhaps to the landowner.

On the other hand, if a cache of gold coins was found in a

leather bag or a container of some kind, perhaps buried beneath a tree or lodged up the chimney of an old house, then this suggests a past and deliberate concealment.

These are the kinds of decision which must be made by the coroner, usually based on evidence obtained for him by the police. The reason for his involvement goes back to twelfth century at least, and possibly further. Once known as the crowner, the origins of the coroner are lost in time, but the office was mentioned in 1194 in Richard I's Articles of Eyre. They provided for the election of three knights and one clerk as custodians of the pleas of the Crown. From this, the early coroners were known as Keepers of the King's Pleas (*Custos Placitorum Coronae*) and their duties were to keep 'the pleas, suits and causes which affected the King's Crown and Dignity.'

The task of an early coroner was really to record matters rather than determine them, but one of his jobs was to ensure that any 'chance revenues' were paid to the King. These included money from 'the forfeited chattels of felons, deodands, wrecks, royal fish and treasure trove.' In other words, the early coroner was little more than a tax-gatherer, although he did enquire into sudden deaths and did supervise the disposal of a deceased's lands and goods. Indeed, his official interest in sudden deaths was then to ensure that the Crown received all its dues.

The forfeited chattels of felons were the belongings of a man who had committed some felony (i.e. serious crime like theft or murder). If he was convicted, all his belongings were forfeited to the Crown and it was the coroner's job to see that it was done.

It is now easy to understand why the coroner had to enquire into every sudden death – it was to determine whether or not it was the result of a murder so that, when a culprit was convicted, the Crown would receive its dues. Deodands are now obsolete: these were the objects which had caused the death by mis-adventure of a person. For example, if a cart accidentally ran over and killed a man, the cart or even just the offending wheel might be declared deodand and forfeited to the Crown. In days of old when this happened, the King would donate the object to the church or to the family of the victim, so that money could be raised for the sufferers. This scheme was abolished in 1846 when it was feared that entire railway trains or ships might be forfeited!

Wrecks at sea are now subject to their own procedures which were recently up-dated by the Protection of Wrecks Act 1973 and the coroner is no longer involved. So far as Royal Fish are concerned, it was Edward II who ruled that all sturgeon caught in British waters belonged to the sovereign and it was the coroner's duty to make sure this was done. I know of no modern law which enforces these provisions, but the practice continues as a matter of courtesy and custom. These, plus treasure trove, were the chance revenues which had to be handed to the King; of them, only treasure trove legally remains, and even now, if objects are declared treasure trove, they must still be handed to the Crown. But now, of course, this means the British Museum.

Upon the coroner declaring a discovery to be treasure trove, the goods will be handed to the British Museum who will then determine the current market value of the find. The finder will then be paid that sum, which shows that, in this case especially, honesty is by far the best policy. In recent years, many rewards totalling hundreds of thousands of pounds have been paid to lucky finders.

The old common-law misdemeanour of 'concealment of treasure trove' has been abolished, but if anyone now finds treasure trove and does not declare it, they can be charged with theft under the Theft Act of 1968 and their find will be confiscated. No reward will be paid either. It is so much wiser to report any of these discoveries, both from a criminal liability aspect and from the nation's need to conserve treasures which might otherwise be lost for ever.

It is not the job of a coroner to determine *ownership* of any treasure found on private land or in private premises; if it is *not* declared treasure trove, it might belong to the finder or the owner of the land or occupier of the house, or indeed to anyone else. That kind of decision is a matter for the civil courts if there is a dispute and so, with this background in mind, I found it both interesting and simple to deal with people who found things in their homes, or in the fields and surrounding countryside. And the number and variety of things discovered was truly amazing.

It is not easy to select the most interesting of the finds which occurred in and around Aidensfield – every one was fascinating in its own way. Mundane objects like old bikes, oil drums and even motor-car spare parts were constantly being located in the lakes, ponds and streams while our woodlands produced cast-off refrigerators, ovens, settees and a bewildering selection of household offal, most of which resulted from the actions of those ghastly people who dump their unwanted rubbish in the countryside. In our streams and waterways, old guns have been found too, and so have Victorian lemonade and beer bottles which are so desired by collectors. There were modern ones too, along with kettles and bedsteads, and in one miraculous case, a diamond wedding ring was discovered in a tiny beck. This was returned to the owner who had lost it several years earlier; she had reported the loss to the police, and our records turned up her name. Needless to say, she was delighted.

But none of these objects was remotely within the scope of treasure-trove rules, neither was an antique flintlock pistol found in the thatch of a cottage, or a beautiful unmarked glass goblet which had been tucked into a hole in a wall, and then boarded over for a couple of centuries. Because our area had been colonised by the Romans, we were often told of discoveries from that era; items of pottery galore like bowls, plates and urns turned up, usually broken into fragments, although very occasionally a complete and flawless example would be found.

These caused immense excitement, and although such finds were always of tremendous archaeological interest, they were generally not of police interest, nor was the coroner officially involved. Sometimes, however, we had to bear in mind the likelihood that any found object might be the subject of a crime – people did steal valuables and then dump them, but in most of our cases they were genuine discoveries from the distant past. Our procedures referred the finder to a local museum or archaeologist; sometimes, Roman coins would be unearthed and we had all coins examined by experts to determine whether or not they were struck in gold or silver; I don't think we ever dealt with a gold or silver coin from Roman times, although I understand that the Anglo-Saxons made gold copies of some Roman coins – these are now very rare. Most of the Roman coins we dealt with looked a dull bronze colour with the head of an emperor crudely portrayed on one side with various inscriptions on the other. None was particularly valuable and there seemed to be so many different types.

In one case, a very enthusiastic and slightly dishonest hunter discovered a hoard of Roman coins on private land and kept them; he was charged with stealing them from the landowner, as he had not obtained permission either to go on to the land nor to seek the coins. Some bore the head of the Emperor Septimus Severus who died at York around AD 211; this gave them a very local interest, but because they were neither gold nor silver, they were not treasure trove.

There was a burst of tremendous excitement at Elsinby when a local farmer turned up an ancient sword. He was ploughing close to the stream which flows through this pretty place when he struck the long, stout metal blade. His fields occupy a patch of land beneath the castle walls where there are strong links between Elsinby Castle and the Civil Wars; it was a regular occurrence for Fred Pullen to find relics of this kind. He regularly turned up cannon balls, musket balls, buckles from belts and spearheads.

But this sword was different. Although the long, heavy blade and hilt had suffered years of rust, he was alert enough to notice two narrow bands of what appeared to be gold which had been incorporated in the hilt. He brought this discovery for me to examine but I could not determine whether or not the bands were fashioned from real gold. That could only be decided by an expert, so we arranged for the sword to be examined.

And those bands were of gold; furthermore, the expert who hailed from the Yorkshire Museum said that the sword was not from the Civil War period. It was very probably an Anglo-Saxon warrior's sword dating from the seventh century, and he believed the gold bands had once bound a leather handle to the sword. But those tiny bands of gold made all the difference to Fred's discovery – because of the gold content, I now had to consider the law on treasure trove and this meant that Fred could not keep the sword – unless the inquest decided it was *not* treasure trove.

I made a formal report on the matter, and included a detailed

statement from the museum's expert together with the circumstances of its discovery in that field beside the stream. The
coroner said he would hold an inquest at some future date – he
always kept such matters on file until a number of cases had
accumulated, and he would then hold several treasure trove
inquests on the same day. Each lasted but a few minutes.

In this case, he decided the sword was not treasure trove –
clearly, it had not been deliberately hidden and had, more than
likely, been abandoned or even thrown away. And so Fred
Pullen was allowed to keep it, but he donated it to the museum
for display.

'It'll be safer yonder, Mr Rhea,' he said with simple logic. 'If
I keep it and then pass on to that big hayfield in the sky when my
time's up, it could get chucked away again. Folks round here
don't recognise history, tha knaws, 'specially them relations o'
mine. They see sike stuff as nowt but old bits o' junk. In my
mind, them bits an' bobs are all a part of history and should be
kept where folks'll appreciate 'em and where they'll never get
lost again.'

I told him I couldn't agree more, and from that time, he
donated many more pieces to local museums.

If Fred's discovery was rather unusual, so was that of Mrs
Dolly-Ann Powell, a delightful lady of mature years who earned
a living by lecturing upon and arranging beautiful displays of
flowers in hotels, shops and other places.

Dolly-Ann was a tiny, slender and very pretty widow of about
forty-five who lived in a picturesque thatched cottage at Briggsby. When dressed in her best clothes, she reminded me of one of
her own flower arrangements, so delightfully neat and attractive
was she. Our paths seldom crossed for she went about her
business in a brisk and efficient manner and her work was
something that rarely, if ever, warranted attention from a
policeman. Every so often, however, I would spend time patrolling around her village and very occasionally I would find her in
the garden, tending her beautiful collection of exquisite
flowers. Many of these were used in her work and I do know
that she sold lots to florists for wreaths and bouquets, or even to
customers who came to the door. To say that her house and
garden were a picture was a great understatement – they were a

sheer delight. On such occasions, we would chat amiably over the hedge, passing the time of day and issuing the customary British small-talk about the weather and gardening.

One of Dolly-Ann's strengths was that she did most of her own renovations to the cottage; rather than employ builders or craftsmen, she would tackle most jobs and, surprisingly, achieved a great deal. It was while undertaking one of her improvements that she made a discovery which puzzled and then intrigued her.

It occurred when she decided to re-lay the sturdy path of sandstone paving-slabs which led to her honeysuckle-covered porch and front door.

Over the years, they had become rather uneven and maybe dangerous, and so she decided to level them all. To make a good job, she lifted every one, including that which formed the threshold. It was here that she made her discovery. Underneath the threshold she found an old glass bottle dirty with age. Some six inches tall with a wide neck, its top contained a large cork which was thoroughly sealed and had remained intact in spite of many years in the ground. She had wiped off much of the grime to find the bottle contained some very strange objects and ingredients, so strange in fact that she was baffled by them.

By chance I arrived just after she had cleaned the bottle, when she was endeavouring to determine the contents, so she invited me in for a look at it. She put the kettle on and sat me in her pretty kitchen among countless vases and arrangements of flowers.

'So here it is.' She plonked it on the table before me. It was a clear bottle, although the glass had a faint greenish tinge to it, and I could see a dried-up, dark and almost glutinous substance covering the bottom. This had congealed many years ago, judging by its appearance, but there were other small metal objects stuck into it, rather like pins or nails, some rusted and others still clean; I could see what appeared to be human hairs and nail clippings too.

And then I knew what it was.

At that point, she arrived with a mug of hot tea and settled down at my side.

'Well, Mr Rhea, have I discovered hidden treasure?'

'Not really,' I smiled, thanking her for the drink.

'Oh.' Her face showed just a hint of disappointment.

'You've no idea what it is?' I asked.

'Not a clue,' she was honest.

'Well, suppose I asked you if your house is troubled by witches?' I smiled at her. 'What would you say?'

'Witches? No, of course not!' she laughed. 'Why, was this a witch's cottage?'

'On the contrary, witches were not welcome here!' I told her. 'This little device was to stop them, to ward off witches and to prevent them from bewitching the house or its occupants. It's obviously done a good job!'

'Really?' She opened her eyes wide with surprise and smiled at my attempt at joking. 'I had no idea!'

I explained my own interest in the folklore of the North York Moors and how, even until little more than a century or so ago, the country folk believed in witches and the power of the evil eye. Even today, some cottages contain witch posts whose original purpose was to protect the occupants from the attentions of witches, and there are other devices which served this purpose: for example, iron nails in beams or bedsteads, circular stones with holes in the centre, horseshoes on the walls of houses and outbuildings and even rowan trees planted close to the dwelling. All were used to deter witches.

She listened as I explained, and when I had finished, asked, 'So what is this bottle?'

'It's a witch bottle,' I told her. 'It was customary to bury them beneath the threshold, or sometimes under the hearth.'

'Really?' She picked it up and tried to identify the contents. 'What's inside?'

'Do you really want to know?' The ingredients were rather revolting and I wondered if she was squeamish.

'Something odd, is there?' she asked, suspicious of what was coming next.

'Ordinary things, really,' I smiled. 'But gruesome at the same time.'

She plonked the bottle on the table and stared at it, her pretty face screwed up in concentration.

'Go on, Mr Rhea,' she said at length. 'Make me squirm!'

'I'm not sure precisely what's in this particular bottle,' I said. 'But the sort of ingredients they put in would include samples of human hair, nail cuttings and metal objects like pins or nails. They'd put urine in too, and human blood . . . '

'Urggh . . . ' she shuddered.

'And!' I was in full flow now. 'Some of them contained the liver of a live frog stuck full of pins, or the heart of a toad which had been pierced with the spikes from the Holy Thorn of Glastonbury.'

She stared at the bottle on her table.

'How revolting!' she shuddered again. 'Why did they make such horrible things?'

'They really worried about the effect of witches on their children and cattle,' I explained. 'If things went wrong, things that couldn't be easily explained, they would blame the local witch. She was usually some poor old woman who dabbled in herbs or reckoned to foretell the future. And to stop any evil that she might perpetrate, they made these bottles as safeguards.'

'So the contents acted as a charm?'

'Yes, they were put under the door to prevent entry by evil spirits or witches. The presence of iron has long been a means of keeping witches at bay, hence the horseshoes, nails, pins and so on. The hair and human nail-parings come from the most indestructible part of the human body, and they believed that if included in a bottle, their presence would stop the witch injuring the family. I'm not sure what the blood was for. The addition of the urine was a terrible thing – they believed this caused the witch's death because she would be unable to pass water!'

I went on to say these charms were used beyond our shores too, examples having been found in Sicily and Germany, and that in some cases three earthenware jars were used with similar contents, in this case each being buried beside a churchyard footpath seven inches below the surface and seven inches from a church porch.

When I had concluded my lecture on local witchlore, she smiled. 'So what am I going to do with this bottle? Is it something you should know about, officially, I mean.'

'No, but thanks for showing it me. You could replace it!' I suggested. 'Or keep it as an ornament . . . '

'No thanks! I wouldn't want that collection of stuff on my shelves!'

I mentioned the local Ryedale Folk Museum and felt it would be a suitable place to keep this bottle and its odd contents. She agreed.

'Mind you,' she smiled with a twinkle in her eye. 'I suppose that if I remove it from the house, I'll then be open to the machinations of the local witches? They might ruin my flowers, cause them to wilt or die, or even create havoc in the house itself.'

'That's the risk you take,' I confirmed with a chuckle. 'It seems this cottage has been free from strife over the years!'

'It's always been a happy house,' she said. 'Always.'

Draining my mug of tea, I left her to make her decision and never asked what she had decided. I felt I should not mention the bottle again, and although I did see her from time to time, she refrained from bringing up the subject. But I have never seen that bottle in the folk museum, and so far as I know Dolly-Ann's cottage and business have remained free from trouble. And her front path is now neat and level, with the threshold firmly in place.

Among the other discoveries was a magnificently ornate silver spoon which a householder discovered buried in the thatch of his cottage; this was identified as a seventeenth-century dessert spoon worth around £2,500, and the coroner decided that it *was* treasure trove. He said due to the peculiar place in which it was found, it must have been deliberately hidden for reasons which we shall never know. So much treasure seemed to be discovered in the thatched cottages around my beat that I was almost tempted to buy one!

But perhaps the most satisfying discovery was the one that occurred at West Gill Farm, Aidensfield, the centuries-old home of Reg Lumley and his family. Only months earlier, I had seen Reg devastated by a terrible outbreak of Foot and Mouth Disease. It had resulted in the slaughter of his entire herd of pedigree Friesians, a herd which had taken him twenty years to establish but which had been wiped out in hours by that most dreaded of cattle diseases. The story is told in *Constable along the Lane*.

I knew that Reg, his wife and son Ted, were struggling to re-build their lives but no new cattle had yet appeared on the farm. I did not like to pry into their affairs nor discuss matters like insurance or compensation, nor did I wish to cause anguish by reminding them of the outbreak, so it was a pleasant surprise when I received a call from Reg. On the phone, he sounded in unusually high spirits.

'Can thoo come, Mr Rhea? Ah've summat to show you.'

'Sure Reg, when's a suitable time?'

'Any time, we're about t'spot all day.'

'How about just after two o'clock?'

'Champion,' he said and rang off.

When I arrived just after lunch, I found the family in the kitchen. They were sitting around their massive scrubbed pine table with huge mugs of tea, and in the centre was a tray full of muddy coins and bits of broken pottery.

Reg, beaming with happiness, shoved a mug into my hand and pulled out a chair. I settled on it, staring at the treasure before me.

'That's it, Mr Rhea. How about that?'

'Reg!' I said. 'Is this yours?'

'That's for you to say, Mr Rhea. Our Ted dug it up wiv 'is plough this morning, down in oor fifteen-acre.'

'Did he now!' I couldn't resist running my fingers through the pile of ancient money. The coins, most of which appeared to be of silver and from the sixteenth and seventeenth centuries, tinkled and rattled back on to the tray, and there seemed to be thousands of them. Upon some of them, I recognised names like Carolus I, Jacobus, Elizabeth, Edward VI and Carolus II. So they were from the reigns of Charles I and II, James I, Elizabeth I and Edward VI. I believe at least one was from the reign of Henry VIII.

'Wonderful!' I beamed. 'Absolutely wonderful.'

'Are they worth owt, Mr Rhea?'

'They must be,' I said, 'but I'm no expert.'

'Can I sell 'em? We could do wiv a bit o' cash.'

'I'm afraid not, Reg. But you could still get money from the find, although it'll take time,' and I told them about the procedure relating to treasure trove. Ted showed me where he had ploughed them up and I noted the place, then took a formal statement from him.

Next, we counted the coins. It took a long time because there were almost 2,000, and I had the unpleasant task of taking them away from the Lumleys in a large sack. I gave a receipt for 1,985 coins. I explained they would have to be examined by experts to determine whether or not they were silver or even gold. The Lumleys probably thought it was the last they'd see of them, knowing they were now subjected to red tape and officialdom.

As expected, the coroner declared them treasure trove which meant they were handed to the British Museum, and they would make their customary valuation based upon the prevailing marked prices. It was some months later when I got a telephone call from Reg.

'Can thoo come, Mr Rhea. I've summat to show you.'

'Not another batch of coins, Reg?'

'Nay, summat else,' his voice contained an air of mystery. 'Thoo'll like this.'

'I'll be there in ten minutes,' I said, curious to learn about his latest discovery.

This time, there was a whopping glass of whisky on the kitchen table when I arrived and the family sat around with huge grins on their faces. Even Mrs Lumley was smiling.

Reg made sure I was settled and insisted I drink the whisky, even though I was in uniform. I didn't like to offend by refusing! After this performance, I was handed a letter. It was still in the official buff envelope which had been opened, but it bore the logo of the British Museum.

'Tak a leeak at yon, Mr Rhea,' invited Reg.

I did. I read the formal letter and was astounded. It itemised every single coin and identified them by year, reign and designation, and an individual valuation had also been added. The letter said that the total official value of the hoard of coins found at West Gill Farm, Aidensfield was £47,884 and a cheque for that amount was enclosed.

I held the cheque . . . I'd never seen, let alone held, such a huge amount of money.

'Whew!' was all I could say.

'That caps owt, Mr Rhea,' said Reg. 'That really caps owt.'

'It does, Reg. It really does cap owt. And I'm delighted for you all.'

Mrs Lumley, a woman of few words and a severe hair-do, just smiled again.

'Nay, it's thanks to thoo,' said Reg. 'I read summat in t'*Gazette* aboot thoo and another inquest on summat found at Elsinby, so thowt I'd better tell thoo. If thoo hadn't said what we had ti deea wiv 'em, Ah might have stuck 'em in t'loft and said nowt. I mean, thoo can't spend 'em, so in my mind they were worth nowt.'

That was a typical Yorkshire attitude, and he continued,

'Ah mean to say, who'd have thowt they were worth all this? So we'll have a party, Mr Rhea. Your missus'll come, eh?'

'We'll be delighted,' I said, and I meant it.

'It'll be soon,' he said. 'I'll ring wi' t'date.'

'Don't spend it all on a party!' I cautioned him with a laugh. 'Make the money work for you!'

'Ah shall, Mr Rhea. Starting next week, me and Ted'll be off to a few cattle marts. There's a few young pedigree Friesians we'd like to get oor hands on.'

I was so happy for the Lumleys, and their party was marvellous. With a farmhouse full of friends and relations, it was a wonderful event, especially as Reg seemed to have overcome the depression which had plagued him for so long. And he did get his new herd started. Now, when I drive past his farm, I see his fields once again full of beautiful Friesians and Reg has still not retired. He continues to build that 'new' herd with just a little help from some past occupants of his lush farmland.

But of all the discoveries made on my patch, it was the one involving Mrs Ada Jowett which was the most intriguing. Ada, a stout and oft perspiring lady in her late sixties, was the church cleaner at St Andrew's Parish Church, Elsinby, a job which she did voluntarily. She had been St Andrew's cleaner for more years than anyone cared to recall, and the lovely building sparkled through her efforts.

The brasses always gleamed, the altar cloths were ironed to perfection, the surrounds were tidy and neat, and she managed to ensure that the flowers were always fresh and readers' lists and other notices were tidily displayed.

In short, Mrs Jowett was a treasure.

The church, always short of money and in need of constant maintenance and repairs, was soon to learn just how much of a treasure she really was. Conscientious as ever, she decided one year to spring-clean the hidden corners of the church. In addition to her normal brushing and polishing, this meant clearing out cupboards and corners, getting rid of years of accumulated rubbish and paper and generally ridding the church of unwanted junk. The job was long overdue, but no one had dared suggest it to Mrs Jowett. For all her skills, she cleaned only what could be seen . . .

No one knew what had prompted her to tackle the cupboards and corners, but she attacked the job with much gusto, lots of mops and dusters and gallons of perspiration. The stuff that was thrown out was bewildering – old curtains and cloths, ancient notices and posters, stacks of battered hymn books and a load of assorted jumble which would have graced the best junk-sale for miles around. It is just feasible that some important documents got lost in her enthusiasm, but she operated like a whirlwind. There was no stopping her once she had started and for days the church was almost lost in a cloud of dust or bonfire smoke.

And then, right at the back of a massive oak cupboard in the vestry, she found a chalice. It had obviously been there for years for it was dirty, very battered and full of dust. Like most other discoveries, she decided to throw it in the bin, so removed it from the shelf and took it outside. Then she had a second look in the strong daylight and for some reason changed her mind about casting it in the bin. It was at that precise moment that I arrived. I was undertaking a patrol around Elsinby and had noticed the frantic activity within the church. Attracted by the piles of rubbish outside, I thought I'd pop in to see what was going on and to pass the time of day with Ada.

As I strolled up the path towards the porch, I saw Ada clutching the chalice; she was peering intently at it.

'Morning, Ada,' I greeted her. 'Still busy, eh?'

'Never been so busy,' she grumbled. 'Wish I'd never started this. The more I chuck out the more I find inside, it's never ending. Makes you wonder where it comes from.'

'You're doing a good job.' I decided to praise her efforts. 'It must be benefiting the church. So, what's that you've found?'

'An old cup,' she said, holding it up for me to see. 'Been stuck in the back of a cupboard for years, it has. Junk I'd say, by the look of it. It's made of tin, I think, been battered about a bit. They'd never use this sort o' thing now for communion.'

She passed the chalice over to me and I held it, weighing it in my hand.

'It's pewter, I think,' I told her. 'And very old by the look of it.'

'It'll not be worth owt, then? It's not gold or silver, is it?'

'No, so what are you going to do with it?'

'I was thinking about chucking it out,' she said. 'Then when I got out, I had second thoughts, I'd like to show it to t'vicar, but he's away at a conference.'

The Rev Simon Hamilton, Vicar of Elsinby, was away at a Diocesan Conference; I knew that because he'd told me that the vicarage would be empty for a whole week and had asked me to keep an eye on it during his absence.

Still holding the chalice and turning it in my hands, I said, 'I think he'd like to see this,' and then, in the strong light of that morning, I noticed the faint engraving on the face. It was very difficult to determine but it looked rather like a crowned sovereign in a sailing ship; he was carrying an upright sword and a shield.

'You take it and get somebody to look at it,' she said quite unexpectedly. 'Then I can tell t'vicar what we've done. You deal with found treasures, don't you?'

'Yes, if they're treasure trove.'

'Well, mebbe it's a good thing you turned up like you did. Do you happen to know anybody that'll look at it, say what it's worth or summat?'

'I'm going into York tomorrow,' I said. 'Off duty, but I've a pal who's in the antique business. I'll show it to him if you like.'

'Aye.' She looked relieved, for the decision had now been taken out of her hands.

And so I took the chalice from her. I found a piece of brown paper among the rubbish and wrapped it up, then placed it in the cubby-hole of the mini-van. Next day, I popped it into a carrier bag and took it to York. Mary and I did a little shopping, had a meal and then I remembered the old chalice. I went back to my car and removed it, then walked along Stonegate to my friend's antique shop.

'Hello, Paul, how's things in the antique world?'

'Hi, Nick,' he said. 'Things are bloody fine. So what brings you here?'

'This,' I said, and I placed the battered old chalice on his counter. 'I think it's pewter but wondered if it's worth anything!'

He took it and held it very carefully, turning it in the strong light of an angle lamp as he first studied the cup itself, and then examined the engraving on the front.

'Bloody hell!' was all he said. 'Where's this come from?'

'One of the churches on my patch,' I said. 'The cleaning lady found it in a cupboard. Been there years by the look of it.'

'Centuries more like,' he said, and I saw his face was flushed. 'You've no idea what this is?'

I shook my head and said lamely, 'A chalice?'

'A chalice, yes. But what a bloody chalice! Worth a bloody fortune,' he whistled. 'A bloody fortune, or I'm stupid. You say she found it in a bloody cupboard?'

I explained the circumstances of its discovery, and then asked why he was so enthusiastic about it.

'Here,' he said. 'Take a look at this engraving. What is it?' he shone the light upon it and pointed to it.

'I think it's a king in a ship.'

'Right, with a sword and a shield, eh? The sort of arms you'd get on a bloody coin, not on a bloody pewter chalice!'

'Oh,' I said.

'This might have belonged to a king, see? Or to the priest who was the king's confessor or something. Henry IV it would be,' he continued. 'Reigned 1399 to 1413, he did. And see this?' He pointed to the shield, but I could not determine precisely what he was showing me. 'His shield, it's only got three fleurs-de-lis, not four. He changed his royal arms, you see; coins with only three fleurs-de-lis are so bloody rare it's unbelievable. And see this rudder on the ship? There's a star on it. Now most rudders on Henry IV coins are blank, but some have crowns on and some have bloody stars. Nick, if I'm not mistaken, this is a bloody rare find – a really rare bloody find.'

'No kidding?' I was awestruck by the thought.

'No kidding,' he said. 'You need expert valuation of this, my lad. Try Sotheby's.'

'I don't know anybody there.'

'I do, and he's a whizz-kid on medieval pewter. I'll fix up a bloody appointment, right now if you like.'

'The vicar hasn't even seen this yet; if it's what you think it is, no doubt he'll want to be involved, and maybe even bring his bishop or the Archbishop into this find.'

'Too bloody right he will when he finds out what it is. Right, show it to him, tell him what I said, then ring me and I'll fix up an appointment at Sotheby's for it to be expertly assessed. Somebody'll have to take it down to London.'

'Right, Paul, thanks. I appreciate your advice.'

'And if your church wants to sell this bloody thing, let me know! I'd mortgage my shop to get my bloody hands on that.'

When the vicar returned, I informed him of this conversation (although I omitted Paul's colourful flow of expletives) and he promptly rang the Archbishop of York who suggested we let the Sotheby expert have sight of it. And, he said, the diocese would pay the train fare of the person who took it. We nominated Ada, with the proviso that she be told to take great care of the chalice at all times. Simon Hamilton felt she could be trusted to look after it – after all, who'd think this countrywoman was carrying treasure?

'I'm off to London,' she said next time I saw her. 'With that cup, Mr Rhea. To show a chap down there. I've never been to London, you know, never even been on a train.'

And so, dressed in her heavy brown shoes, lisle stockings, headscarf and her only overcoat which was of heavy tweed, Ada Jowett set about the journey of a lifetime. Excited both at the prospect of travelling to London and of riding on a train, she was driven to York Station by the vicar and would be met at King's Cross by the man from Sotheby's. He'd promised to care for her during her visit, bearing in mind the circumstances. I've no idea what he made of Ada when they met, but she had a most enjoyable day. Upon her return that same evening, she was collected from York by taxi and the vicar invited me to go along and hear how she'd progressed at Sotheby's.

The vicar's wife had arranged a late supper for her and I was invited. And when Ada came in from the taxi, she was carrying the chalice in a brown carrier bag; in fact, she'd put one bag inside another to give greater protection to the chalice! That was her notion of taking care of it.

'Well, Ada,' began Simon Hamilton. 'How did it go?'

'By, yon train goes fast,' she said. 'And then in London, they rushed me down some stairs under t'ground and there was more trains, coming every few minutes . . . I've never seen owt like it . . . and folks! Thousands of 'em all pushing and shoving . . . there's no wonder folks get bad-tempered with all that rushing about.'

'Yes, but the chalice . . . '

Ada ignored the vicar and continued to enthuse about London, giving her highly colourful interpretation of life in the capital. She rambled on about guards in funny hats at Buckingham Palace, messy pigeons, Eros, Big Ben, the Houses of Parliament, the department stores, the different nationalities she noticed, buses that came every few minutes instead of twice a week and trains whose doors shut without being pushed by the travellers.

Eventually, she ran out of talk of the City and Simon took the opportunity to mention Sotheby's and the chalice.

'They would have nowt to do with it, Mr Hamilton.' She shook her heavy grey head. 'Didn't want to know. This young chap met me off t'train and took me in a taxi where I saw the chap you mentioned, him what reckons to know summat about cups like that.'

'And he examined it?'

'He did, in a manner o' speaking. It took nobbut a minute or two, and that was that.'

'And what did he say?'

'Not a lot.'

'You offered to leave the chalice for a more thorough examination, as I suggested?'

'Oh, aye, I made that clear. I said I'd leave it for him to have a better look and he could mebbe post it back, but he said he'd have nowt to do with it, Mr Hamilton.'

'Nothing to do with it?'

When I heard this, I wondered about Paul's assessment – Paul would never have allowed Ada to go all the way to London with a dud. I was sure Paul knew his antiques . . .

'Nay, nowt. Summat to do with insurance, he said. He wouldn't take it off me, so I had to fetch it back.'

And she dug into the paper carrier bag and lifted it out.

'Is that all?'

'Well, he said he'd be having words with you about it, I told him your telephone number. Tomorrow, he said, all being well. He'll ring.'

There was clear disappointment on Simon's face and I knew mine also showed similar feelings. It seemed that the so-called experts in London had merely fobbed off poor old Ada. The vicar should have gone, he should have taken it and presented it in a more sophisticated manner.

'Leave it with me, Ada,' said Simon. 'We'll see what they say tomorrow, eh?'

'Aye, and it's my bedtime now. See you tomorrow,' and off she went.

I remained with Simon for a while, each of us expressing our sorrow at her apparently callous treatment in London, and then I went home. Then at lunch-time the following day, I got a call from Simon Hamilton.

'Can you spare ten minutes, Nicholas?' he asked.

'Of course,' I said. 'I'll come now.'

When I arrived at the vicarage, he showed me into his kitchen where Ada was seated at the table. Mrs Hamilton was also present and I noticed a glass of wine at each place setting. And in the centre was the dirty old chalice.

When we were all gathered together, Simon said, 'Ada, PC Rhea, I'd like to thank you both for your work in rescuing this chalice. I've had a call from Sotheby's this morning, Ada, and they thank you for taking it to them.'

'The cheek of 'em!' she pouted. 'Nearly threw me out they did . . . didn't want to know about me . . . '

'I think you have misunderstood them, Ada.' He spoke

softly. 'They did a proper and expert examination; it's a Henry IV pewter chalice, a very rare object and more so because of the arms which it bears. It seems pewter chalices were used in medieval times, but most of them were buried with the priests when they died. Very few from this period have survived, especially of this quality. Now, did he say what it was worth?'

'Well, he muttered on about it being worth summat in the region of half a million pounds. Now I ask you, Mr Hamilton! Half a million pounds for that bit of awd tin?'

'And you didn't believe him?'

'I did not! I reckoned he was having me on 'cos I'm a country woman who doesn't know about such things.'

'Ada, he does genuinely believe it would bring that amount in a sale at his auction rooms. It is unique, Ada, a real treasure.'

'You're all having me on!' She flushed deeply now and looked very embarrassed. 'That's why I said nowt to you about what they'd said it was worth. A bit of awd tin can't be worth that much, it just can't.'

'No, we're not teasing you, Ada, none of us. His problem was that he could not keep it overnight because he was not insured for that particular cup. So you took it sight-seeing . . . '

'Aye, and I nearly lost it over London Bridge, an' all,' she said grimly. 'Can't say I'd have missed it.'

'So you've a problem now.' I put to him. 'Your church will never afford the premiums to insure this!'

'I must speak to the Archbishop,' he said. 'This is a real shock, Ada, a massive shock. I'm reeling from the thought that this has been standing in my vestry for years and, but for you, would have been thrown out . . . '

'Half a million pounds!' she said. 'For that bit of awd tin? I'd not give it house-room!'

She was steadfastly refusing to accept the truth of that statement, and left the vicarage shaking her head. After being assured Simon would place it in a bank vault for safe keeping, I followed her out, stunned that I'd carried it around in my car and had left it unattended in a York car-park!

It would be about a month later when Rev. Simon Hamilton called me again. 'I thought you'd like to know the outcome of the chalice saga,' he said.

'Love to,' I said, and drove to his vicarage for a coffee with him.

When I was settled, he said, 'As you've been involved with this from the start,' he strode up and down his spacious kitchen, 'I thought you'd like to hear the Archbishop's decision about the chalice.'

'Yes, thanks, Simon. I appreciate that.'

'It is a problem, Nicholas,' he said. 'We cannot keep it because of the risks and the necessarily high insurance premiums. We could not afford them. And, as you know, we do need a regular supply of money for upkeep of our church.'

I let him take his time on this explanation.

'If we allowed Sotheby's to auction it on our behalf, it might raise that huge sum; half a million pounds does seem excessive, but I am assured it could bring as much as that on the open market, maybe from international buyers.'

'So you're selling it?' I asked.

'Not by public auction. As the Archbishop says, if we did sell it through Sotheby's, it might go out of the country. There is no telling where it might get to. We don't want that – we want such a unique chalice, our chalice, kept in England, Nicholas. It must never leave these shores.'

'But you're in a cleft stick, Simon,' I said. 'You can't afford to keep it, and you can't dictate where it goes if it is sold. You cannot issue conditions for sales of that kind.'

'A solution has been reached, Nicholas,' he said. 'A museum has offered us £45,000 for it; it will be put on display and kept in this country for all time.'

'But that's a fraction of its true value,' I protested.

'Perhaps, but it's all that museum can afford. If we invest that cash, it will give the church a very nice income for years ahead and that will safeguard it and permit us to maintain it in the manner it deserves. After all, we want nothing more than that. You see, this method pleases everyone because the chalice can be viewed by the public, we get some income from it and it will never again be lost or taken out of England. It's an admirable solution.'

'But you're throwing money away!' I said.

'Not really, because we're getting more than we've had

before, and we don't really need half a million, Nicholas.'

'It's a real Christian decision,' I heard myself say.

'It was made by the Archbishop, I might add,' said Simon as if that explained everything.

Today, Ada's name is upon the notice which provides a history of the chalice as it stands in a famous museum, and soon after the sale, Ada got a new apron, some new brushes and dusters. So the chalice was of benefit to her as well.

And she still refuses to believe that such a 'piece of awd tin' was worth so much money.

4

The crime of theft, known legally in England as larceny until 1968, is among the earliest of criminal offences; not only is it a crime, however, it is also a sin, and as such features in the Ten Commandments. 'Thou shalt not steal' could hardly be a more direct prohibition.

A universal loathing of theft has, over the centuries, provided it with many penalties, some of them dreadfully severe. Some five hundred years before Christ, for example, the Romans hanged those who stole crops at night. They were executed at the scene of their crime as a sacrifice to Ceres, goddess of the harvest. Here in England during Danish times, a thief could be killed without fear of having to pay compensation to his family because his act of stealing had rendered him valueless. During medieval times, theft continued to be a capital offence along with others such as murder, treason, arson, burglary and robbery; Henry II, however, said that crimes which involved the theft of five shillings (25p) or less could be punished by amputation of a foot instead of death.

By the middle ages, reforms were gradually reducing the barbarity of our penal system, although as late as the seventeenth century a woman was drowned in Loch Spynie in Scotland for committing theft, and across the Channel in France the infamous guillotine was utilised against thieves.

After many tests, France's wonderful new death-dealing

66

machine was perfected by Tobias Schmidt and fitted with a slanting blade on the advice of Louis XVI. In fact, he was later to die by that very blade. However, after being installed on 15th April 1792 as the official method of execution, the guillotine's very first victim was a thief. He was Nicholas-Jacques Pelletier who was guillotined at 3.30pm on 25th April 1792 by the Executioner of Criminal Sentences, Charles-Henri Sanson. The machine was thoughtfully painted red and white, and Pelletier's execution had been delayed so that he could have the honour of being the first to be executed by the guillotine.

Even by the early years of last century, some forms of theft in this country carried the death penalty. In 1810, the reformer Samuel Romilly was horrified by the number of offences which did carry the death penalty, and he tried to introduce bills in Parliament to change these laws. At first, he failed; he tried, for example to remove the death penalty which had been reinstated for stealing objects up to the value of five shillings (25p), and also for stealing objects to the value of £2 from houses and for stealing from ships in navigable waters.

He achieved partial success when Parliament abolished the death penalty for stealing from bleaching-grounds. In spite of his efforts, in 1819 there were still over two hundred capital offences on the statute book, one of which was impersonation of a Chelsea Pensioner!

Examples of the contempt in which theft was held occurred in 1827, when a man called Moses Snook was awarded ten years transportation for stealing a plank of wood, and another man was sentenced to death for stealing 2s 6d (12½p). But the spirit of change was moving, and Robert Peel, founder of the modern police service, made a tremendous impact upon legal reform. His influence reduced three hundred Acts of Parliament to only four, and drastically reduced the number of capital offences. The death penalty continued to exist however, even for some crimes of theft such as stealing goods to the value of £2 or more from a dwelling-house.

But the juries hated the death penalty for such crimes and they would deliberately undervalue the stolen goods to save a criminal from death. One jury valued a £10 note at £1 19s 0d (£1.95) to save a criminal from death; other examples involved sheep-stealing and horse-stealing, both of which carried the death penalty. A jury found a thief guilty of stealing only the fleece of a sheep instead of the whole beast, and guilty of stealing only the hair of a horse instead of the entire animal.

By 1956, when I joined the Force, theft, in its many and varied forms, carried penalties which ranged from a maximum of five years' imprisonment up to and including life imprisonment, although fines were often imposed in the less serious cases. It was then called larceny, a term which still creeps into some publications.

Stealing from one's employer, for example, carried a maximum penalty of fourteen years' imprisonment; an officer of the Bank of England who stole securities or money from the bank could get life imprisonment. The stealing of horses, cattle or sheep carried up to fourteen years, while stealing postal packets carried life imprisonment. In 1957, a murder committed during the course of or in the furtherance of theft carried the death penalty, and on 13th August 1964, Gwynne Owen Evans and Peter Anthony Allen, two Lancastrians in their early twenties, were hanged for murdering a van-driver during the course of theft. These were England's last judicial hangings.

In 1968, the law of theft was completely overhauled. The definition of the crime was both altered and simplified, and from that time it has carried a maximum penalty of ten years' imprisonment, with associated offences such as burglary and robbery carrying a maximum of life imprisonment in some cases. Those penalties still apply, for theft is still regarded by some as a sin, by others as a major crime and by yet more as a normal part of life.

People help themselves to 'souvenirs' from hotels, restaurants and cafes; they take stuff home from work and fiddle expense accounts. They 'borrow' with no intention of returning, lift plants from garden centres, purloin precious objects from stately homes and have expeditions to our cities for shoplifting. And it is all theft with a ten-year maximum jail sentence.

In our modern society, the scope for theft is infinite; hundreds of thousands of such crimes are committed daily but massive numbers go unreported because they are accepted as 'normal', and so the true incidence of theft in this country can never be known nor even estimated. But taken as a whole, and supported by most police officers, this will suggest that we live in a very dishonest society.

A statement of this kind, taken from knowledge but unsupported by statistics, will anger politicians who are to the left of centre, but such a claim will be agreed by most business and professional people. They know that thefts occur from their premises and many are dealt with internally, so why report those for which there is no chance of detection? A cafe-owning friend of mine cheerfully told me that he had about a hundred and twenty teaspoons and thirty-six ashtrays stolen *every week*, but he never reported any of these crimes to the police. The incidence of unreported theft would make a marvellous study for a university student . . .

But while the Church continues to denounce theft as a sin, and socialists continue to regard it as a symptom of a society deprived of its basic needs, police officers continue to regard it as a crime committed not by those in need, but by those who like to get their hands on something for nothing and don't mind who suffers in the process. I must confess that I know few, if any, thieves who genuinely had to steal in order to survive; they stole out of pure greed. And that is why thieves are so despicable.

Although so many thefts are not notified to the police, considerable numbers *are* formally reported and investigated before being fed into the nation's crime statistics. For the operational police officer, however, such academic matters are of little importance; his work involves knowing what constitutes a theft, and how to catch the villain responsible. Statistics are of little interest to him.

The 1916 definition of larceny was as follows, and this was the wording which we had to learn parrot-fashion. It was the equivalent of learning the Lord's Prayer or the alphabet, and although I learned this more than thirty years ago I still remember it. Since then, of course, I had to learn the new definition of theft which is contained in the Theft Act 1968, but the old words stick in the memory. The 1916 wording may seem ponderous, but it does have a certain rhythm and indeed one poet wrote it down in verse form.

The definition is as follows, according to section 1 of the

Larceny Act 1916, now repealed. 'A person steals who, without the consent of the owner, fraudulently and without a claim of right made in good faith, takes and carries away anything capable of being stolen, with intent at the time of such taking permanently to deprive the owner thereof.

'Provided that a person may be guilty of stealing any such thing notwithstanding that he has lawful possession thereof, if, being a bailee or part-owner thereof, he fraudulently converts the same to his own use or to the use of any person other than the owner.'

I frequently imagine a Shakespearian actor quoting this definition, with due pauses at all the commas and full-stops, but our task was to learn it and understand it, along with all the other variations of larceny such as stealing by finding or by intimidation, stealing by mistake or by trick, larceny from the person, larceny of trees and shrubs, and a whole range of other associated crimes like embezzlement, burglary, housebreaking, robbery, false pretences, frauds by agents and trustees, blackmail, receiving stolen property, taking of motor vehicles, etc.

It was fascinating stuff and the precise interpretation of that definition has kept lawyers occupied and earning fat fees for years. We had to know it in our heads so that we could instantly implement its provisions in the street, even if our actions did result in appeals to the High Court or House of Lords in the months to come. But in a volume of this nature, there is no space to enlarge upon the wonderful range of legal fiction which resulted from this and similar statutes. But imagine a thief maliciously cutting someone's grass and leaving the clippings behind on the lawn . . . would it be larceny? Were the clippings 'taken and carried away' or indeed, is grass capable of being stolen? And, how many crimes would be committed? One only? Or one for each blade of grass? Was there intention permanently to deprive the owner of his grass? Or was the whole affair a crime of malicious damage? Such points could keep a class of students occupied for hours and reap rich fees for lawyers.

But police officers tend to deal more with the ordinary crime than the exotic, and few interesting cases of larceny came my way at Aidensfield. Most of them were very routine, often committed at night by pilferers who sneaked around the village picking up things left lying around. For example, one farmer had a brand-new wire rat-trap stolen from his barn, a house-holder had a selection of pot plants stolen from his greenhouse, a child's tricycle was stolen having been left outside all night, and someone managed to steal a full-size horse trough. Coal was occasionally nicked from the coal yard, wood was taken from the timber yard and, as happens in most villages, there was a phantom knicker-pincher who stole ladies' underwear from clothes-lines. It seems that almost every village, and in towns every housing estate, has a resident phantom knicker-pincher, most of whom are peculiar men who operate under cover of darkness, many of whom are usually caught in the act of satis-fying their weird addiction. When their houses are searched, a hoard of illicitly obtained exotic and colourful underwear is usually found. Publicity rarely brings forth claimants because many ladies are too shy to report the initial theft or to admit ownership of some of the magnificent and strikingly sensual underwear thus recovered. The courts are then left with the task of ordering suitable disposal.

Apart from the mundane thefts, several interesting cases did cross my path and one of them involved a picture hanging in a village pub.

It was one of those background pictures, some of which are delightful, which adorn the walls of village inns but which are seldom appreciated until someone steals them or mutilates them in some way during a fit of pique or drunkenness. In this instance, however, the picture remained safely in its position above the black cast-iron Yorkist range, enhanced in the colder seasons by the flickering flames of the log fire below and in the warmer seasons by a vase of flowers positioned on the mantel-piece.

The picture was an oil painting of Winston Churchill as the British Prime Minister and it depicted him with his famous cigar between his lips. It showed him at the height of his powers, a confident and forceful personality who had guided our nation to victory during World War II. In the picture, he was contemplating something across to his left (maybe the Labour party!) and was shown seated in his study with books around him and papers scattered across his desk. It was a fine picture of a widely respected statesman and it had been in the Moon and Compass Inn for several years.

It was one of those pictures which brighten the bars of our village inns, and many a glass had been raised to Winston, later Sir Winston, in his silent pose above the cosy, welcoming fire of the Moon and Compass. During my official visits to the inn, Sir Winston was still alive and I had admired the picture and complimented David Grayson, the landlord, upon its merits. This pleased him, although he had acquired the painting with the fittings of the pub.

The possibility that there could be a problem associated with that picture never entered my head until I received a visit from a tourist. He arrived on the stroke of two o'clock one Wednesday afternoon just as I was about to embark upon a tour of duty in the mini-van. I noticed the sleek grey Jaguar 340 glide to a halt outside my house and a smart man in his sixties emerged. He was dressed in light summer clothes of the casual kind, and his wife remained in the car. I met him in the drive to the police house.

'Good afternoon,' I greeted him.

'Ah, I've obviously just caught you, Constable. Are you in a hurry? You can spare a minute or two?'

'Yes, of course,' and I offered to take him into my office but he said he could tell me his business where we stood in the front garden.

'You know the Moon and Compass Inn, at Craydale?' he put to me.

'Yes, it's on my beat,' I said.

'Ah, well, there is a problem. A delicate one, I might add,' he began. 'I hate to make accusations which I cannot substantiate, but I feel you ought to be aware of this . . . '

I wondered what was coming next, but waited as he gathered his words together.

'It's the picture of Winston Churchill,' he said eventually. 'You know it?'

'It hangs over the fireplace in the bar,' I informed him. 'A nice picture, very realistic. I know it well.'

'And so you should!' His voice increased in pitch. 'It was

commissioned from a special sitting – Churchill actually posed for that picture, Constable. It's not a copy, not a print but the original by Christopher Tawney. It's the only one in the world, Constable.'

'It must be valuable, then?' I said inanely.

'I have no idea of its value,' he said shortly. 'No idea at all; it's not an old master so we're not talking in huge sums, but I'd guess it can be measured in thousands, if not tens of thousands. And this is why I've called, Constable. That painting has been stolen. It should not be there; that pub has no right to that picture, no right at all.'

'Stolen? But it's been in that pub for years,' I told him. 'Long before I came here. Eight or ten years even. Are you sure it's the one you think it is?'

'I've never been so sure in my life, Constable. You see, I had it done, I was the person who commissioned the artist and persuaded Winston to undertake that sitting. I know that picture like I know my own belongings. If you care to examine it, you'll see Tawney's signature in the bottom left-hand corner too.'

'You'd better come into the office,' I said.

I asked Mary to make a cup of tea, and to include the gentleman's wife who waited in the car. She was persuaded to come into the lounge where Mary and the children entertained her as I discussed this matter with her husband.

His name was Simon Cornell and he was a retired director of one of Britain's largest and most famous manufacturers of cigars.

'I retired about six years ago,' he said. 'And now Jennie and I spend a lot of time touring England, seeing places we've never been able to visit until now. Always too busy, you know, leading the hectic life of a businessman.'

'So what about the painting?' I was taking notes. 'What's your involvement with that?'

'It was done for an advertisement series,' he said. 'Winston was happy enough for us to use that picture in our adverts – restrictions weren't so rigid then, although he did ask for us to give the equivalent of his fee to a charity of his choice. So we had the oil painting executed by Christopher Tawney; several prints were run off it and you might have seen copies of them on cigar-box lids, adverts in the papers and magazines and so on.'

'Yes,' I admitted. 'I thought I'd seen that picture before. To be honest, Mr Cornell, I didn't pay a great deal of close attention to it . . .'

'Exactly, because there are so many copies still around, a lot of them hanging in pubs, by the way, like this one. They're the same size too. But the one in the Moon and Compass is the original. I can vouch for that.'

I took a long handwritten statement from him which confirmed what he had told me, and then noted his address and telephone number for future use.

I did extract from him that he was not acting in any official capacity on behalf of the company for whom he had worked; he was merely drawing police attention to a theft which had occurred many years ago. He did inform me that, so far as he could recall, the picture had been hanging in the boardroom and it had been painted soon after Churchill had won the Nobel Prize for Literature in 1953. Some time around 1956, it had disappeared.

'Company records will give the exact date of its disappearance,' Mr Cornell informed me. 'But that's roughly the sequence of events.'

'So it might have been here at least ten years?' I said. 'And I do know the present landlord has been here only four years. He bought the picture with the inn, by the way; he told me that when I was admiring it some time ago. He did not bring it with him – it was part of the fittings.'

'So who does it belong to now, eh?' smiled Cornell.

'I think that's a matter between the company and the landlord of the Moon and Compass,' I said. 'But clearly, you'd be interested in tracing the thief?'

'I think that would be impossible now,' he said. 'But perhaps you will contact the company and inform them of my discovery, and perhaps warn Mr Grayson, your landlord, of this conversation?'

'Yes, of course. And I'll let you know what progress I make.'

And so Mr Cornell left me with this problem.

As he drove away, his wife chirping with delight at her warm reception by our little brood of four children and I was left with the thought that David Grayson had no idea he was in possession of stolen property. I was equally aware that the matter could not be ignored, but knew that if I mentioned the affair to Sergeant Blaketon, he would charge into action like the proverbial bull in a china shop. His heavy-handed, rule-bound methods would wreak havoc every inch of the way as he had me arresting everyone in sight for theft or for receiving stolen property. It was my belief that this allegation, for it was nothing more than an allegation at this stage, required some rather delicate handling.

And so I waited for Sergeant Charlie Bairstow to come on duty. I felt he would adopt a more reasoned approach. It meant a delay of just one day, but I felt it was justified. I caught him during a quiet moment over an early-morning cup of coffee in the office at Ashfordly, and presented him with the story. He listened carefully and I showed him the statement made by Simon Cornell.

'A tale of villainy if ever there was one,' he smiled. 'What do you reckon?'

'About the truth of it, you mean?' I asked.

'Yes, is Cornell having us on, or is that picture the genuine thing as he says.'

'I believe him.' I spoke as I felt and, of course, I had witnessed Cornell's reaction as he had relayed his tale.

Sergeant Bairstow thought for a while and I knew he was weighing up all the problems that might accrue, both emotional and legal, and then he said, 'We'd better go and have a look at it. And we'd better warn Grayson of this.'

'He bought it legally,' I pointed out.

'Yes, and that gives him a claim to the painting,' he said. 'A claim of right made in good faith, as the Larceny Act so aptly puts it.'

And so we drove out to Craydale and popped into the Moon and Compass. David was working in his cellar when we arrived, stacking crates and cleaning out his beer pumps. He was happy enough to break for a coffee.

'Well, gentlemen.' He took us into the bar which was closed to the public as it was not opening hours. 'This looks business-like, two of you descending on me.'

'It is a problem,' Sergeant Bairstow said. 'Nick, you'd better explain.'

I told him of Cornell's visit and allegations, and he listened carefully, a worried frown crossing his pleasant face as I outlined the theft of the picture from the cigar company. We closely examined the painting and it was clearly executed in oils and signed, and on the back was a certificate of authenticity. It was the genuine thing; of that, there was no doubt. David kept looking at the image of Sir Winston and was clearly upset at our unpleasant news.

'So what do I do now?' he asked us both, looking most anxious and apprehensive.

'Nothing,' said Charlie Bairstow. 'Just sit tight; there's no suggestion that you stole it, we want you to know that. Our next job is to contact the cigar firm and tell them the picture has been found. But you do have a claim to it, David, because you bought it in good faith, as part of the fittings of the pub.'

'When did you say it was stolen?' he asked.

'1956, as near as we can tell,' I said.

'That was two landlords ago,' he added. 'I took it over from Jim Bentley, and he came here in 1959. I'm not sure who was here in 1956.'

'Our liquor licensing records will tell us,' said Bairstow. 'We'll chase up that angle.'

'But I don't want that bloody picture hanging here if it's worth a fortune!' he cried. 'Somebody might pinch it!'

'It's been there years without that happening,' Bairstow said. 'Anyway, I'd say it's yours now, David, but you might need a solicitor to do battle for you, from the ownership point of view, especially if the cigar people decide they want it back and make a claim upon it.'

'I think I'll hide it upstairs,' he smiled grimly. 'So what happens now?'

'Leave it with us,' said Charlie Bairstow. 'We will contact the cigar company and see what they say.'

'Thanks for telling me all this first,' David was clearly grateful for our action. 'So I might be sitting on a fortune after all this?'

'Cornell thought it was worth a lot of money,' I said. 'But he wouldn't commit himself to an amount. Don't forget that this is the original, David.'

'How can I? It's funny this has arisen,' he added. 'I've often said to Madge – my wife that is – that this looked like an oil painting and not a copy. I know some copies look so realistic now, even down to a rough surface, but well, this did have a genuine feel to it. I never thought of looking at the back for that certificate!'

'Well,' said Sergeant Bairstow. 'You hang on to it, and we'll see what happens next.'

'Thank you, Sergeant,' and we left him to his thoughts.

Back in the office, I compiled a report on the matter for despatch to the Chief Constable of Surrey Constabulary in whose area the cigar factory was based. In the terminology of the time, I asked him if he would allow an officer to search his records in an attempt to locate the report of the original theft, and then allow an officer to visit a senior official of the cigar company to inform him of the painting's present whereabouts. Sergeant Bairstow also asked me to include a paragraph to ask whether, in view of the passage of time, Surrey Constabulary required any further action by us in this matter.

The reply came ten days later. A detective sergeant in Guildford had established that the crime had been reported on 28th April 1956, the picture then being worth £850.

The original's disappearance had not been noticed for some time because one of the copies, in an identical frame, had been substituted. It had never been recovered, nor had the thief been arrested. Enquiries at the time had revealed that one of the suspects had been a salesman who had subsequently resigned from the company, but nothing had ever been proved against him. That man's name was not supplied, but Surrey Police did say the file had never been closed; they went on to add that it would be appreciated if steps could be taken to ascertain the name of the person who had sold the painting to the landlord of the Moon and Compass.

We did trace the long-retired landlord, an old character called Ralph Whalton who now lived with his married daughter in a bungalow at Eltering. He did not remember anything of the painting, but his daughter did. A plain girl approaching her thirties, she remembered its arrival.

'Oh, yes,' she said. 'You must remember, Dad!'

The old man shook his head. 'I'm too old now, Jill. They gave me all sorts of publicity stuff, I stuffed most of it in the cellar. I couldn't put it all up in the bar.'

'Well, I remember it well. I was about eighteen or nineteen at the time, and helping behind the bar. A salesman came in, not the regular one, with a box of those cigars you always bought. And he had that picture of Churchill. He said every pub was being given one and he hoped we would display it in a public area.'

'Was I there?' he asked, clearly puzzled.

'You might not have been,' she now realised. 'Maybe not, maybe that's why I was helping out. Mebbe you'd gone away somewhere. Anyway, we took a picture down, it was one of those pen-and-ink drawings of a Scottish mountain scene, and hung Sir Winston instead. He's been there ever since.'

She was unable to provide a description of the salesman and did not know his name. We passed this information to Guildford Police and it was about three weeks later when I received a telephone call to say that Guildford Police were closing this file because (a) the picture had been located and (b) their suspect salesman was now known to have died in 1962. Apparently, their records showed he was working in the North Riding for a short period during the spring of 1956. He was a very positive suspect.

So who did the picture now belong to? I knew that if someone was convicted of stealing it, the court could make an order for its restitution to the cigar company, but this was impossible in this case because several innocent buyers had since been involved and, apart from that, no one had been convicted of its theft. This latter fact alone ruled out this form of restitution through the criminal courts; now, of course, no one would ever be convicted for stealing it.

David Grayson, landlord of the Moon and Compass, now had a strong legal right to that picture, and I do know that he changed his mind about hiding it upstairs.

He was very proud of it, particularly as it had spawned so many copies throughout the country, and he told me that the cigar company had eventually offered him one of the many surplus copies in an identical frame, but he had refused. They desperately wanted the original to be returned for display in the company head office, but they did not offer him any money or compensation for it. After all, he had paid good money to acquire it quite legally and perhaps the company should have made some form of financial gesture.

Instead, following David's refusal, the company had made a half-hearted threat of attempting to recover the painting through the civil courts, but that was never proceeded with. I don't think it would have succeeded. So even now, if you go into the bar of the Moon and Compass at Craydale, you will see Sir Winston Churchill's image beaming over the customers. And no one knows how or why it came to be in this remote North Yorkshire pub.

One theory is that the salesman managed to steal it from his head office and that he mistakenly gave it away while delivering the advertisement copies. Or, of course, he might have become terrified at the thought of being captured with it in his possession, and decided to get rid of it in this way, hoping that no one in remote North Yorkshire would realise it was something special. But David Grayson did tell me that, when he decided to leave the pub, he would return the picture to the company for display in their boardroom above a little notice saying "Donated by Mr David Grayson."

I thought it was a nice gesture, a moral compromise and a means of ensuring the picture never again went astray.

While that episode caused more than a flicker of professional interest, there were countless mundane crimes and one of them, or to be more accurate, a series of them, involved the village store at Crampton. It was a typical village store, the kind of emporium found in every self-respecting small community. It dispensed almost everything from lawnmowers to tins of beans by way of socks, bread loaves, paperback novels, eggs and some of the finest cooked ham in the area. The high walls were filled with shelves of wines, exotic foods and sweets, tins of fruit, boxes of screws, nails and washers, dishcloths and kitchen utensils.

The owner was a small sprightly bachelor of indeterminate age. He was called Mr Wilson and had run his well stocked shop for as long as anyone could remember. No one seemed to know his Christian name because everyone called him Mr Wilson and no one knew much about his private life. A secretive but marvellously tidy little fellow, he seemed to be involved in no social or community activities, for his entire life was spent running his shop. It was his pride and joy, and if he could not supply any requested item from stock, he would always obtain it from somewhere. On one occasion, I asked if he knew where I could find a belt for our twin-tub spin-dryer, for the existing one had become worn and stretched until it would not properly turn the pulleys. Mr Wilson had one in stock.

His range of cheeses was remarkable, as were his liqueurs, chocolates, fresh fruit and beautiful vegetables, and I know one man who even bought a wheelbarrow wheel from Mr Wilson's stock – and it was the right size.

During the course of my duties, I learned that people respected Mr Wilson highly and relied upon him to cater for all their daily requirements. 'You'll get it at Mr Wilson's,' was the slogan, and so I was a frequent visitor, both on duty and off. He never complained, never seemed flustered or worried and was always in complete control of his stock and in touch with his customers' changing needs.

And then, one breezy day in May, he rang me and asked if I would pay him a visit, preferably between 1pm and 1.45pm when he would be closed for lunch. I was asked to go around the back, to his cottage door, because he wished to discuss a matter without interruption by his customers.

Intrigued by this, I drove across to Crampton and knocked on his cottage door. When he met me, he had a deep frown on his small, pink face and for the first time, to my knowledge, his immaculate head of pure white hair looked untidy. I detected worry in his eyes and there was no doubt he was more than a little agitated.

'Come in, Mr Rhea,' he invited. 'You'll have a coffee with me? Have you eaten?'

'Yes, thanks, I had lunch before I came out, but a coffee would be very welcome.'

He led me into his neat living-room; it was very plain and lacked the touch of a woman. There were no flowers, for example, and everything was in its place, untouched by children, visitors and family. There was not a speck of dust anywhere and his collection of brasses sparkled in the light of the bright spring weather. He indicated a plain leather easy chair and I settled in it as he busied himself with the coffee.

'You'll be wondering why I've called you in,' he said, sitting opposite me and crossing his legs. I was surprised at the tiny size of his shoes, so highly polished and well kept. I'd never seen his feet before, because he was always behind his counters. Now, without those protective barriers, he was like a little elf as his bright blue eyes scrutinised me.

'It must be important,' was my response to that remark.

'Yes, and confidential,' he said. 'Er, am I permitted to discuss something with you unofficially, off the record in a manner of speaking?'

'Of course, we are allowed discretion, you know. We do not enforce every rule by the letter – that would make it a police state!' I wondered what was coming next.

'I have a shop-lifter among my customers'. He drew in a deep breath and then spat out those words. 'A clever and persistent shop-lifter, Mr Rhea. I do not know what to do about her.'

This problem was the scourge of many city shops, and it was also affecting some rural ones which encouraged self-service by their customers. Mr Wilson's was such a shop, for the three counters which formed an open square as the customers entered each bore a selection of goods upon their tops. Sweets, cakes, delicacies, preserves, novels in paperback, spoons, fruit and so forth occupied space upon them.

'You know who it is?' I put to him.

He nodded. 'Yes, it's been going on for some time now, months perhaps, but I've been keeping a careful eye on things recently. I have made myself certain of the identity of the culprit, Mr Rhea.'

'You've confronted her about it?' I asked.

He shook his head this time. 'No, that is the problem, that is why I need your advice.'

'So what's she been doing?'

'General thieving, I think you'd call it,' he smiled a little ruefully. 'She is a good customer, Mr Rhea, a very good one. But I noticed that she began to linger in the shop when other customers were present, allowing me to serve them while she examined my stock. Then she would make her purchases, but I began to realise things had disappeared from my counter surfaces after each of her visits. She was picking things up while I was busy, you see, and hiding them in her shopping-bag.'

'Valuable things?' I asked.

'Not really, more like silly things. Apples, plastic teaspoons, tins of sticking-plasters, tubes of toothpaste, indigestion tablets, bars of chocolate or tubes of sweets, a bottle of wine on one occasion, biscuits, cakes . . . '

'If I am to prosecute her, I'll need to catch her in possession of the stolen goods,' I said. 'I cannot take a person to court without real evidence.'

'No, I don't want that,' he was quick to say. 'I don't want to prosecute her, that's the problem. I just want to stop her.'

'Confrontation would be advisable in the first instance,' I advised him. 'You'd have to catch her in possession of something that you could positively identify has having been stolen from your shop. Then threaten her with court action. That might stop her.'

He hesitated and then said, 'I did halt her on one occasion,' he said quietly. 'I had placed a bottle of French perfume on the front counter, where I knew she had been taking things from, and it disappeared when she was in my shop. As she was leaving, I said. "Miss Carr, the perfume, that will be £3 17s 6d please".'

Unwittingly, he had revealed the name of the shop-lifter but I did not comment on this just yet.

'And what did she do?' I asked.

'She looked at me full in the face and said, "Mr Wilson, I have no perfume, I never use that horrid French stuff".'

'And did you search her bags?'

'Oh, no, I couldn't do that,' he said. 'That would drive her away.'

'You want her driven away, surely?' I put to him.

'On the contrary, Mr Rhea, I do not. That is my dilemma.

You see, she is a very good customer. She spends heavily in here, buying all sorts and she always pays cash, except for the silly things she steals. She is not like some customers, Mr Rhea, who run up bills and need pressing to pay them. She pays cash for every honest purchase, so she's a very valuable customer in that sense.'

'You couldn't afford to lose her then?'

He shook his head. 'No, but there's more, you see. She is aunt to lots of people around here. She's one of a very large family, the Carrs, most of whom live around Crampton. Farmers, villagers, professional people – you'll know them as well as me. They're related to the Bennisons, the Tindales, the Haddons, the Newalls, the Lofthouses and others too. Many have accounts with me, Mr Rhea, they're all good spenders. She buys for them, as well; she's very generous you see, always buying things for her army of nephews and nieces, always giving them presents from here. Bottles of wine, expensive cheeses, perfume, tins of exotic fruit and so on. They're things she pays for, by the way.'

'Are you saying that if you banned her, they'd all stop coming as well?'

'It's a fear at the back of my mind,' he admitted. 'They are a very close family, Mr Rhea, and I know they'd never believe that their generous Aunt Mabel was a cunning thief.'

In some ways, it was the classic case of a nasty thief taking advantage of a kindly village storekeeper, and in real terms this was a case which well justified prosecution. I explained to Mr Wilson that we could secrete a camera inside the premises to catch her actually stealing an item, and then take her to court by using that film as evidence. Or we could mark certain objects with a fluorescent powder which would adhere to her hands and clothes, and which would glow under certain lights. By using technology, we could catch her in the act – all this presented no problems.

'No, I couldn't bear that,' he said. 'Not for such a good customer, Mr Rhea, and I must think of her reputation and that of all her relations. The publicity would be terrible in a community of this size.'

'So how can I help if you do not want official action?' I asked.

'I thought you might have knowledge of other methods of prevention, Mr. Rhea. I know shop-lifting is a problem, and I thought you might know of some way I could prevent her, for her own sake really, without resorting to court action.'

'I could have a word with her,' I offered. 'I could try to warn her off. Maybe a lecture from a policeman would help. I could frighten her off, maybe.'

'She might take umbrage, Mr Rhea, and boycott my store if she thought I'd been making accusations behind her back.'

'So we've reached an impasse,' I said. 'You will not confront her with your suspicions, and you will not allow me to confront her either. Really, Mr Wilson, if you do not want official police action, the remedy must come from you. You've got to decide either to let her continue, or to ban her from the shop, with all the possible consequences.'

'Oh, dear,' he said. 'I know that if I do ban her, the others will boycott me, and I could not afford that. There are some very good customers among her relations, Mr Rhea. It seems I must grin and bear it, then.'

'Sorry,' I said. 'I only wish I could be more helpful.'

'Well, I had to talk it over with someone impartial,' he said. 'I shall keep a closer eye on her, that's all.'

And so I left him to his worries. But later that afternoon, as I drove around my picturesque beat, I felt I'd let him down. Even though he did not wish me to take official action, I felt there could have been some advice or help I might have produced. But what?

How could I involve myself in this problem in an unofficial capacity? In some ways, Mr Wilson had placed me in a dilemma too and as I drove around, I passed Miss Carr's fine house. A magnificent detached stone-built house, it occupied a prime site about a mile out of Crampton and as I drove past, she drove out of her gate in her new Volvo.

Money for Miss Carr was no problem; a confident, fine-looking woman in her early fifties, she paid her way and was openly generous to her nephews and nieces and indeed to others who needed help. The village could tell of many acts of kindness by Mabel Carr. For these reasons, it seemed very odd that she was systematically stealing from this hard-working little shop-

keeper. My own instinct was to prosecute her for this unkind-
ness towards him, for I felt it was the only answer. I drove on,
and it would be about a week later at lunchtime when I was next
in Crampton. Mr Wilson's shop was closed so I decided to walk
around the village, then pop in to see him. And as I walked
among the pretty cottages and flowering meadows, I had an
idea.

'Ah, Mr Rhea,' he beamed. 'Good of you to call.'

'Good afternoon, Mr Wilson,' I smiled. 'How's things?'

'Very well, thank you,' he said. The shop was empty, so we
chatted about the weather for a while, and engaged in our usual
small talk, and then I asked about Miss Carr.

'Is she still stealing?' I asked.

'I'm afraid so,' he said. 'As bold as brass, really. She got away
with a small liqueur on Monday, slipped it into her shopping-
bag as quick as lightning. I think she's getting bolder, Mr Rhea.
I do wish I could find a way of halting her.'

'I think I have an answer,' I said. 'Highly irregular, I'm
afraid, and very unofficial, but it might work.'

He smiled. 'I'll listen to anything.'

'First, I must ask this, you're not making it easy for her to
take things, are you? Putting temptation in her way? Placing
things where she can't resist them?'

He shook his head. 'No, the stuff she takes is my normal
stock which is regularly on the counters for sale. I've always
displayed it there, Mr Rhea; in fact, I've been trying to make
things a little more difficult for her by putting out larger items,
like the bottles of liqueur. But after she'd been in, one was
missing. She was too quick for me, Mr Rhea; it had gone in a
twinkling and she was out of the shop before I realised what
she'd done. That's how she operates; I have kept an eye on her
and she knows it, but she's too quick and clever, a real expert. I
can't clear my counters because of her; besides, that kind of
open sales technique is a valuable source of income.'

I knew that his neat and tidy mind would instinctively
realise when something had been taken; he'd know if a solitary
tomato or roll of mints was stolen from his stock, so organised
was his mind and his business.

'I had to ask,' I said, 'because it's the sort of question that you might get asked by her relations if you implement my little scheme.'

'Short of banning her, Mr Rhea, I've done everything to make it harder for her to steal. So what is your plan?'

'Her relations, nephews, nieces, cousins and so on, how many of them are your customers?'

'Most of them who live hereabouts,' he said, opening a drawer behind the counter. 'I'll check for you.'

He lifted out several small red notebooks, each with a customer's name on the front, and sorted through them. He put several to one side, and then counted them.

'Seven,' he said. 'Seven have monthly accounts with me, these are their books.'

'And are there others without accounts?' I asked.

'Just one,' he said. 'Mrs Ruth Newall, Mabel's elder sister. She pays cash for everything. Why do you ask?'

I side-stepped that question for the moment by asking, 'And are they fond of their Aunt or Cousin Mabel? They'd not want her to get into trouble with us, the police?'

'Oh, they love her, Mr Rhea, they're a lovely family, so close.'

'Good, so this is what I suggest. I suggest that every time Miss Carr steals something, you add its cost to one of those relations' accounts. In other words, you make the family pay for her sins through a form of communal responsibility.'

'They'd know they hadn't bought the goods in question, Mr Rhea, and query it. It's almost dishonest . . . '

'But that's the idea, Mr Wilson, to encourage them to query their account. Then you tell them why, you tell them it's for a bottle of liqueur that Miss Mabel, er, took, without paying. You tell them quite clearly what she's doing, Mr Wilson.'

'I think they'd be very upset.'

'Yes, but that's where you score because you say that she's been stealing for many months, that you've done all in your power to stop her, and short of taking her to the magistrates' court, this is your only redress. I'm sure they'll appreciate your actions in not prosecuting her – after all, she is giving them presents and money . . . besides, that bottle of liqueur, for example, might well be sitting on one of their own shelves right now . . . '

'Yes, I suspect it is, Mr Rhea.'

'The idea is that the responsibility is placed upon her family; it lifts the burden from you and it means you are not losing money or sleep because of her actions.'

'I'll think about it,' was all he said.

It was several weeks later when he called me into his cottage behind the shop.

'Mr Rhea,' he said over a coffee. 'That system you suggested for Mabel Carr. I thought I'd let you know that it is working very well.'

'Is it? Then I'm delighted!'

'I must admit I was uncertain at first, and indeed I ignored it, but then she got away with a full bottle of brandy. I put it on Mrs George Haddon's bill – George is a nephew, and I explained why. It seems Mabel had given him the bottle anyway! But he called a family conference and they invited me up to the Haddons' house to explain things to the whole family, without Mabel's knowledge, of course.'

'That's an excellent move, so they took it well?'

'Yes, very well, they were sorry that she had placed me in such a position, but they fully understood. And they agreed to my actions. They were pleased I had told them.'

'And they will be trying to persuade her to stop shop-lifting?' I smiled.

'Er, no,' he said. 'They do not want to upset her, so we will all allow her to continue, and they will pay for everything she steals. They feel it is a symptom of her time of life, you see, and that she will overcome it eventually. So they're keeping my actions secret from her.'

'And does this please you, Mr Wilson?' I asked.

'Yes, it does, Mr Rhea, and thank you.'

In the days that followed, I wondered whether the actions of Mabel Carr now amounted to the crime of theft and felt this could produce a marvellous challenge for a defence lawyer if such a conspiracy ever reached court. But it never did. Mabel's huge complement of relations continued to pay for her indiscretions and I heard no more about it.

Years later, though, I did learn by sheer chance from one of her sisters that, throughout her youthful and indeed middle-aged years, Mabel Carr had conducted a very one-sided love affair with Mr Wilson. And not once had he shown the slightest romantic interest in her – I don't think he ever knew of, or suspected, her yearnings and devotion.

Maybe her shop-lifting was a last desperate attempt to attract his attention?

5

'Where is the man who has the power and skill
To stem the torrent of a woman's will?'

Anonymous

It was Shakespeare who said that a railing wife was worse than a smoky house, and Thomas Moore who wrote in his 'Sovereign Woman' that "Disguise our bondage as we will, 'Tis woman, woman, who rules us still." Those poets, and the anonymous gentleman who wrote the opening lines at the head of this chapter, must have had some personal knowledge of the awful effect that a nagging wife can have upon the happiness and peace of mind of a husband.

Down the ages, and in spite of modern scientific progress, it has been impossible to stop some women from nagging. One terrible attempt was made by the introduction of the brank; this was an iron framework which was placed upon a woman's head and padlocked in position. At the front, it had a plate from which protruded a spiked or sharp edge, and this fitted into the mouth of the woman. If she moved her tongue, therefore, she injured herself; if she kept quiet, she was not hurt.

With this upon her head, the scold, as she was called, was paraded through the streets by one of the community officials. This object, known variously as the brank or scold's bridle, was thought to have been first used in 1623 in Macclesfield, although there are hints that is was used in Scotland as early as 1574. In 1600, it is thought, the brank was used in Stirling to punish 'the shrew.'

Around the country, some branks are preserved in our

museums, and a famous one is linked to the church at Walton-on-Thames. It was presented to the parish in 1632 by a man called Chester because he had lost one of his estates through the actions of a lying and gossiping woman. Mr Chester presented the brank with this accompanying verse:

'Chester presents Walton with a bridle
To curb women's tongues that talk too idle.'

It is difficult to ascertain when the brank was last used, although there is an account of one in the early part of last century. At Altrincham, a woman who caused great distress to her neighbours by her ceaseless and malicious gossip was punished by being paraded around the town wearing a brank. But she refused to walk with it on and would not agree to this punishment. As a result she was then placed in a wheelbarrow and wheeled around the principal streets and market place. History assures us that this had the desired effect of curbing her tongue.

Another device for dealing with scolds was the ducking-stool; this varied in detailed construction but was based on something akin to a long plank, rather like a see-saw, which had a chair or seat at one end. It was positioned with the chair over a pond or river, and so the scolding woman, after being tied into the chair, was lowered repeatedly into the water to cool her tongue. This punishment usually attracted a crowd of local folks who came along for the so-called fun.

One account dated 1700, written by a Frenchman upon a visit to England, says, 'The way of punishing scolding women is pleasant enough,' and he then describes the ducking-stool, after which he adds, 'They plunge her into the water as often as the sentence directs, in order to cool her immoderate heat.'

Like the brank, the ducking-stool's last known use occurred in the early years of last century, probably in 1809 at Leominster. The lady was called Jenny Pipes and the first thing she did upon release from the stool was to utter a string of foul oaths as she cursed the magistrates.

Of these two methods, contemporary reports said that the brank was better than the ducking-stool because 'the stool not only endangered the health of the party, it also gave her tongue liberty 'twixt every dip.'

The nagging woman has been a topic of writers, poets and comedians for years, and remains so. I like the story of a man who called his wife Peg, when her real name was Josephine. Someone asked him why he called her Peg and he said, 'Well, Peg is short for Pegasus; Pegasus was an immortal horse and an immortal horse is an everlasting nag.'

There is also a view that nature has given man the apparatus for snoring to compensate for the woman's capacity for nagging. She nags him during the day, so he retaliates by snoring at night, for which she nags him during the day . . . . and so a type of noisy if uneasy balance is achieved.

But not all naggers are married to snorers and not all snorers are married to naggers, which means that many innocent people suffer from vitriolic and poisonous tongues while others must tolerate nights of oscillating and very tuneless olfactory muscles.

One would hardly expect the village constable to become involved in marital battles of this kind, but in fact all police officers, whether rural or urban, do find themselves involved in what the police call 'domestics'. These are breaches of the peace which generally occur among families; if the battles remain behind closed doors, we are not too concerned, but when warring women spill into the street armed with frying-pans, rolling-pins and sharp tongues, then we are sometimes called in to quell what could otherwise develop into a breach of the peace in a public place. As a rule, we try to avoid these because the moment the peace-making constable arrives, the sparring partners both turn upon the unfortunate constable. But at least that stops the quarrelling and perhaps personifies the constable's unsung role in maintaining public tranquillity. He keeps the peace while being attacked from all sides.

It would not be possible in this book to list all the 'domestics' in which I became officially involved, but they did conform to this pattern and few terminated in court. They were usually settled by a stern talking-to or threats of having 'binding-over' orders levelled against the parties, for most were of a sudden and temporary nature.

But there were cases when nagging wives caused domestic upsets of a more permanent kind. One involved a man called

Joseph Pringle who had a wife called Roberta. They lived in a neat little bungalow in Aidensfield, just off the Elsinby Road, where it nestled cheerfully among trees with a fine view to the south. With no children, the Pringles were a quiet couple who rarely involved themselves in village matters. Mrs Pringle's socialising was done in York.

I first became aware of Joseph when I noticed his car halting outside the Brewers Arms at Aidensfield around seven each weekday evening. He always popped in for a swift half of bitter on his way home from work, and sometimes I came across him when I was on official business in the pub. If I had any confidential enquiries to make of any landlord, I would pop in before the customers filled the bars. And so I became acquainted with Joseph Pringle.

Aged about forty with a balding head of greying hair, he was one of those insignificant men who are hardly noticed among a crowd of three. Of average height and average build, he wore average clothes and drove an average car at an average sort of speed. He lived in an average house on an average income, but, as I was to learn later, he suffered from a higher-than-average amount of nagging. He had married a true virago, a real warrior of a woman who constantly and cruelly nattered him during his every moment at home. She never gave him a moment's peace; she nagged and nagged and nagged.

Roberta Pringle was a loud-mouthed, energetic and very forceful woman who played hell with everyone; good-looking in some ways, she was approaching forty and had a fine figure topped with an equally fine head of dark hair which framed a handsome, rather than pretty, face. Slightly taller than her husband, she was always very well dressed, but went about her daily routine playing hell with the postman, the dustman, the milkman, the paper-boys, the butcher, the grocer, the vicar, the policeman, her neighbours and anyone else with whom she had any dealings. And of course, when they were not available, she played hell with Joseph.

Because most of them learned, by experience, to keep out of her way, Joseph bore the heaviest burden. He was continuously told off because of the government, the rates, the parish council, the state of the nation, the cost of living, the sloppy work of builders, plumbers, electricians, motor mechanics, doctors, dentists and nurses; she played hell about the roads, snowploughs, weather forecasters, British Rail, bus timetables, canteen ladies, rubbish bins, cafe proprietors, village shops, the post office, tinned beans, the telephone system, television, women's fashions, men's trousers, hotel beds, the water supply, long grass, bruised apples, cold Yorkshire puddings and fatty ham.

And she never stopped complaining and nagging, which meant that her range of subject-matter was never exhausted. Indeed, it expanded, with the meek Joseph having his ears lambasted during all his precious moments at home.

As a result, of course, he started to come home later, a ploy which enabled him to avoid some of her vitriol and which was part of the reason he paid his nightly visit to the Brewers Arms. It gave him peace from both work and wife.

Joseph owned and ran his own gentlemen's outfitters in Eltering. It was a modest shop which sold fairly cheap clothes whose quality was not of the highest. He now faced competition from the major department stores in York and elsewhere for they stocked good clothes within the cheaper range, while those men with money patronised their own bespoke tailors. Joseph had no drive and ambition; he did not wish to become the owner of a chain of shops nor did he strive to change his own dwindling circumstances. He seemed content to let things drift down-wards, and I began to learn of his shrinking fortune in the course of my patrolling.

Some hint of his problems arose when I popped into his shop to buy some black socks. He was on the telephone, and was saying words like, 'Yes, dear. No dear. Yes, I will. No, I will not be late tonight. There isn't much in the till today. Yes, I know the car needs attention, the brakes, yes. I'll see what the garage says.'

When he saw me at the counter, he said, 'I have a customer, dear. See you tonight,' and he replaced the handset.

'Women!' he said, recognising me. 'All they think about is money and status! Well, Mr Rhea, what can I get you?'

'Two pairs of black socks please, Joseph,' I said.

He obtained them and I paid, then he said, 'There are times I wish I had your job, Mr Rhea. A regular salary, interesting life, varied work and the means of travelling around the district. I'm stuck in here, day in and day out, it does get a bit monotonous.'

'It's funny, you know,' I said. 'Lots of policemen say they'd like their own business.'

'It has some advantages, Mr Rhea, but times are not good for my trade. Multiple stores, cheaper mass-produced clothes, foreign imports – small shops are finding it hard, very hard to compete. I'd pack it in tomorrow if I could.'

'You surprise me,' I was honest when I said that.

He seemed anxious to talk so I did not rush away.

'Roberta likes to live well, to dress well, to socialise and have a nice home. I can't give her all she wants, Mr Rhea, it does worry me.'

'Could you sell up and try another business?'

'I would have trouble selling this shop, I feel. But you don't need burdening with my worries! Thanks for listening, I needed someone to say that to. Not that you can help, but at least you did listen.'

'I'll listen whenever you want, Joseph.' I tried to show a little understanding. 'Maybe I will come across someone who wants a shop just like yours. As you say, I am out and about a lot.'

'Thanks, I'll buy you a half next time you're in the Brewers Arms,' he offered with a sad smile.

Further hints of Joseph Pringle's problems came to me over the next few months. A businessman friend from York, for example, asked if I knew the Pringles of Aidensfield; my friend's wife was a member of a York Ladies Luncheon Club where Roberta Pringle was also a member. It seemed she had told her fellow members that Joseph ran a men's clothing manufacturing business with outlets all over the country. In fact, there was an internationally known manufacturer of men's high-quality clothing at Eltering, but it was not Joseph's business. Roberta's skilful story-telling had led her friends to believe he was a very successful businessman and that those premises were his. I began to see that Roberta was living a life of fiction, a life of fantasy, a life of dangerous expense for poor old Joseph.

It explained why she socialised away from home, why she kept away from those who knew her well, why she dressed so expensively, why she was always nagging at the tired Joseph to improve his status and income. And, as eventually I learned, she was spending all his cash.

I met him on a walk one Sunday morning and he wanted to talk again. 'You've not found anyone who might want my shop, Mr Rhea?' was his opening gambit.

'Sorry, Joseph.' I had asked around, and had in fact come across a retiring police sergeant who was thinking of starting a shop in Eltering. Not a clothes shop, however, although he did express interest in the premises. But he never went ahead.

I promised Joseph I'd keep my ears and eyes open on his behalf.

'I'm getting to the point where I can't pay my bills,' he said. 'I can't get credit to buy my stock . . . '

'How about a sale?' I suggested. 'Why not sell off some older stock?'

'I have,' he said. 'It's Roberta, you see, she is a partner and she never stops buying clothes for herself. She does need them, you see, for her luncheon clubs and theatre outings and so on, and it's not fair if I stop the only enjoyment she has in life. She has to be smart, she's mixing with the right people, you see . . . '

It's all right telling a man to be firm with a wife who is ruining him, but it's a different thing persuading that same man to take positive action. I never knew why Joseph did not take a firmer stance for I'd heard that she demanded a new outfit every month so that she could keep up her social appearances . . . poor old Joseph. Much of his dilemma was due to his own fault and his weakness with his awful wife, but I could only commiserate with him. Tentatively, I asked whether Roberta might help in the shop, perhaps by selling other lines, baby clothes, for example, or ladies' wear.

'Oh, no, she wouldn't do that, Mr Rhea, not Roberta. She doesn't believe in women having to work.'

'But if it's to save your business, your livelihood . . . '

He shook his head. 'She won't, I've tried that idea. In fact, I think a general clothes shop would go well, but I'd need finance to establish it, and I'd need staff to run it, but can't afford either.'

Surely Roberta would have worked with him, for no wages, to establish a thriving business and to enable her to continue her desired way of life? But she would not. He was adamant about that. After this chat, there was no doubt in my mind where his problem lay. Over the weeks that followed, I saw him spending longer and longer in the Brewers Arms, not getting drunk because he wasn't that kind of man. He just wanted relief from her nagging, but then she started ringing the pub. She began nagging at George, the landlord, demanding that he send Joseph home, and when Joseph got home, he was faced with more nagging.

Roberta continued to nag George day in and day out until, whenever poor Joseph went in for a quick half, George would say, 'Come on, Joseph, don't spend all night here, I don't want that wife of yours hogging my telephone and nagging me. Folks come here to get away from nagging.'

Poor old Joseph. There was no escape.

As for Roberta, she continued to strut around the village in her finery, holding her head high and nagging at everyone she met until the end came. Joseph went bankrupt. It was all done quietly with very little noise from Roberta, but his ailing shop closed, and they sold their bungalow. But this did not stop Roberta.

I was to learn that they had moved into York where, according to Roberta, Joseph had become a director of one of the city's department stores but where, in fact, he was an assistant on the men's shirt counter.

And she continued to attend her important social functions in the finest of clothes. Looking back, she would have been a fine candidate for the brank or the ducking-stool. and I'm sure plenty of volunteers could have been found to administer that punishment.

Since then, I've always felt sorry for the Josephs of this world, but really, who was to blame?

Another case of a nagging wife had a very different outcome.

Benjamin Owens was a hill farmer in a fairly small way and his untidy clutch of ramshackle buildings occupied a remote hillside in Rannackdale. Always in need of painting, glazing, tidying-up and general maintenance, his mediocre spread barely earned him a living. He managed to scrape together a few pounds every week by selling milk from his small herd of cows, and by selling eggs, poultry, sheep for mutton and some wool when he sheared his little flock of moorland sheep. A tiny patch of land was cultivated and he would sometimes sell turnips, potatoes or cabbages to the local shops. He earned just enough for subsistence; he never bought clothes nor went out socially, except once a month to Eltering Market to sell his stock and to buy more.

Even then, he went in his scruffy old clothes which he'd worn every day for about fifteen years.

Benjamin, who was about sixty-two years old, had farmed at Helm End, Rannackdale, all his life; his parents had run the tiny farm before him and his grandfather before that, so there was no mortgage to worry about. The farm had been handed down from father to son for generations, but Benjamin had no heirs. His massive wife, Kate, who was perhaps a couple of years younger, had never produced a litter, as he once said.

The income from such a small hillside small-holding did not allow luxuries or extras; Benjamin ran a battered old pick-up, an even more battered old tractor and his untidy wife never worried about dusting the house, washing their clothes regularly or doing any form of extra housework. She did the essentials like baking, cooking their meals and some shopping, but little more.

As I got to know them better, I realised they never went anywhere together. Benjamin's only outing was to Eltering Cattle Mart once a month. The rest of his time was spent at home. Kate, however, did go out once a week. Dressed in her long, scruffy overcoat and black wellington boots, she caught the bus to Eltering every Friday to do her shopping and seemed to enjoy these trips. She also went to the WI meetings once a month and on special occasions, such as the Anniversary, would visit the chapel high in the dale.

In those early days, I wondered whether they shared a bed,

97

for they seemed to live separate lives, seldom speaking to one another but never fighting. Each got on with his or her own work as they had done for years, and they ate together, their main meal, a hot dinner, being at 12 noon prompt. It was a mutual understanding, a convenient arrangement and neither seemed to mind this form of life.

I saw them once a month when I went to inspect their stock registers, and Kate always produced a mug of hot tea for me, along with a plate of fine home-made scones or rock buns. Benjamin would join us at the kitchen table, we'd discuss business and local matters, and then I'd leave.

I must be honest and say that I never noticed any discord between them but, on reflection, never noticed any warmth in their relationship. They seemed to exist side by side, to live beneath the same roof without any overt problems, but without the love or understanding that one finds in most families.

But, as I grew to know them better, and as I gained the confidence of other local farmers, especially those in Rannack-dale, I learned more of the Owens' way of life.

'Never slept in t'same bed ever,' one stalwart informed me. 'She's never let him near 'er; poor awd Benjamin's nivver covered that missus of 'is, nivver. He was a bit of a stallion as a lad, but she's kept him short. It's a bit late now, mind, cos t'farm'll etti be sold up when they're called up ti yon small-holding in the sky.'

As I was realising I'd never heard of a child of their union, he continued.

'Ah doubt she'll produce a lad noo. She's ovver awd for that sort o' caper; if she was a coo, they'd have her put doon. She's neither use nor ornament, if you ask me.'

He was right, because Kate was far from pretty. In fact, she was downright ugly, a large, loose and untidy woman with hairs on her upper lip and a floppy body which seemed to spill at random out of her ill-fitting clothes. Her iron-grey hair was pulled tightly back into a bun behind her head and she had awful teeth, many of which were rotten or missing. I could fully understand why Benjamin had never 'covered her' as his colleague so aptly put it.

But Benjamin wasn't much of a catch either. A wiry fellow

with freckles all over his balding head of thin gingery-grey hair, he looked more like a retired jockey than a farmer. Bandy-legged, thin as a lath and often unshaven, he was not the kind of man who would appeal to a woman.

I was to learn also that Kate nagged him. She nagged him about getting more work done about the farm. The poor little fellow seemed to work every hour except those trips to mart, but Kate demanded more. On one occasion when I called, I could hear her lashing him with her tongue.

'If thoo didn't spend si much time messing aboot wi' these coos, you'd have more time ti spend on yon field, growing crops, selling tonnups, cabbages and t'like.'

'Coos need care,' he countered. 'We need coos for t'milk cheque . . . '

'That's a woman's job, our Benjamin. Coos is for milkmaids, not fellers.'

'Then you do it.'

'Nay, Ah've enough on what wi' t' hens and t'house.'

From what I gathered in my rounds, she did nag at him, her chief antic being that whatever he was doing at any particular time, she thought he should be doing something else. If he worked on his sheep, she thought he should be working on the cows; if he was with the cows, he should be in the fields, and if he was in the fields, he ought to be tending his sheep. If he settled down for a rest at night, he ought to be fixing the tractor, and if he was fixing the tractor, he should be tidying the garage.

I understand that poor old Benjamin had tolerated this for years. Her constant irritation had led him never to argue or talk with her, except when it was essential during moments like 'Pass t'tea pot, will yer?' or 'Get us a roll o' binder twine if you're in Atkinson's.'

Then I had a spell doing pig-licence duty at Eltering Cattle Mart and noticed Benjamin with his cronies. He was in a group of farmers of his own age, and was clearly enjoying himself. He noticed me and came across for a word.

'They've let you away from t'missus an' all, have they?' he said, grinning from ear to ear.

'Now, Benjamin,' I greeted him. 'Good to see you out and about, getting away from that busy spot of yours. And, yes, they have let me loose for today!'

'That's what cattle marts are for, Mr Rhea, to get us fellers away from them wimmin folk. Ah mean to say, we could sell cattle in other ways, but, by gum, it's a grand way of having a day out.'

'You've left your missis at home then?' I knew he always came without Kate, but used the phrase to make conversation with him.

'Aye, she's better off there. Couldn't fetch her here, tha knaws. If she saw me standing here, she'd say Ah should be standing ovver there, and if Ah was looking at them Red Polls, she'd say Ah should be thinking of Jerseys and if Ah took her into t'Black Swan for a beef sandwich, she'd want to go to t'Golden Lion for a ham sandwich. As things are, Ah can do as Ah like; Ah allus does, mind, cos I don't let that nagging get to me. It just maks her go on a bit more, but doon here, wiv me mates, I can have a day off nagging.'

'Enjoy it,' I smiled.

'Don't you worry, Mr Rhea, Ah shall.'

I could appreciate his genuine need to get away from the farm, and then, as I performed more of those market duties, I noticed that Benjamin's group of market friends included a tall and very attractive blonde girl. She would be about twenty-five years old at the most, and I noticed he spent a good deal of time talking to her.

So fascinating was her style and beauty that most of them were taking a keen interest in her, and I noticed that she attended every mart. My own curiosity was such that I wanted to find out more about her, and the opportunity came through Benjamin himself. He came to my little wooden shed at the mart for a pig-movement licence, saying he thought he'd try a few store pigs for fattening in the hope that the bacon factory would eventually buy them from him.

'Who's your friend, Benjamin?' I asked him, nodding towards the direction of the tall blonde.

He blushed just a fraction when he realised I was speaking particularly of her, then said, 'Oh, yon's awd Harry Clemmitt's lass. Rachel. Fine lass, that. She does all his buying and selling at mart; knows her beasts, she does. Ah gets all my stock from her, Mr Rhea. Knows his breeding stock does Harry Clemmitt, and she does, an' all. You can rely on Harry Clemmitt for good breeding stock.'

'She's taken a shine to you!' I laughed, for she seemed to be very happy in Benjamin's company, even if their ages and appearances were poles apart.

'Ah used to be a good 'un at chatting up the wimmin, Mr Rhea,' he chuckled. 'Ah reckon Ah've lost nowt o' me touch!'

'I can see that!' I said, and he walked off, beaming with pride at his achievement with the girl. But I was not to realise, until some time later, that Benjamin and the girl were considerably more than just good friends. For one thing, they met here regularly and he took her to lunch.

The full realisation came to me about six weeks later when I called at Helm End Farm to make my routine check of the Owens' stock registers. I went into the untidy kitchen for my customary mug of tea and buttered scone, and was welcomed by Kate. As she fussed over me, the door opened and in walked Benjamin, followed by the tall blonde girl.

'Morning, Mr Rhea,' he beamed. 'Good to see you.'

'Hello, Benjamin.' I couldn't take my eyes off the girl; even when dressed in her rough working-jeans and old smock, she was gorgeous. Her erect bearing, long blonde hair, smooth skin and lovely features were so out of place here. I could even visualise her on the catwalk of a fashion show, such was her elegance and stylishly slender build.

'This is Rachel,' he introduced her. 'My new milkmaid.'

'Milkmaid?' I said, puzzled.

'Aye, Kate said coos were wimmin's work, and cos she wouldn't take 'em on, Ah thought Ah'd better get a milkmaid. Rachel here knows about coos and got a bit sick o' working on her dad's farm, so I've takken her on. She sleeps in, Mr Rhea, so she's part of t'family now.'

'Hello, Rachel,' I said to the milkmaid.

'Hello, Mr Rhea,' she said, moving sensually across to the cupboard for a jug of milk for our tea.

It was impossible to guess what was going through Kate's

mind at this time, but I think she felt this stunning girl would never be interested in her thin, scruffy and ageing husband. But Kate was wrong.

One night, she came back early from a WI meeting because the speaker had failed to turn up for his engagement, and poor Kate caught Benjamin and the girl together in bed. The outcome was not one of the famous 'domestics' we were so accustomed to on council estates, but merely a rapid and discreet exit by Kate. She simply packed her bags and left that same night, without a fight and without an argument. She stayed that night with a friend, and told her, 'I would never let him touch me, the filthy old brute, so she can't be very choosy! I'll not live in the same house as a hussy like that and he's welcome to her!'

Even now, I do not know what happened to Kate, for no one saw her again. So far as I know, she never returned to the district and I never heard of any divorce. But Rachel Clemmitt continued to live with Benjamin at the remote farm, and during my monthly calls, I noticed the transformation to the premises, and to Benjamin himself. The entire place was smartened up, the house was cleaned from top to bottom, new licks of paint were added, the farmyard was tidied up and the whole enterprise appeared to be buzzing with new life. Rachel had transformed the farm.

She had transformed Benjamin too. Uncharacteristically, he appeared in the pub one night with Rachel, and he sported a smart new jacket and trousers; his face was bright and alert and he behaved like a prosperous farmer, and a happy one. I was later to learn that he was prosperous; in spite of outward appearances, Benjamin had made lots of money.

Another benefit of his life with Rachel was that he looked and behaved as if he were ten years younger, and in time, Rachel started to call herself Mrs Owens. She looked very happy too and it wasn't long before she was pregnant. At this news, Benjamin strutted around like a proud bantam cock, as pleased as any man could be, and in due course, a son was born.

I called about a month afterwards and saw the baby in his smart new pram. Rachel was fussing over her son, whom she called Patrick, and Benjamin insisted on lifting him out for me to examine.

'Marvellous,' I congratulated them both. 'How marvellous for you both. You must be very proud!'

'Ah allus said t'Clemmitts had good breeding stock, Mr Rhea, and Ah was right. There'll be a new line of Owens to continue this farm now. Ah did it just in time.'

I smiled and said, 'So you did, Benjamin.'

'Ah was a bit oot o' practice, mind, but wiv a bit o' training, Ah soon got caught up again. Like a lad Ah was, in full strength. And see that, a fine lad, as bonny as you could wish to see anywhere. And he's mine, all mine.'

'And mine,' said Rachel gently.

I was pleased for Benjamin, but even now I cannot understand why such a lovely young woman had given herself entirely to this curious old character. She'd seen him as a poverty-stricken, unkempt old hill farmer during his visits to the mart and she knew his background and his age.

In spite of all that, she had fallen in love with him and had then transformed his life. Albeit at the unfortunate Kate's expense, it was something of a miracle and it only served to make me more curious about the way a woman's mind operates. That is something I have not yet discovered! But Benjamin became a local legend because of this romance; his prowess as a lover was the talking-point of the market and of the surrounding villages, and none of the eligible young men of the area could understand why they had lost to this ageing Lothario from Rannackdale. Nor could anyone else.

As one envious old farmer said to me. 'He got shot o' that nagging awd bitch of a wife and won hisself yon fit-looking lass who looks good enough for a duke and fit enough for a young buck of a lad. And he did it all without missing one hot dinner.'

Another character with a chattering wife was Horace Pitman who ran a small garage and taxi-service in Waindale. His was an old-fashioned garage which had been operating since the first cars came to these dales. Stocked with spare parts in neatly marked and carefully arranged boxes, and with a pair of tall green petrol pumps outside, Horace's garage was always busy. He worked from seven each morning until ten each night, except when he was on rural or county council business. On those occasions, he would take a day off and hire a driver/pump attendant should anyone require a taxi or some petrol.

I seldom saw Horace dressed in anything but a pair of navy blue overalls heavy with grease and equally greasy black boots. He did all the mechanical work himself and somehow coped with everything that came his way.

Horace was a big man. In his late forties, he must have weighed at least sixteen stone and had a jolly, calm face which never seemed troubled by anything or anyone. Balding on top, and with a monk's hair-style of sandy hair, he wore rimless glasses and, oddly enough, always sported a crisp white shirt and coloured tie beneath his overalls. I think that was in case he got a sudden taxi job – he could throw off his overalls and put on a blazer type of jacket he kept hanging in his garage.

Everyone liked Horace, which is probably why he found himself elected to the rural district council, and then to the county council. With so little spare time, he did manage to accommodate his council duties, and often went to meetings at Northallerton in his white shirt and working clothes. These comprised a pair of dark crumpled trousers, that blazer-like jacket which he kept in the garage, and his greasy black boots. One snag with his trade was that his hands were never clean; black oil had engrained itself into the skin of his hands and his fingernails were always black. Scrub as he might, he could never get his hands clean. Those who knew him paid no attention to his mode of dress or dirty hands, but I often wonder what the other councillors thought.

But Horace was a good man, a fine councillor and a very able person in every respect; perhaps in other circumstances, he would have become a top-flight businessman or even a politician. But he was utterly content with his busy village life – he loved cars and he liked being a councillor, and his way of life gave him the best of both his chosen worlds.

His wife, Dora, was an ideal companion for him. A tiny, virile woman in her early forties, she was a bundle of energy who had a family of three fine teenage children and who busied herself with the Red Cross, Women's Institute, night classes and various other charities. She was secretary to countless village organisations, including the parish council and parochial church council, and she also did the office work and accounts for Horace's garage.

And she was a non-stop chatterer, unlike Horace who was a man of very few words. What he did say usually made sense, but she could not stop talking, and the village knew that if she cornered anyone for a two-minute chat, it would continue for half an hour if her time was short, and for well over an hour if things were progressing in a more leisurely manner. Horace, however, allowed her flow of constant chatter to drift away to oblivion over his head and he had that happy knack of saying 'Yes, dear,' at frequent intervals while never listening to a word she said. For Horace, Dora's voice was nothing more than background noise, there to be ignored where possible.

He did respond when she called 'Coffee's ready,' or 'Dinner' or 'Tea's up,' usually by simply arriving at the table or desk where she placed his morning cuppa. Even in council meetings, he said very little, consequently when he did say something, everyone listened. With his wife, however, no one listened, least of all Horace.

For all her chattering, she was a lovely woman and he was a fine man; they were a popular and hard-working pair of people who deserved the best. If anything, Dora was perhaps a little more ambitious than Horace although not in the same league as Mrs Pringle. Dora loved and respected her husband and felt that his work for the council, both at local rural level and at county level, deserved some recognition.

But Horace was not interested; he went along to the meetings, said his brief piece and came home to his garage. And that, in his mind, was that. He rarely told Dora what had transpired and if she asked what had happened, he would usually say, 'Nowt much.'

I caught a hint of Dora's ambitions one day when I was in his garage. I was asking about stolen cars, and had provided him with a list of their registration numbers in case any were brought in for petrol; he would ring me or our divisional headquarters if he spotted one. As we chatted, Dora came in with his coffee and invited me to have one. I agreed, and she joined us, chattering non-stop.

'I mean,' she said, 'they never say thank you, not one of them out of the whole village and they expect Horace to trek over to Northallerton month in and month out to say his piece for them and to fight their fights about rates, drainage, the water works and sewage and I mean, he does do well for the village, don't you think, Mr Rhea? More than some I know, more than some who make much more of a fuss about it and you'd think they would make a bit of a fuss about a man who works so hard for other folks and who's got a business, two businesses in fact, taxi and garage, to run as well. It's not as if he's retired or on a private income, you see . . . '

I wanted to say that councillors did not work for thanks but she would not let me get a word in.

'Dora . . . ' I began.

'Well, you would think they'd do something for people like my Horace, Mr Rhea . . . '

And so she went on, so I drank my coffee while Horace rubbed at a piece of car engine with some emery paper.

She rabbited on for a long time and I found myself becoming like Horace. Everything she said drifted over my head and once I caught sight of Horace, smiling to himself. This was a regular event for him.

I could see that his wife had some social ambitions for Horace even if he did not have any for himself, and it would be about a month later when I next came across the voluble Dora. I was on duty in Waindale when she was shopping and she spotted me; before I could leap into the mini-van to avoid a marathon session of her brand of verbal diarrhoea, she had presented herself before me.

'Ah,' she began a little breathlessly. 'Just the man who might help me. Mr Rhea, I know you are familiar with the county council and how they operate because our Horace never tells me a thing because he just goes along to those meetings and says nothing, then comes home and says nothing has happened until I read in the paper that they're building new schools here, police stations there, libraries and fire stations, new roads and putting the rates up and he would know all that and yet he never says a thing to me about it. You'd think he would, wouldn't you, I mean I am his wife but the reason I've stopped you, and I won't keep you because you must be a very busy man with lots of enquiries to make and jobs to do apart from talking to women like me, is that I thought you might know something about the Buckingham Palace thing. I met this lady at WI whose cousin is a councillor from Malton just like my Horace and he's been on years, she says, sitting on the Finance Committee and the Highways Committee and really getting involved . . . '

'The Buckingham Palace thing?' I was baffled and managed to register my curiosity as she turned to smile at a friend.

'Yes, you know,' she said. 'You must know, being a policeman, but that lady didn't know much about it because her husband had never gone on it and I wondered if you know what it was, Mr Rhea, and whether I, well, Horace really, could go along as well, I mean, it would be nice, wouldn't it? It would be a sort of thank-you for Horace for all he's done and I could wear a new hat and lovely coat and meet the Queen and all those important people. I've always wanted to go to a posh place like that, Mr Rhea, in one of those large hats with a wide brim, you know, the sort society ladies wear at races and operas and things like that . . . '

As she chattered on, I began to gain a glimmer of understanding.

'You mean the selection procedure for the Garden Parties?' I said during another momentary lull in her chatter.

'Yes, so you do know! How marvellous. What do I have to do, well Horace really, what does he have to do? I mean, does he write to the Queen or how does he get there? I mean, I'm sure Her Majesty has never heard of my Horace even though he does do an awful lot of good work for the council and the village but he's so quiet about it and never makes a fuss while other folks who don't do so much seem to get down to the Palace for tea with the Queen.'

Now I realised what she was talking about because my own grandfather, himself a County Councillor, had once been invited to Buckingham Palace for a garden party.

Dora stopped chattering to say a long "Hello" to a passing friend, and this gave me the chance to say, 'Horace will have been told about the system, you know.'

'He never tells me anything, Mr Rhea, you know my Horace, tight as the proverbial duck's, well, you know what and he always says nothing's happened at the meetings, then I hear of Mr and Mrs So-and-So, then Mr and Mrs This-and-That going off to London to meet the Queen and I ask myself why isn't our Horace getting himself there, and why isn't he taking me? I would love to go and wear my new hat, Mr Rhea, I really would, it's not as if I get far, you know, what with the business and my other interests, so this would be a once-in-a-lifetime outing, a really lovely one . . . '

'There's a draw for tickets,' I managed to tell her. 'I'm not sure when it's done or how often, but according to my grandfather, all councillors who want to be considered must put their names forward, and then a draw is made. Those drawn out of the hat, in a manner of speaking, are then invited to the Palace Garden Party. But Horace would have to find out exactly how the system operates. Get him to put his name forward, Dora. But you realise it's something of a lottery – not everyone can go, so there's no guarantee Horace would win an invitation.'

She beamed with happiness.

'Oh, Mr Rhea, I know he'll get there if only he'll do something about it . . . I will have a word with him straight away; now I mustn't keep you, I know you're very busy.'

She kept me standing there another ten minutes, saying how busy I was and how busy she was, and then she sailed away home in a very cheerful mood. Horace, I knew, was in for a session of chatter from her, with strict instructions to put his name forward next time Buckingham Palace asked the County Council for Garden Party nominees.

It would be four or five weeks later when Horace mentioned this; I had popped into his garage on a routine enquiry and he said, 'Mr Rhea, our Dora said summat about you suggesting I put my name down for t'Buckingham Palace jobs?'

'Yes,' I said. 'She was asking how councillors like yourself managed to get invited to Buckingham Palace, so I told her about the draw they have.'

'Aye, well, I can't say sike affairs are much in my line, but my name's gone down. They asked us at t'last meeting, and a few

councillors sent their names in. I thought I would, then if our
Dora goes on at me, I can allus say I put my name forward.
That'll keep her quiet, cos I shan't win. I never win owt, Mr
Rhea.'

I was surprised that he had bothered to actually do this, for it
would have been easy to tell a white lie, to tell Dora he had
submitted his name even if he hadn't. But the surprising thing
was that Horace won. His name was drawn from the list and he
was notified by a telephone call, following which detailed instructions about the event would be sent to him.

Dora spent hours rushing around the village telling her
friends, and then she went off to York to buy an entire new
outfit, including one of those huge wide-brimmed hats that
were her heart's desire.

Then the formal instructions arrived by post.

And Dora's world fell apart.

Horace had certainly submitted his name, but he had failed to
understand that he had also to nominate his wife; he had failed
to include her name, and so the invitation was for him and him
alone. A maiden lady councillor from Whitby had also won an
invitation – she had been issued with the one that should have
gone to Councillor Horace Pitman's lady.

Dora's anger and disappointment was acute and she kept
herself hidden from the public for some weeks after this bad
news. Then on the day before the event, I saw Horace getting
into one of his cars, and went across. He was dressed in the dark
blazer he used for taxi-driving; he had on a dark tie and white
shirt, and some crumpled trousers which he usually wore under
his overalls. His boots were clean but very greasy and he carried
a brown paper carrier-bag.

'Going shopping, Horace?' I asked

'Nay, it's for t'hotel tonight, Mr Rhea. I'm off to London. A
clean collar and me razor and toothbrush. I need nowt else. I'm
off to Buckingham Palace.'

And so he was; thus equipped, he got into his car and started
the engine. I had no idea whether he intended to drive all the
way to London or catch a train from York, but he sat there,
smiling at me but saying nothing as he ran the engine of his car.

And then Dora came rushing out, looking like a dream. She

wore a beautiful new suit, a matching wide-brimmed hat and high-heeled shoes. She carried a small suitcase and a matching handbag.

'Off to see the Queen, Dora?' I asked.

'I am not, and I'm glad I'm not, not with our Horace looking like that. You'd think he would have got some new clothes if he's to shake Her Majesty by the hand . . . no, Mr Rhea, he's not getting away with this! I'm going to London to see the sights, a play maybe, and then the shops. I wouldn't be seen dead with our Horace dressed like that . . . '

And Horace engaged first gear and drove off with a big smile on his face. I wondered what Her Majesty would make of him. Upon their return, Dora never stopped talking about her trip. She'd had a marvellous time and had crammed a host of exciting events into her short visit to the city. As for Horace, I asked him what he thought of the Buckingham Palace Garden Party.

'Not much,' he said. 'T'food was nowt but a load o' ket.'

A translation of that dialect word would, I doubt, not please those who arranged the teas.

6

'If this be not love, it is madness,
and then it is pardonable.'
William Congreve, 1670-1729

One of the recurring duties of the sympathetic police officer involves dealing with people in distress; there are times when that distress is self-inflicted either by accident or design, and there are times it is inflicted upon us by other people or by a single event or even a series of unfortunate occurrences. Officialdom, bureaucracy and red tape can also inflict distress in their own inimitable manner, the latter being revealed when puzzled pensioners receive threatening letters from computerised accounts departments when their rates or other bills have been paid.

Minor examples of distress might include those who lock themselves out of their homes or whose motor cars run out of petrol, or who are locked out of their homes by others during arguments or stupidity, or whose cars run out of petrol because their teenage son has surreptitiously done a trip to Scotland and back. Other people can inflict distress upon us, by simple things like persistent telephone calls or playing football in our front garden, or by greed such as burglary or through dangerous actions like reckless driving, playing about with firearms or indeed anything else. The possibilities of trouble are endless and it seems we are continually at risk either through our own behaviour or from the actions of others.

In the course of police work, therefore, the constable often comes across examples of this kind and seeks to comfort the

111

victims where possible. A kind word and some assurance that the world isn't going to end is generally sufficient, albeit tempered with advice on how to cope with the unexpected and harrowing predicament.

In dealing with jobs of this kind, however, it becomes evident that of all the root causes of man's predilection for disaster, that which causes most problems is man's love for woman. Through their vast experience of people, police officers know that men get themselves into some of the most curious situations in their undying efforts to prove their love to the lady of their dreams. Constables know that love is one of the most powerful of urges, so strong that at times it removes every scrap of common sense from the skulls of those whom it infects. A poet who remains anonymous once said that 'Love is a passion which has caused the change of empires' – in short, men do the daftest things when they are in love, and I have mentioned some of their misadventures in previous 'Constable' books.

But because this symptom provides a never-ending series of dramas, sagas, mishaps, problems and (to be honest) a few chuckles in the process, every constable has witnessed and can recount stirring tales of love. They would fill a volume, so I thought I would place on record a few more tales of the love-lorn countryman.

One example occurred during the depths of winter. While I was the village bobby at Aidensfield, one of my less pleasant duties as Christmas approached was to man road-checks at various lonely points. This meant stopping all cars to check them and their boots for stolen chickens, turkeys, drinks and other festive fare. We were also seeking those who stole holly from gardens and Christmas trees from our acres of local forests. It was a task that country constables had undertaken for years and the only time I found any game in a car was when I halted and searched a Rolls-Royce which, it transpired, had a boot full of pheasants. His Lordship was not too pleased; he was delivering them to his tenants.

The timing of those road-blocks varied, but they were usually of two hours' duration, perhaps starting at 8pm, 9pm, 10pm, 11pm or even midnight, and on each occasion we selected a different check-point. Word generally got around the local pubs that the police were checking cars at Bank Top or The Beacon or Four Lane Ends which probably meant the poachers took alternative routes. But we did get results – we found cars with no insurance, drivers with no licences, cars not taxed, cars with dirty number plates and cars in a dangerous condition. We caught drunken drivers, car thieves and burglars and, once in a while, we caught a Christmas poacher with a boot full of illicitly acquired game or liquor, or a hard-up dad who had risked digging up a Norway spruce from the local Forestry Commission plantation.

We referred to these duties as turkey patrols, although I've never known an arrest for having a boot full of turkeys. On one occasion, however, I caught a youth riding a bike without lights. It happened like this.

It was a pitch-black night with no moon and I was manning a road-check at Elsinby Plantation. It was about 8.30pm and I was alone for it was a very minor road which ran right through the centre of the conifer plantation which comprised Norway spruce, Scots pines and larches. We'd had reports of Christmas-tree thefts and so I was out to catch a thief.

Almost numb with cold, I suddenly heard the distinctive swish-swish of bicycle tyres and as I peered into the pitch blackness, I could not see any lights. And then the noise came closer and I could hear the sound of breathing as the rider pedalled up the slight gradient. And so I shone my torch upon him.

He cried with alarm, for my sudden action had terrified him. In the light of my torch, I saw it was young Ian Spellar from Elsinby and he stopped when he realised it was me.

'Oh, Mr Rhea, hello.' He was slightly out of breath.

'Now, Ian, what's all this then? Riding without lights, eh? You could get yourself killed on a night like this, you know. Car drivers can't see you; you realise you're putting drivers in an impossible situation?'

'Aye, sorry, Mr Rhea. I won't do it again.'

'Where are you going anyway? It's a bit off the beaten track up here!'

I shone my light on his bike and upon his back to see if he had anything which might carry a small tree or any other Yuletide trophy, but he wasn't equipped for transporting anything save himself. I knew he wasn't stealing.

'I'm not pinching things, Mr Rhea, honest. I'm off to see my girlfriend.'

'And who's she?' was my next question.

'Linda Thornhill,' he said. I knew where she lived and this was on the route to her parents' isolated farm.

'Right,' I said. 'Off you go, but be careful. And next time, get some batteries in those lights, and get them switched on, OK? Or I'll book you!'

'Yes, Mr Rhea. Sorry Mr Rhea.'

'And be careful – remember you can't be seen!'

Knowing few cars used this quiet track, I allowed him to continue to see his love, although the lad might be a danger to other road users. Maybe I should not have relented, but I decided in his favour. Ian was a pleasant youth. Just turned eighteen, he worked in a local timber yard and was a hard-working lad from a decent working-class background. I'd had to tell him off once or twice about drinking under age but he never got into serious trouble. Under-age drinking and riding a bike without lights was the extent of his lawlessness.

Then, only a week later, I was manning another check-point in that vicinity, this time at Flatts End, when I heard the same swish-swish of bicycle tyres. I shone my torch upon the on-coming rider and again it was Ian.

'Same rider, Mr Rhea!' he said, halting at my side.

'Same constable, Ian!'

'Same excuse!' he countered.

'Same warning!' I said. 'Now what about those lights?'

'I never got round to putting them on, Mr Rhea, sorry,' and he bent over his lights, back and front, and switched them on. After telling him once again of the dangers, I let him go.

'It'll be a summons next time, Ian!' I shouted after him as his red rear light disappeared into the gloom.

It puzzled me that he should be riding in such darkness without lights when both his lamps were in good working-order. It didn't make sense. Then some ten days later, one Saturday night, I was manning yet another check-point, this time at Swathgill Head, and once more, I heard the panting sound of someone pedalling heavily, and the accompanying swish-swish of bicycle tyres. I groaned. I would now have to be harder with this youth.

I switched on my torch and waved him to a halt. I was right; it was Ian Spellar.

'Same cyclist, Mr Rhea,' he said, this time not so chirpily.

'Same constable,' I retorted, sternly.

'Same excuse,' he said, wondering what my reaction would be as he switched on both lights.

'Same threat, Ian!' I sounded angry. 'Now look, this is getting beyond a joke. This is your final warning, right? Next time, you go to court, I can't have you putting yourself and car-drivers at risk . . . '

'If I hear a car coming, I stop and put 'em on,' he said. 'I'd never let 'em run me down, Mr Rhea, I'm not as daft as that.'

'Why ride without lights when your lamps are in working-order?' I asked. 'There's nothing wrong with them!'

He just shrugged his shoulders in reply, and I watched him ride off once again. Each time I'd seen him, he'd been on a different road, albeit within the same general area of the heights above Elsinby. Any of those roads would take him to Linda Thornhill's remote home, but his attitude defeated me. It wasn't defiance of the law, it was more a strange sort of lethargy. Now, however, I felt he had got the message. But I was wrong. Only a week later, I was again on the lane running through Elsinby Plantation when I became aware of an approaching cyclist without lights. My heart sank. I could distinguish the swishing of the tyres and the sound of a man breathing as he climbed the gradient, and so, once more, I shone my torch on Ian Spellar.

'Same cyclist, Mr Rhea.'

'Same constable, Ian.'

'Same excuse,' he recited what had become a kind of ritual response.

'Same results, Ian.'

'Same apologies, Mr Rhea.'

'And this time, it's the same summons, Ian. You're clearly ignoring my warnings, so it's a summons this time,' and I took down his name, age, address and occupation, then reported him

115

for riding a cycle without obligatory lights.

'I'm really sorry, Mr Rhea,' and he switched on his front and rear lamps.

'Look, Ian, this is serious, you're risking an accident and putting too much faith in other drivers . . . they just cannot see you in darkness. Why are you doing this?'

He hung his head, embarrassed at my questioning, but his demeanour told me there was a reason for his odd behaviour. Even so, he did not reveal this to me. I must admit that I was against submitting a formal report against him; on paper, it seemed such a trivial matter and my superiors would probably think I'd become drunk with power. But Ian had to be taught a lesson, and so I did submit a report with an accompanying account of the reasons for my action.

And then, even before a decision had been made upon that report, I caught Ian once again.

'Same constable, Ian,' I shouted at him. 'And it'll be another summons for the same offence. What on earth are you playing at?'

'Same cyclist, Mr Rhea.' He sounded very subdued now. 'And same excuse.'

'You're going to see your girlfriend again?'

'Aye,' he said. 'I am, and well, Mr Rhea, I'm sorry, I really am. I know it's wrong, but, well, it's so important . . . '

'Go on, Ian, I'm listening,' I said.

'Well, you know where the Thornhills live, down at Birch Bower Farm?'

'I know it well,' I paid a visit to this farm about once a month and it was an awful trek from the road. The farm lay at least a mile and a half from the road, and although the first quarter of the track leading to it was surfaced, the remainder was an unmade lane full of ruts and pot-holes and littered with partly buried rocks. It was a diabolical road and Ted Thornhill never seemed inclined to repair it. Everyone who used it grumbled.

'Well, old Thornhill doesn't like me courting his lass, Mr Rhea, so I go in secret. Linda can't get out at night, you see, being only sixteen anyway, so I have to ride out there if I want to see her. She goes into her room to do her homework, you see, but she sneaks out at nine o'clock. Well, her dad might catch me riding down that lane if I show lights, Mr Rhea, and 'cos I need to adjust my eyes to ride down when it's pitch dark, I practise on these quiet roads, you see . . . I allus have lights on in the village, or on main roads, but not here where there's nowt but 'trees.'

I believed him. I knew the value of working without light when operating at night because one's eyes do become accustomed to the darkness.

'So you're practising that ride and using different roads to avoid me, eh?' I put to him.

'Yeh, well, when you first nabbed me I reckoned you'd often be on that road, seeing Christmas is coming up and there's poachers about. So I went the other way round, then you were there an' all, Mr Rhea . . . '

'And I've no doubt you've been riding those roads other nights, Ian, when I've not been on duty?'

He laughed with a silly sort of giggle. 'Aye, well, you have to, haven't you? Just the quiet bits, mind, and that lane down to Birch Bower.'

'I'm not interested in Birch Bower Farm Lane,' I said. 'That's private property. I'm concerned with public roads.'

'So will they take me to court, Mr Rhea?'

'It depends on the Superintendent,' I said, which was the truth. 'He'll read my report and decide what to do.'

'Tell him I'm sorry, then. But mebbe he was a lad an' all, at one time? Going courting.'

'I'll see what he says,' was all I could promise.

The Superintendent met me at one of my rendezvous points a few days later and took the opportunity of asking me about my 'no bike-lights' report. I explained the situation and included Ian's odd reason.

'Christmas is coming up, PC Rhea,' said the Superintendent. 'Would you agree that a written caution is appropriate in this case?'

I smiled. 'Yes, sir. I think it would be very appropriate.'

And so that was Ian's punishment. Within a few days, he would receive a written caution from the Superintendent which would inform him that he would not be prosecuted on this occasion, but that the letter must be regarded as a warning. Any future offences of this nature could result in a court appearance.

I saw Ian in Elsinby one Sunday afternoon just before Christmas and told him what to expect.

'Thanks, Mr Rhea. I'm grateful.'

'Wish Linda a happy Christmas from me,' I said.

'Thanks, Mr Rhea. I will. And I'm sorry I've been a nuisance, I was daft really. But there was nowt else I could do, was there, if I wanted to see Linda?'

'I can't encourage you to break the law.' I smiled at him. 'Mind,' I added, 'I'm not sure how you'll sneak down to Birch Bower in the summer without her dad knowing.'

'Me neither, Mr Rhea. I'll have to find a way in somehow, although she might be able to go for walks when it's light at night.'

'Let's hope so, Ian. Oh, and by the way,' I said. 'We finish those check-points this coming Saturday night.'

'Thanks, Mr Rhea,' he said. 'Happy Christmas.'

One of the funniest incidents involved a man whom I shall call Ronald Youngman, a salesman who lived in Ashfordly. I was never very sure what he sold, although I think it was something linked to the building-industry like scaffolding. A dark-haired, attractive man in his early thirties, he was a lively character who played a lot of tennis, cricket, football and badminton. When he was not selling scaffolding or playing one of his sports, he was exercising his considerable charm upon the local ladies.

In the latter case, he made ample use of his company car which was a Ford Cortina with reclining front seats; he used this to take his many conquests for outings, frequently making trips to rural pubs after which he would take his charmed girl to a remote rustic location, there for mutual enjoyment. For this reason, his distinctive gold-coloured car was often to be seen parked in lonely places, sometimes with steamed-up windows and generally in complete darkness.

Most of the local police officers knew the car and they knew of Ronald's insatiable appetite for lovely ladies, consequently they never checked over the car or its occupants when they found it in a far-away place. Normally, our procedures were to check every car found in a remote place to see if the occupants were safe and sound, to see if it was someone trying to commit suicide or whether the car had been stolen and abandoned. It might contain the proceeds of crime, or it might be used for crime – there were many other valid reasons for checking such vehicles.

If I was patrolling late, therefore, and came across Ronald's car upon the moors or deep in a forest, I ignored it. After all, I didn't want to embarrass either Ronald or his lover of the evening and if neither was breaking the law there was no need to make myself a nuisance.

But late one night – in fact it was after midnight – I was working a patrol and around 1am, my route took me high into Waindale. Tucked away in the corner of a quarry behind Wether Cote Farm was an explosives store; it belonged to the quarry owner and because it contained explosives and deto-nators used for blasting, we had to check it regularly for security. It was little more than a very solidly built chamber, part of which was underground, and it seldom contained a large amount. But it had to be checked and our checks had to be recorded.

With this in mind, I parked my mini-van off the road near Wether Cote Farm and decided to walk the couple of hundred yards to the explosives store. The route was along an unmade lane, full of pot-holes and with the quarry gates closed, there was very little room for turning a vehicle around. It was much safer to walk. And so, in the gloom of that night, albeit armed with a torch which I did not use during the walk, I made my way along the track. Rather like young Ian Spellar, I found I could see without the light from a torch. And then, in a corner right next to the store, I came across Ronald's car. It was in darkness but I could recognise the outline. Ronald was at it again.

Having no wish to become a peeping Tom or to disturb him in his moments of bliss, I tried to creep past the car to carry out my essential check. But as I was going past, I could hear cries for help . . . and they were being sounded in a man's voice! I halted a while, listening; I thought it might be the car radio, a disc jockey fooling about or perhaps a character in a play or it could be Ronald playing games. After all, he had no idea that I, or indeed anyone else, was standing just outside his passion-wagon.

But the cry was genuine . . . and a woman's voice was calling too. Who on earth they were hoping to attract in such a remote part of the moors was beyond me, but I listened carefully, just to ensure that these were genuine cries for help. I did wonder if it was some odd part of their love-making, but in spite of being muffled by the closed windows, they were, I felt, very genuine cries of distress. And, they sounded rather weak.

I had to investigate.

I switched on my powerful torch and pulled open the driver's door. The interior light came on and there, in the most bizarre situation upon the passenger's reclining seat was Ronald. He was face down and beneath him was a woman. Both were completely naked. And neither could move.

'Who's that?' he asked, with a mixture of relief and embarrassment, unable to turn his head towards the door.

'PC Rhea, Ronald.'

'Oh, thank God . . . . get me out . . . '

In the weak glow of the interior light, I could distinguish a tangle of bare legs; I could not identify the woman, and she was saying nothing. In fact, she was hiding her face by turning her head towards the wall of the car. But Ronald was saying 'My foot, Mr Rhea, my leg . . . '

'What's the problem?' I asked, baffled by this discovery.

'My legs . . . my feet . . . they're trapped . . . can you loosen them . . . '

I could now see that his right foot had disappeared through the cubby-hole of his car; it seemed he had been exerting pressure with that foot as a result of which it had dislodged the plastic back panel of the cubby-hole. His foot and much of his lower leg had then slipped through the hole to become trapped among the wires and bodywork, and he could not pull it out. That sudden action had then caused his left leg to make an involuntary movement, and his foot had gone through a gap between the spokes of the steering-wheel. That leg was also trapped due to the weight upon it.

'Interesting position, Ronald,' I said as I examined his predicament.

'I can't move, Mr Rhea. I just can't move . . . '

His entire body weight was resting upon the woman beneath;

she could not roll free because the driver's seat was not in a reclining position, nor could she slide towards the rear due to the slope of the seat upon which she was trapped, and Ronald's position prevented a forward escape.

Besides, one of her legs was somehow curled between his which well and truly anchored her. Unfortunately for Ronald his own trapped position and the weight of his body meant he could neither rise nor free his own legs.

'I wish I had a camera, Ronald, this is one for the record books!'

'Give over, Mr Rhea, just get me out . . . I've been here ages . . . I thought nobody was going to come . . . '

'They wouldn't, at least not until the quarry opens in the morning – it would give the lads summat to talk about. I just happened to be coming to the explosives store. Now, let's see if I can shift one of these legs.'

I went around to the passenger side and opened that door, upon which the woman turned her face the other way. It was almost the only part of her that I had not seen, but I set about removing Ronald's foot. By pushing my hand through the cubby-hole, I could dislodge the panel which had secured his foot, and then, by heaving on that leg and getting him to bend his knee, I could release that foot. But he could still not help himself. Gradually, I eased the other foot out of the spokes of the steering-wheel, got into the rear of the car and dragged him towards the back seat by his shoulders, and then he was free. Aching, stiff with cold and very, very embarrassed, he rolled into the driver's seat.

And then the woman could move and I recognised her.

'Good evening, Mrs Stamford,' I greeted her.

She was the wife of an hotel owner in Ashfordly but she made no response, not even a thank-you. As I clambered out of their car, she began to get dressed in total silence as Ronald grabbed his clothes and began to pull them on in the lane as he talked to me.

'Look, Mr Rhea, we're men of the world. I mean, I've committed no crime, no offence . . . You don't have to take action, do you? Report this, or anything? She is a respected lady from the town, you see, she's never done this before, not with me anyway. Her husband's away, He's at an hoteliers' conference in Harrogate . . . '

'There's no need to say anything, Ronald. Rescuing damsels and knights in distress is just part of our service. Well, it's made my night interesting, but, Ronald . . . '

I paused.

'Yes?' He was fastening his shirt by this time.

'I'd love to know how on earth you managed to get yourself into that position. I'll bet a contortionist would have a job to achieve that!'

'You'll not tell a soul, will you, Mr Rhea?'

'It's our secret, Ronald, ours and Mrs Stamford's.'

And I have never mentioned it to anyone. Ronald often greets me and insists on buying me a drink when I'm off duty, but the humiliated Mrs Stamford never speaks to me.

But when I returned home and booked off duty that night, I realised I had omitted to do one vital thing. I'd completely forgotten to examine the explosives store.

Possibly the most dramatic love story that came my way involved Mr and Mrs Colin Blenkiron and a notorious cross-roads called Pennyflats Cross. So difficult and accident-prone was this stretch of road that my predecessor, and then I, kept a stock of blank scale-drawings of the roads for use in our accident reports. The number of traffic accidents which happened at that point kept us in regular work!

Wherever a road traffic accident occurred which resulted in a need to examine all the evidence with a view to prosecution, we had to submit detailed plan drawings of the scene. These were carefully drawn to scale and contained the positions of the vehicles involved both before, during and after impact. This was for the benefit both of our senior officers in deciding whether or not to send the case to court, and later the magistrates if it did get to court. This system helped enormously to simplify a difficult explanation of the events. A stock of neatly drawn plans depicting this road, with all the constant measurements, the position of warning signs, indications of gradients, type of road markings, etc., did save a lot of time.

At Pennyflats Cross, the main road, which had a 'B' classification, ran from Ashfordly to York and crossed Pennyflats, an area of elevated scrubland covered with small conifers, gorse bushes and heather. As it reached the crossroads, the road dipped suddenly and quite steeply, although this short gradient was well signed in advance.

Nevertheless, many drivers who were strangers to the area were, when approaching from Ashfordly, largely unaware of the undulating nature of the road. They sailed over the summit without knowing and apparently without caring what lay beyond. That in itself could be regarded as careless driving or even dangerous driving because, just over the summit, within a matter of very few yards, was a minor road. It crossed the Ashfordly–York road at an oblique angle, emerging almost unseen from a plantation of conifers at one side and a copse of young silver birch at the other.

Defence solicitors always maintained that these crossroads were badly placed and it was unfair to convict anyone of driving carelessly here. The police, however, assured the court that the crossroads was well signposted from all directions, and that, in any case, a driver should always drive at a speed and in such a manner that he or she could deal with any unexpected hazards.

But a similar problem afflicted drivers coming out of the side road on to the main road. Upon emerging on to the main road, their vision was grossly impaired by the angle of the road and the profusion of trees. The chief problem was that those on the main road often crested that hill at speed only to find a slow car emerging into their path. So short was the stopping-distance that very few could pull up in time, not even those who pottered along in a leisurely style. Fast or even moderately fast drivers had no chance at all.

Accidents were inevitable, and although we, the police, grumbled at the highway department and the district council for improvements to be made, nothing was ever done. Their argument was that the crossroads were not dangerous because no one had been killed there, and, oddly enough, that was true. There never had been a fatal accident there, although some nasty injuries had occurred. Everyone said that, one day, somebody would be killed, but happily in my time at Aidensfield that did not happen.

I was not surprised therefore, one Sunday afternoon in May,

when I received a frantic phone call from a passing driver to say he had come upon two cars which had clearly just been involved in a traffic accident. He was chattering nervously as people tend to do when they are reporting urgent matters to the police, but I tried to calm him down by slowly asking the obvious questions.

I learned that the location was the infamous Pennyflats Cross, and that both drivers were injured. In his view, the injuries did not appear to be too serious although he said an ambulance was required. The road was not blocked and he had not witnessed the accident; he had come upon it moments after it had happened. I thanked him and said I would be there in less than ten minutes; I assured him I'd call the ambulance before I left home. He said he would wait and attend to the injured drivers.

The accident was one of the kind that regularly happened here. A young woman in an Austin mini-car had come out of the minor road on to the main road just as a young man in a sports car had crested the brow of the hill. He'd reacted quickly and had attempted to swerve to his right to avoid a collision, but she'd kept coming across his path from the left. He had collided with the front of her car. This had spun her off the road and she had collided with a telegraph pole while he had veered further to his offside, ending his short trip by crumpling his MGB around a sturdy ash tree.

A quick visual appraisal of both drivers showed that neither was too badly hurt; happily, neither was unconscious and I could detect no arterial bleeding; the girl, however, did say that her right arm hurt a lot and the youth complained of intense pain in his left leg. Tenderly, I examined both their injured limbs and was in no doubt that each was fractured; there were abrasions too, and some degree of shock. Hospital was a necessity for both.

At that stage, the ambulance arrived. The injured pair were well enough to tell me their names and addresses before the skilful ambulancemen lifted them out of their vehicles, wrapped them in blankets and in no time had placed them aboard stretchers. In seconds, they were being borne towards York County Hospital for treatment. I thanked the passing driver for his assistance and confirmed that he was no longer required as he was not a witness. Then I radioed our Control Room with a request for a breakdown truck.

The rest of my action was routine. I obtained measurements of the positions of their cars, cleared the scene, swept up the broken glass and made arrangements for relatives to be informed. The breakdown truck took away both cars, lifting one on board and towing the other, and I went home. Using my stock plan of the crossroads, I entered the position of each of the cars and completed my accident report as far as I could. I rang York Police with a request that an officer be allowed to visit the hospital when the injured couple were well enough, and that the officer be allowed to obtain from each their version of events.

If they were not well enough, then other arrangements would be made; I also had their driving licences and insurance certificates to check.

When all this was done, I submitted my report to the sergeant for onward transmission to the Superintendent and I was to learn later that he recommended 'No prosecution' on the grounds that there was no independent witness. No one could say precisely what had happened, for it was a case of the man's word against the girl's. And that, I thought, was that.

But there was more to follow.

Some time during the November that followed, I received a telephone call from a Mr Colin Blenkiron.

'It's Colin Blenkiron speaking. Is that PC Rhea?' the voice asked.

'Speaking,' I confirmed.

'Ah, good, well, I wondered if you'd like to come to a party, you and your wife.'

'Me? Well . . . '

At that instant, I couldn't recall knowing anyone called Blenkiron and I was hesitant until he said, 'That accident at Pennyflats Cross last May, Mr Rhea. It was me in the MGB Hardtop.'

'Oh!' Now it all came flooding back. 'I remember now, that Colin Blenkiron! Well, thanks, what sort of party and where is it?'

'It's my engagement party, Mr Rhea, and it's at the Hopbind Inn, Elsinby, a week on Thursday night. Half eight.'

'Well, that's very kind of you,' I was surprised at this. 'Very kind. I'm off duty that night,' I said. 'And I know my wife would love the outing, but . . . '

I was about to say that I was surprised at the invitation because Colin's parents' farm, which he ran in partnership with his father, was not on my beat. I did not know him or his parents, although I did know they were very wealthy and successful.

'It was because of that accident, Mr Rhea, you looked after me, and Susan. Got us to hospital, and there was no court appearance for us either. So we'd like you to come to our party.'

'She's your fiancée?' I was surprised.

'Not then, she wasn't. I didn't even know her then! She's my fiancée now, we met in hospital, you see.'

'What a way to meet!' I laughed.

'Yes, well, it was. Actually,' he chuckled, 'we met in the ambulance, but we weren't exactly on speaking-terms then! I was blaming her for the pile-up . . . I still am, by the way, and she was blaming me . . . anyway, in hospital, one thing led to another and here we are, getting engaged!'

'What a lovely tale!' I said. 'Yes, then we'd love to come and wish you a happy future!'

'Marvellous. We're inviting those ambulancemen as well, they were great. See you then.'

And he rang off.

Mary was delighted. From time to time, one of my 'customers' produced an offer of this kind, a form of genuine and heartfelt 'thank-you', even if my part in their romance was very minor. We went along to the party and met their respective families, friends and relations. Susan Ascough, Colin's fiancée, was a secretary in a big department store in York and lived in Ploatby, which was on my patch. She drove into York every day. I knew her parents by name, but had never met Susan until this evening.

During the party, there were ribald jokes about their method of meeting, their respective injuries, their time in bed in hospital and the prospects for their future together. It was a very happy gathering and a real tonic for me, and even more so for Mary. Diplomatically, we left the party at closing-time for I did not wish to make them feel uncomfortable if they decided to stay awhile at the pub.

'I enjoyed that,' said Mary on our way home. 'They seem a real nice couple, and their families are nice too.'

'It makes you think that that accident was fate,' I said. 'I wonder if they'd have met each other if it had never happened?'

'We'll never know,' she said. 'And thanks for leaving the pub at closing-time!' she added. 'I hate people staring at you as if you're a leper when the landlord calls time.'

'A little drink after hours always tastes better,' I said. 'It's like kids pinching apples – they're always better than the ones at home, and drinks laced with a spot of law-breaking taste all the better for it. A hint of naughtiness will put the final seal on their celebrations!'

'That's if they *do* drink after hours!' she laughed. 'You'll never know, will you?'

'I don't want to know,' I said, truthfully.

I thought that would have been the last we'd see of Colin and Susan, but it wasn't. The following March, we received an invitation to their wedding. It was fixed for the weekend before Easter in Elsinby Parish Church, with the reception at Craydale Manor. This was a fine country house which had been converted into an hotel and restaurant, and we looked forward to the whole celebration. The wedding was superb. In Elsinby's historic parish church, the atmosphere and setting were both dramatic and moving. Susan looked a picture in her long white wedding dress with its train and eight tiny bridesmaids in the most delicate of pinks.

Colin and his best man looked handsome and splendid in their top hats and tails, and the happy couple were united before a full congregation of family, friends and well-wishers. Beyond doubt, it was this district's wedding of the year. Mary and I thoroughly enjoyed the occasion; we lingered as the photographs were taken outside the church, savouring every moment and participating in the sheer happiness of the newly-weds. As the village constable, it was so nice being part of this joyful event.

Eventually, the photographer had taken all that he wished and the best man shouted for us to rejoin our cars and follow the bridal procession to the reception, after which the presents would be on display at the bride's home in Ploatby. And so we

all went off to Craydale Manor in a long procession of gleaming
vehicles led by a silver Jaguar car with white ribbons fluttering
from its bonnet.

The reception was splendid; the excellent meal was run with
flair and efficiency, Colin's speech and those of the other dutiful
men were fluent and entertaining, and the toasts were drunk
with style and aplomb. The wedding had started at 11.30am and
by the end of this reception the time had crept around to
2.30pm.

At this time, the best man, a friend of Colin's, said, 'Ladies
and gentlemen, the presents are on display at the bride's home,
Sycamore Cottage, Ploatby – you are invited to view them. The
bride and groom will leave the bride's home for their honey-
moon at four pm. You might like to see them off.'

Mary, who always loves a wedding, said she'd like to view the
presents and see Susan's going-away outfit, so we agreed to visit
Sycamore Cottage, Ploatby. As we were leaving the reception,
several other cars were doing likewise, and leading the first
flush of departing vehicles was the silver Jaguar containing the
bride and groom.

The uniformed chauffeur had been hired with the car, both
coming from a York firm which specialised in this kind of
service. In an orderly fashion, the procession of cars filed out of
the spacious grounds of the hotel and began to speed through
the lanes towards Ploatby.

I was somewhere towards the rear with perhaps ten or a dozen
cars ahead of me. I simply tagged on behind and others followed
me, for some of the guests were strangers and did not know the
route. I made it clear I would show them the way. As we moved
off, there was a good deal of merriment with people waving at
each other out of car windows, flying their silk scarves, throwing confetti, shouting and laughing as we passed through the
splendid Ryedale countryside.

And ahead was the fine Jaguar, its polished silver bodywork
glistening in the bright sunshine of the day as the happy couple
waved and blew kisses to everyone. It disappeared around the
sharp corners and was frequently hidden from my view by the
high hedges and the distance between us.

As we motored along Hazel Burn Lane which joined the

Ashfordly–York road, I lost sight of the powerful Jaguar; its lead had become quite substantial but I did not try to keep pace with it, for I had no wish to lose those behind me who were relying on my guidance. And then we were on the main road, the B-class highway which led towards York. Driving steadily, I was approaching the dangerous portion over Pennyflats Cross, and even as I neared the place, I saw several smart-suited gentlemen waving us to a halt.

'Oh, no!' I groaned at Mary. 'What now! Don't say there's been an accident today of all days!'

With every passing yard, it was clear there had been an accident, for cars were strewn across both lanes of the highway and people were milling about, shouting at us to slow down and stop. I pulled on to the grass verge, making sure my car was clear as I went to investigate. Upon my advice, Mary remained in her seat – the fewer people about the scene, the better.

When I crested that notorious hill, my heart sank. The silver Jaguar was on its side, its roof crushed against the very same ash tree that Colin had hit only months ago. Also lying on its side in the middle of the road was a tractor and trailer, the trailer having carried a load of manure. It was spread across the carriageway and other cars were scattered randomly about the road with anxious people milling about . . .

I ran to the Jaguar.

I knew Colin and Susan were inside and the awful silence about the car made me fear the worst; I was no longer a wedding guest, but a policeman who had suddenly found himself on duty. As I ran down the road, weaving between irregularly parked cars, I saw that several had been slightly damaged. The accident was one of the shunt type when each car runs into the back of the one ahead. Seven or eight had been damaged, but I was not concerned with those. I arrived at the Jaguar to find a knot of helpers trying to reach the bride and groom who were in the rear seat. No one seemed to be worried about the chauffeur, and at this stage I was not even aware of the tractor driver's injuries.

Susan, her wedding dress stained with blood and dirt, was crying as she lay on top of Colin; he was curled up in an untidy heap as he lay among the broken glass and shattered metalwork of the car body, and he was bleeding about the head and face. I told the helpers who I was and they stood aside as I wrenched open the rear door which now lay uppermost and somehow, I don't know how, I found myself crouched inside the rear compartment, mysteriously avoiding trampling on the couple.

They were conscious but hurt; I shouted for someone to call two ambulances and to stress the urgency due to the number of casualties, then call the police, a local doctor and finally a nearby garage to arrange lifting-gear and cutting-equipment. I asked the volunteer to give a detailed account of the multiple accident; he said he would cope.

I thought Colin or the chauffeur might be trapped, such was their position in the wreckage. Each was lying on the side of the car which was on the ground, the roof being caved in around them. I asked the gathered menfolk to care for their ladies and other guests, and to ensure that there was adequate warning for approaching vehicles. I didn't want more pile-ups and I asked them not to move their cars; their position was vital for the subsequent official report.

But I must see to Colin and Susan. Speaking to them in what I hoped were soothing terms, I managed to move Susan to a more comfortable position. Then I made a very brief and almost cursory examination of Colin. He was sighing with pain and I daren't move him in case he had broken bones or internal injuries which could cause further damage. One of his arms seemed to be trapped somewhere beneath him and careless handling could aggravate any injuries he might have.

Relieved that he was alive, I now looked to the unfortunate chauffeur; he was lying trapped too, unconscious and pale with a spot of blood on his face, but he was breathing quite smoothly. I did not touch him. This release required the skill of experts and the injured people needed medical attention. I hoped the messages for help would receive the attention they required. And I was not disappointed.

The sequence of events moved rapidly ahead. In what seemed a very short time, the emergency services arrived; a motor patrol car based at Scarborough had happened to be patrolling nearby and two capable officers, not closely known to me, came and dealt very efficiently with the multiple accident, paying immediate attention to the casualties. Two ambulances came and, with the help of us all, and the garage's lifting-gear, we soon had the casualties free and on their way to hospital.

The chauffeur was placed in a second ambulance and the tractor driver, who seemed to be forgotten by most of us, was also placed on board. The other casualties were all suffering from minor injuries and shock, and Doctor Archie McGee, summoned from Elsinby, was able to treat most of them without hospitalisation.

I sent Mary home while I remained to help the two officers with the statement-taking, clearing the scene and generally making myself useful. Under the circumstances, I'm not sure if anyone went to the house to see the presents, but we didn't. I was shattered by the awful turn of events, the enormity of which did not register until some time later.

This is a feature of police work; you deal with a harrowing incident in a cool and professional way, and it is later, when relaxing at home, that the sheer horror of the incident registers. I'm sure many police officers have wept with sorrow and anger after dealing with terrible incidents.

But this was not such a serious case for there were no fatalities. That, I felt, was another example of fate. With so many cars involved, there could have been carnage.

I rang the hospital to enquire after each of the casualties and learned that Susan had fractured an ankle and had suffered lots of bruising to her body. Colin had a broken arm, a minor fracture to his skull and lots of cuts about the face; the chauffeur, a man from York called Eric Wallis, had fractured six ribs and had facial injuries due to impact with the steering-wheel and windscreen. The tractor driver, a 56-year-old farm worker called Eddie Harper, had been knocked from his machine to suffer a broken shoulder blade, a broken arm and severe lacerations to his face and hands.

The following day, I rang the two motor patrol officers to explain about my battles to get the junction made safer either by more signs, better advance warnings and a clearer view from the minor road and they assured me this would be incorporated in their report. Their enquiries, based on witness statements, suggested that poor old Eddie Harper had pulled out of the minor road with his slow-moving tractor and trailer, and the fast-moving Jaguar had crested the blind summit of that hill driven by a man who was accustomed to city traffic, not country roads. The Jaguar had hit the tractor, and the following cars had each collided with another vehicle. Nine of them were damaged, and fifteen people had been injured.

It was the worst accident on my patch and I hoped it would result in some improvements to that road. And then, about six or seven weeks later, I received a phone call.

'It's Colin Blenkiron,' said the voice. 'We're out of hospital, Mr Rhea, Susan and me, and we wondered if you and Mrs Rhea would like to see the wedding presents? I know it's a bit late, but we're having friends in, a few at a time . . . how about Sunday afternoon, say three-ish?'

'We'd love to!' I enthused.

'Drive carefully!' he said, laughing.

It was pouring with rain as we went along to their lovely cottage and we found both of them still wearing dressings on some of their injuries and both chuckling at the absurdity of the situation.

'That crossroads has got it in for us!' Colin laughed as he poured the wine. 'It's put us in hospital twice now . . . I never go that way when Susan's with me. I'm not risking another accident, I can tell you!'

'You met me because of Pennyflats Cross!' she retorted with good humour.

'And I got put in hospital twice because of it!' he said. 'And that first accident was all your fault . . . '

'It wasn't! It was yours!' she cried. 'You were going far too fast . . . '

'Here's to the pair of you!' and as the driving rain beat upon their cottage, a flash of lightning was followed by a crack of thunder which rattled the windows.

I raised my glass to them and then, for some odd reason, I remembered the words of Samuel Beckett in, I think, *All That Fall*. I quoted them as a toast, "What sky! What light! Ah, in spite of all, it is a blessed thing to be alive in such weather, and out of hospital!'

And Colin kissed Susan.

7

'A difference of taste in jokes is a great
strain on the affections.'

George Eliot, 1819-80

Society will have its jokers. Throughout the ages there have
been many classic pranks, some on a large scale and others of a
very minor nature. In the countryside, April 1st has always
been a good time for practising pranks upon one's friends,
relations and workmates. I remember one joker who claimed
that hens' eggs could be stretched if they were collected immediately after being laid because at that moment, their shells
are still soft. He said they could be stretched to appear larger
and so fetch a better price.

In our area, one newspaper printed a story that the castle at
Barnard Castle was to be demolished to make way for a bridge
across the River Tees, and there was a joke that almost went
wrong when a man walked into a park and picked up a new park
bench under the nose of a policeman. He was stopped on
suspicion of theft and claimed he wanted the seat for firewood.
He was promptly arrested and when he explained that it was
merely a joke no one believed him. He did, however, manage to
prove that the seat was his own, as he'd bought it specially for
the joke only the day before.

One Yorkshire lad tricked his family and friends when he
organised a spoof wedding. He and a girlfriend had apparently
got married, had their photographs taken, and then driven
around town in their wedding outfits for all to see.

One of my favourite jokes was the news that British time was

133

to be decimalised. It claimed that, in order to rationalise Great Britain with the move towards metrication and decimalisation, the year would no longer have twelve months. Instead, Britain would have 10 months, each comprising 10 weeks; there would be 10 days to each week, and 10 hours to each day. Each hour would have 10 minutes and each minute would be split into 10 seconds. A year would be called a Kiloday, a month would be a hectoday, a week would be known as a decaday, while a minute would become a centiday and so forth.

Furthermore, to coincide with the change, Big Ben would become digital and there would be wage adjustments to cope with each Leap Kiloday.

Harmless, and at times very believable, jokes are great fun, such as the time our local zoo claimed they had found the Loch Ness Monster and even fooled the Scottish police into halting them at the border as they tried to smuggle out the carcase. It was in fact a huge type of seal, but the police had unearthed a byelaw which forbids the taking of certain rare species out of Scotland and so they were halted at the border in the belief they had the Loch Ness Monster in their possession!

One 'animal' which is a regular victim of April Fool jokes is the famous White Horse of Kilburn. It overlooks the North Yorkshire countryside from its vantage point just below the rim of the escarpment near Sutton Bank.

This huge white shape of a horse, over 105 yards long, was cut from the hillside in 1857 from plans drawn by John Hodgson, the headmaster of Kilburn village school. Helped by his pupils and a group of local men, Hodgson carved the horse from the hillside where it remains a landmark for miles around. It is the only hillside sculpture of its kind in the north of England and can be seen from over 70 miles away. It was filled with white lime and so the outline of this magnificent horse continues to dominate the countryside around Kilburn, not far from Aidensfield. But on April Fool's Day, the horse is liable to change! From time to time, it has been transformed into a zebra, a cowboy's horse with a rider and, in recent times, a well endowed stallion.

I think it is fair to say that most of us enjoy a clever but harmless joke and police officers are no exception. A clever

April Fool joke is always appreciated and so are jokes perpetrated at other times of the year.

I well remember one young rookie constable who was ordered to place traffic cones around York Minster one Sunday morning which happened to be April 1st. He had been told that today was the annual Archbishop's Foot Race, when every clergyman in the York Diocese was expected by the Archbishop to run a short race around the Minster, all dressed in their cassocks and surplices. The lad had therefore coned off the entire Minster moments before the regular services were due to start. If he kept his cones there, no one could enter the Minster.

The situation was rectified at the last minute when he received a radio call, supposedly from Police Headquarters, to say the race had been cancelled because the Archbishop had influenza.

Other jokes included leaving notes for the night-shift sergeant to the effect that the Chief Constable had requested an early call at 5am, and a similar one backfired when an unsuspecting constable was ordered to wake up the warden of the local dogs' home at 5am by knocking on his door. He was told that the warden had made this request and that he had insisted that the police keep knocking until he answered the door. He was a noted over-sleeper and had a very important meeting that day. The truth was that the warden didn't live on the premises; in fact, no one lived on the premises except hundreds of dogs, and the resultant continuous loud barking roused the entire town.

It was when I called at Eltering Police Station one day on duty that I found myself involved in a practical joke on a new constable who had recently arrived. His name was Justin Pendlebury, a man of about twenty-eight years of age, and he came from a very wealthy background; it seemed his family were from the stockbroker belt of Surrey, but Justin had decided to break away from both family and environment to become a constable in the North Riding of Yorkshire. We never knew why he had done this, but in fact he proved himself a very capable young officer.

But he had one annoying character trait. He was rather pompous and always boasted about the style and quality of his clothes. Certainly, he dressed well, far better than the rest of us. His suits were beautifully cut, he wore hand-made shirts and shoes, exquisite silk ties and his casual wear was of the very highest quality.

Justin certainly looked very stylish and smart, but he made everyone aware of the fact, telling us tales of how his tailor was the very best in London's West End, how the fellow made all his suits by hand and dressed film stars, politicians and City business people. Justin scorned the cheap suits and flannel trousers that we wore, saying we ought to be more clothes-conscious. But none of us copied him or ever tried to emulate his style. If our clothes kept us warm and dry, then that was good enough.

Although everyone liked Justin and admired his professionalism when on duty, we did get sick of his continual talk of fine clothes, men's fashions and popular styles. He talked of Ascot, Glyndebourne and Epsom as we talked about the back row of the Empire Cinema or the cheap end at Thornaby Races and Cargo Fleet Greyhound Track.

As I entered Eltering Police Station that day, I walked into a discussion about clothes. And, as usual, it was led by Justin. He was having an animated conversation with PC. Alf Ventress and two visiting officers, PCs George Henderson and Harry Pitts.

Alf Ventress was known to us all as Vesuvius because his uniform was always covered in ash and he was likely to erupt at any time; he was a huge, grizzly-haired constable of the old-fashioned type whose trousers always needed pressing, whose tunic was constantly smothered in dandruff and cigarette ash, whose boots always needed cleaning and whose shirts always sported crumpled collars. He was the last person to be discussing smart clothes with Justin.

'Ah, young Nick,' he said as I walked in. I had my bait-bag with me, bait being the name for my sandwiches and coffee. I was to take my meal-break here this evening.

'Hello.' I nodded at them all as they were seated around the kitchen of the police station, with the kettle boiling and a bottle of milk on the table.

'Just the chap!' said Vesuvius to me. 'Nick, a few months ago, you were telling us of a tailor you knew, one of the old-fashioned kind who makes suits by hand. He sits on his table cross-legged, you said, and you can see him at work through his window.'

'Golding,' I said. 'John Golding,' for this was his name and I remembered telling them about him.

'The best for miles around, you said,' continued Vesuvius and he winked at me in what I recognised as the beginnings of a conspiracy of some kind.

'He does a lot of work for the local folks,' I agreed. 'Yes, he turns out some good stuff, our farmers love him.'

'Justin here was saying he needed somebody local to make him a good suit,' Vesuvius continued. 'I was telling him of that chap you mentioned; couldn't think of his name or where he works.'

'Ah, well, John Golding,' I said to Justin. 'He's a bit old-fashioned, but he sits there in full view of the street making suits, jackets, trousers and so on. He'll tackle women's costumes, children's coats and, well, everything, even rugs for horses or car travellers. He's always busy.'

'Really, where's he operate?' asked Justin.

'Elsinby,' I said. 'If you're ever out there patrolling, park near the church and then go up the little alleyway just opposite. You'll see his window. It's a little stone cottage and there's a sign on the top of his window with his name, and it says "Ladies' and Gentlemen's Alterations".'

This was true; people from far around took pictures of that curious sign with its double meaning, but John reckoned it brought him customers!

'And can you recommend him?' asked Justin. 'I need a brand-new suit, you see, urgently. I've been invited to the wedding of Lord Gauvey in Westminster Abbey and I must have a new suit. Duty commitments mean I cannot get to London to be measured, and Vesuvius recommended this fellow.'

At this stage, both the other constables began to praise the old tailor and I suspected a plot of some kind.

I had no idea what they'd been saying before my arrival, so I adopted an impartial stance by saying, 'I've never had anything made by him.'

'But your local farmers use him?' Justin said.

'Oh, yes.' I knew this to be the case. 'They keep him going with their jobs.'

'Just like your farmers from the south, they are,' said Vesuvius. 'Smart, plenty of cash, and always out to impress. Gentlemen farmers, you know, stylish and up-to-date.'

Now I knew something was going on. Many of the local farmers didn't care two hoots how they dressed or what they looked like. If they had one smart suit for funerals and weddings, that was sufficient; the rest of the time was spent in any old working-togs they could muster. They would rarely buy a new outfit, the main visits to Golding being by bachelor farmers who wanted to have tears mended or patches sewn on knees and elbows of worn-out clothes which they thought had ten or twenty years of wear left in them. Those who were married received this attention from their wives.

I realised no one had told Justin that Golding's suits never fit anyone properly; they were always far too big or far too small; one sleeve or one leg would be longer than the other and the general rule was that his clothing only fitted a customer who was misshapen. Throughout the district, John Golding was known for his awful tailoring, although the material he used was of very superior quality. 'It's stuff,' said one farmer to me. 'Real stuff.'

John Golding always used the finest of materials and we never really knew his source, although it was thought he had family connections with the textile industry at Halifax, West Yorkshire. But his cloth was his strength, and those who commissioned John to tailor their clothing invariably knew the outcome. They would received an ill-fitting outfit made from the very best of materials, so they would take it to another tailor to have it altered. Because he was more than generous with his sizes, making clothes that were far too large, such alterations could usually be achieved. This system kept John in work, for his fees were modest, and at the end of the operation, the customer did have a very fine article of clothing which would last a lifetime.

The outcome of that visit to Eltering Police Station was that Justin Pendlebury did call on John Golding. He was duly measured and ordered his suit. He selected the very best Yorkshire worsted and was highly impressed by the quality of material kept in this tiny village tailor's shop.

'Amazing,' he said to me over the telephone. 'You'd never expect quality of that kind up here! It's top quality, you know, genuine too, the real stuff.'

Two or three weeks later, I received another telephone call from Justin. 'Nick,' he said. 'Can you do me a favour? I've had a call from Mr Golding to say my suit's ready. I wondered if you could pick it up for me and drop if off at Eltering Police Station? I see you're covering the whole section next Friday.'

'Yes, of course,' I offered.

That Friday morning, I called at John Golding's little shop and collected the parcel. I completed my morning's patrol and at lunch-time telephoned Justin who was on duty in Eltering until 3pm. He was working 7am–3pm that day, and I said that I had the parcel and would bring it to the police station around 3pm. I arrived just before three o'clock and Justin was already there, awaiting his treasure. The wedding was the following day, and he was to travel to London later this afternoon.

Vesuvius had obviously spread the word around because four other constables from the villages had, apparently by sheer coincidence, come into the office at that time, and Sergeant Charlie Bairstow was there too. They had brewed a cup of tea and it seemed that Justin, even though he didn't realise it yet, was about to have a fitting.

'I had one earlier, you know,' he told us when we pressed him to try on the suit. 'Mr Golding called me in last week . . . the final fitting . . . it was a really good fit . . . '

'Come on, Justin,' pleaded Vesuvius. 'Let's see how a city man should look. We know nowt about smart clothes up here on t'moors, you know. You've been telling us to dress well, so now's your chance to show us how to do it, right from scratch.'

The rest of us echoed those thoughts and pressed Justin to try on his new suit. In the face of such demands, he disappeared down the cell passage to change.

A few minutes later, he emerged in his new outfit. In a handsome dark worsted, it was a three-piece in the very latest style and it was a perfect fit. Justin was the epitome of a smart and successful City gentleman.

There was a stunned silence from his audience.

'How about that, then?' he beamed, doing a twirl. 'This is style, gentlemen,' he said. 'I never knew such clothing was obtainable in the north.'

'Bloody hell, you must be deformed!' laughed Vesuvius, going across and tugging the jacket. 'It's perfect . . . '

And so it was. We admired the suit; it was superb in every sense and the quality and fit was undeniable. Justin was so proud and, to be honest, we were all pleased for him. Looking back, it would have been a tragedy if it had been a gross misfit, and so later that afternoon he hurried away to travel down to the wedding in London.

Our joke had misfired, and perhaps it was a good job it had. But later that evening when I was relaxing at home, the telephone rang. It was John Golding.

'That suit you picked up this morning, Mr Rhea,' he began. 'Have you still got it?'

'I haven't, John, no. I delivered it to my colleague.'

'Where is it now?' he asked.

'In London, I'd say,' I told him, and explained the reason.

'Oh, crumbs,' he said. 'That's torn it!'

'Why?' I asked, wondering what John's problem could be.

'Well, it was the wrong one,' John said. 'That should have gone to a chap in Thirsk, and I reckon he's got that 'un your friend ordered. He reckons it doesn't fit him.'

'I think he's mistaken, John,' I said, trying to cover for Justin. 'Justin's was perfect, he's gone to a wedding in it and he was delighted. I saw him wearing it, he got the right suit, I'm sure. Maybe you could alter the Thirsk one and say nothing about the possible mistake?'

'Aye, mebbe I should. I'll tell yon Thirsk chap he's got the right 'un, they're t'same cloth. Thanks, Mr Rhea.'

I never told Justin he'd been given the wrong suit, nor did I tell Vesuvius and the other constables. I let Justin think we could produce the finest suits, and it was several weeks later when there was another repercussion.

'How did the wedding go?' I asked Justin one day when we were chatting.

He told me all about it and then, as an afterthought, he

140

added, 'Oh, by the way, that suit you helped me with. You should have seen the admiring looks I got; my family and friends were most impressed, Nick, most impressed. In fact, several of them are ordering suits from Mr Golding. I can't wait to see their faces when they receive them.'

'Neither can I,' I said with some honesty.

One of the funniest jokes was the one played upon poor Douglas Gregson and his girlfriend Deirdre. Douglas was a farmer's son who lived in Crampton with his parents.

Aged about twenty-five, Douglas was not the brightest of lads; in fact he was very simple-minded and worked as a labourer on his parents' large and busy farm. He was capable of doing as he was told, and his physical strength enabled him to undertake most of the tasks about the farm. A very good worker, he was not mentally ill, but merely rather slow when it came to using his brain.

He was strongly built with powerful shoulders and a neck like a bull, although he was very gentle-natured. With his short brown hair and big brown eyes, he was a fine-looking lad, but as his father said, 'Oor Douglas was at t'back o' t'queue when God was dishing out brains.'

His parents were ordinary hard-working farmers, and his father enjoyed working with horses; indeed, he kept several on the farm, as well as a collection of fine horse-drawn vehicles including a stage coach and several traps. He would take these to local agricultural shows and galas, where he would provide rides in them for charity. Douglas was quite a capable driver too, and would often take the reins of his father's coaches, carts and traps.

Then Douglas found a girlfriend. Deirdre was the niece of a couple in Crampton and she came to visit them from time to time. She was not too bright either and was a plain but pleasant girl a couple of years younger than Douglas. She wore her dull brown hair in a bobbed cut and had pretty pink cheeks and grey eyes. Heavily built and somewhat slow in her movements, her surname was Wharton.

Deirdre lived in Middlesbrough where she had a mundane job with the Corporation and she loved to come to the countryside. Her long-standing, platonic friendship with Douglas meant she paid regular weekend visits to Crampton and there is no doubt the couple were ideal for one another. She loved to go on outings alone with Douglas and they were sometimes accompanied by his family or her aunt and uncle.

It was during one of those outings on a lovely summer day in June, that someone played a prank on the happy pair. Douglas had been allowed to take a pony and trap for a drive and this delighted Deirdre. With her sitting in the trap like a lady, Douglas had driven along the lanes until he had found a place to halt. It was a field through which a footpath led to a lovely walk along the banks of the river to an old mill, and then across the water via a footbridge and back to this field over another pack-horse bridge. The local people enjoyed this as a Sunday afternoon walk, for it took a little over an hour.

At the entrance to the field, Douglas had tied the horse's long reins to a small tree beside the five-barred gate and had then escorted Deirdre upon this delightful stroll. The horse could move around and was able to munch the grass, even though it was still between the shafts of the trap. But a prankster saw a wonderful opportunity for a joke upon Douglas. This unknown person had discovered the unattended pony and trap and had clearly known it belonged to Douglas.

He had unhitched the pony and, with considerable skill, had manhandled the light trap. This was really a governess cart of the kind used for taking children on outings; it had two seats facing inwards, mudguards over the wheels and a low rear door. Ideal for country lanes, it was very light and manoeuvrable, even by hand. The prankster was able to place the tips of its twin shafts between the bars of the gate and the gap between the bars was sufficient for the entire length of the shafts to go through. Thus the front panels of the cart were tight against the gate, with the shafts protruding at the other side, and then the joker had backed the pony between the shafts and had re-hitched it.

When Douglas and Deirdre had returned, this sight had baffled them. Neither could understand how the pony had somehow caused the gate to become inextricably intertwined with the shafts of the trap. And Douglas, not being the brightest of lads, could not see a way to undo this problem. His answer was to use his strength. The space between the bars allowed him to lift the gate off its hinges, then he put Deirdre aboard the trap and jumped up himself.

And then he set a course for home with the gate still fastened in position; its width filled the lane and provided the wonderful sight of a mobile five-barred gate being carried between a pony and trap. And that's how I found them. I was driving my mini-van towards Crampton when this sight confronted me. I could not get past on the narrow road and pulled on to the verge where I signalled Douglas to stop.

'Now then, Douglas,' I said. 'What have we got here?'

'A five-barred gate, Mr Rhea, from yon field down by t'beck.'

'Ah.' I knew the field in question. 'And how's it come to be here? Did you run into it or something?'

'Nay, I didn't, but how it's come to get tangled up with my cart is summat I shall never know, Mr Rhea,' he said with all seriousness.

'Why, what happened?' I was now very curious about it for at this stage, I did not know what had occurred. As he pondered aloud, Deirdre sat silently in the trap, frowing as she puzzled over the answer.

'Well,' he said slowly. 'I got into t'field, tied up my awd pony and set off walking. I mean, we didn't crash through t'gate or owt like that. It was in t'field by this time, safe and sound, Mr Rhea, both t'pony and t'trap. And when we got back, yon pony must have got loose or summat, because it had got itself tangled up like yon. Now how it managed to do that, I'll never know, so I thought I'd take it home and get yon gate off. I might have to saw it off, it looks fairly well fastened on, eh?'

'If we unhitch your pony,' I said. 'We could slide that gate off, eh? And then we can put it back before somebody thinks you've stolen it.'

'Stolen it? I'd never do that, Mr Rhea.' He looked very worried at this suggestion.

'I know you wouldn't, Douglas, so let's get it off.'

I felt that the best way would be to drive pony and trap back to the field, for this was the easiest way to carry the gate to its former position. To manhandle that gate off those shafts as the trap stood here on its two wheels wouldn't be easy, so I jumped aboard and Douglas drove us back to the field. There, he skilfully positioned the trap into the space between the hedges and we inched the gate into its former position. There was sufficient room for me and Douglas to manipulate it back on to its hinges while still resting upon those shafts, and when it was secure, we unhitched the pony, withdrew the trap from the gate, and re-assembled the unit.

'There,' I said to Douglas and Deirdre. 'Now you can go home without this gate.'

'By gum, Mr Rhea, that was a clever move. Who'd have thought of that, eh?'

'Who indeed?' I wondered who had done this to Douglas and guessed that, sooner or later, the culprit would approach him to find out how he'd coped with the gate. Maybe I would never know of that discussion.

But the happy couple then drove home and I heard no more about the prank with the five-barred gate. I'm still convinced, however, that neither Douglas nor Deirdre thought it was the work of a prankster. They thought the pony had done it.

Prominent among the wonderful aspects of welfare within the police service are the police convalescent homes. There are two in England and they provide facilities for serving or retired officers who are recuperating from sickness or injury. Supported by voluntary contributions from every serving officer, they are havens of rest for those who wish to recover quietly from a serious ailment or injury. Many officers make use of them, for it is here they can enjoy a relaxed and cheerful atmosphere coupled with the undivided attention of dedicated staff. These are not hospitals; their function is to consolidate the work of the doctors and hospitals by providing after-care facilities for rest and recuperation away from domestic and professional pressures. And most certainly, they do a fine job.

The following account is not mine, therefore, because it comes from a friend who spent some time in one of the convalescent homes, and I feel it is worthy of inclusion at this point as we are discussing practical jokes.

I will call my friend Dave; after a serious illness he was advised to spend some weeks in the Northern Police Convalescent Home in order to encourage a full recovery. Once inside, he was one of a group of about thirty officers, men and women of all ranks representing most of the northern police forces. The friendly atmosphere was evident from the moment he stepped inside, and one of the things he noticed, as a constable, was that the rank structure was abolished.

In the workaday routine of the police service, especially among the provincial forces, ranks are strictly honoured, with sergeants always being called 'Sergeant' by the constables. Sometimes, very unofficially, they would be called 'Serge', but the lower rank must never address anyone of higher rank by his or her Christian name.

Sergeants and constables then address inspectors and anyone above that rank as 'sir'; inspectors call chief inspectors 'sir'; both call a superintendent 'sir', and so forth up the scale. Chief superintendents, assistant chief constables, deputy chief constables and chief constables are all 'sir' to those who are subordinate to them. In the London Metropolitan Police, the higher ranks include commanders, deputy assistant commissioners, assistant commissioners and a deputy commissioner with, of course, the Commissioner himself, all of whom are addressed as 'sir'. In the case of lady police officers, sergeants are called by that name, whereas inspectors and those of senior rank are addressed as 'ma'am'. Within the CID hierarchy, the ranks are the same, i.e. detective constables, detective sergeants, detective inspectors, detective chief inspectors, detective superintendents and detective chief superintendents.

Throughout the service, this hierarchy is strictly honoured because police officers are members of a highly disciplined body with an enormous amount of formality; inevitably, this leads to a powerful consciousness of rank through every aspect of a police officer's life.

For officers of all ranks to be thrown together into a common pool can be a traumatic experience, especially if they are supposed to be off duty and recovering from sickness in a friendly environment. No one wants his boss breathing down his neck when he is recovering from sickness. This was recognised by those in charge of the convalescent homes, and it was felt that, within those walls, all distinction between ranks should be abolished. After all, a constable could hardly feel relaxed if his table companion or snooker partner was known to be a deputy chief constable, albeit from another police area.

When officers were admitted therefore, their ranks were not known to the other residents. They were simply Miss, Mrs or Mr. Obviously, instances did occur when one officer was known to another which meant that his rank was also known, but this was a comparatively rare event because of the huge catchment area. Many officers found themselves sharing their convalescence with complete strangers, and this was the ideal situation. The decision whether or not to reveal one's rank rested with individuals.

It was Dave's misfortune, therefore, to be admitted at the same time as his own deputy chief constable. Within moments of arriving, the Home's insistence that ranks should be ignored was made known to them, and to give the Deputy his credit, his first words to Dave were, 'Ah, Dave. I'm Bill. I mean that; I'm Bill, so forget my rank. I'm Bill Short, got it?'

'Yes, sir, er . . Bill, . . sir . . . '

'Bill,' said the Deputy.

'Yes, sir . . . er . . . Bill.'

It was very difficult to abandon that habit which had developed over many years in the service, but Bill Short did his best to make Dave relax. The others, a mixture of men and women of all age groups and from widely varying aspects of the job in distant police forces, had no trouble referring to Bill as Bill. They did not know his rank, and he did his best to ensure Dave didn't tell them. But for Dave, it was not easy; it took days for him to be able to refer to his second most senior officer as Bill.

Inevitably, he did slip up from time to time and called Bill "sir" in front of the others. They, of course, did not mind for there were other "sirs" among them, happily unaware even then of the precise ranks involved. And then there developed a strange situation which completely relaxed Dave and put his boss in a wonderful new light.

One Friday evening, the residents gathered around the notice-board to study the list of forthcoming arrivals who were due at the Home on the following Monday.

'Bloody hell!' cried Stan, a man from Lancashire Constabulary. 'See that? He'll not go along with this "no rank" idea. He's the most rank-conscious man I know – he even gets his wife to call herself Mrs Superintendent Welsh. He never speaks to lower ranks when he's off duty – he's a right pain, I can tell you!'

The rest of them crowded around the board in an attempt to read the name of this unwelcome guest, as Stan went on:

'He crawls to the bosses – he'll grovel like hell to anybody higher than himself. He'll put a right damper on this place, you'll see.'

'Who is he?' asked Bill Short.

'Superintendent Adam Welsh, the Admin. Superintendent in one of our Divisions in Lancashire. Special-course man, a flier, passed all his exams and shot up the tree. He's a right toffee-nosed bastard! He doesn't know me, thank God, but we all know him!'

Bill laughed.

'Right,' he said. 'If he's coming here to flaunt his rank, we'll be ready for him. I have a plan. We can take him down a peg or two, as they say. Everyone agreed?'

They asked Stan to give a detailed account of the behaviour of the newcomer, after which they agreed they would listen to Bill's idea. In short, Welsh seemed a most objectionable man whose chief aim in life was to rise through the ranks by creeping to those who were senior to him. After hearing this, Bill took them all into the lounge and explained his system.

'Right,' he said. 'The first thing is not to react to him if he toes the Home's line; I mean, he might join in with everyone and forget his exalted rank. If he does, then we don't bring our plan into action. OK? We let him set the pace – we must give him a chance to join us.'

They all agreed to that.

'But,' he continued, 'we shall need plans if he tries to pull rank on the rest of us. To get the maximum benefit from this, you should know that, although I'm Bill to each of you, I am really a deputy chief constable. But from the moment this man enters this Home, you will let him know that I am a constable.

I'm the sort of constable who has never been in line for promotion, never passed my exams, and at my age there is no hope for promotion!'

They smiled at the idea.

'Now,' said Bill addressing a man called Keith who came from Newcastle upon Tyne. 'Keith. You are a very well spoken man, if I may say so. You do not have a Geordie accent, not even a trace of one and you do have the presence of a senior officer.' Bill's ability to assess a person shone through.

'I'm originally from Surrey,' said Keith.

'You sound very like a deputy chief constable to me!' smiled Bill. 'At least a deputy, perhaps even a chief constable. You're not, I know, because I know all the chiefs, deputies and assistants in the north. So do you mind telling us your rank – for this important exercise?'

'No, I'm a constable, that's all. I never got promoted because I never passed my exams!'

'Right,' said Bill. 'From the moment this Lancashire character arrives and plays the rank game, you will be a deputy chief constable. I shall inadvertently call you "sir" from time to time and we'll see how he reacts.'

'I'll love that!' said Keith.

To avoid further confusion, the little meeting of conspirators decided that no one else would adopt a false rank, although there was nothing to prevent them pretending they were higher than superintendent if the moment justified it. They all agreed that Keith would be their deputy chief constable for this exercise, and that Bill would be a constable on a beat in Scarborough.

It was with some interest, therefore, that the company awaited the arrival of Mr A. Welsh. After being attended to by the receptionist, he settled in his room and came to join the rest of the guests in the lounge just before lunch.

His first remark, to a grey-haired man called Cyril was, 'Where are the officers' toilets, please?'

'There aren't any,' said Cyril. 'Men's and women's are separate, but we don't use ranks here, Mr Welsh.'

'This is a *police* establishment,' was his retort. 'I should not be expected to share toilets with the lower ranks. I shall speak to

148

the management. And for lunch? There will surely be officers'
tables? With linen cloths and napkins?'

'No,' said Bill Short, entering the conversation. 'We all muck
in, we don't ask for ranks here, Mr Welsh.'

The cheek muscles in the taut white face of this man tight-
ened noticeably; he was a tall, thin man with an almost gaunt
expression and his fair hair was cut short and plastered back
with hair oil.

He showed no inclination to smile and his eyes, darting
rapidly around the room for indications of support, rested on
Keith. As Bill Short had recognised, Keith, for some reason,
had the demeanour of a very senior officer and Welsh addressed
him:

'Is this true? Am I to believe that in this police establishment,
the achievement of rank is not recognised?'

'Yes, Mr Welsh, that is so,' said Keith in his finest voice. 'We
are all guests, men and women of equal status as we recuperate.'

'Then I think this is appalling. I haven't worked my way up to
superintendent rank for nothing! I am Superintendent Welsh, I
wish everyone to know that and to remember and respect that
fact during my stay here!'

And with that statement, everyone knew what to do.

'What do you think, sir?' Bill Short asked Keith, slipping in
the rogue "sir" with astonishing ease. 'Should we revert to our
ranks?'

'I think it is a matter for individual choice,' said Keith.
'Speaking purely personally, I am happy to be called Keith by
everyone here, including Superintendent Welsh.'

Keith played his part with such aplomb that the others almost
applauded him and this set the scene. Later, they learned that
Welsh had quietly sought the advice of one of the guests about
Keith's rank, and was told, in the strictest confidence, that he
was deputy chief constable from Newcastle upon Tyne City
Police.

In the days that followed, Welsh followed Keith around like a
pupil with a crush on a teacher, having been assured that
everyone else here was below his own rank and therefore
unworthy of his companionship. He carried Keith's golf clubs,
invited him out for drinks, joined him at snooker and card

games, discussed policy matters with him and generally shut the others out of his short convalescence.

For Bill Short, this was excellent and he was enjoying himself testing Welsh's reactions; he tried to win his confidence by inviting him out for a drink, by offering to play snooker with him, by inviting him for walks into the town for shopping or sightseeing, but each of Bill's overtures was politely rejected. Welsh made it abundantly clear that he did not consort with lower ranks, especially constables who drank pints and played snooker.

Stan's assessment of Welsh had been absolutely accurate for he was a snob, and a rank-conscious snob into the bargain. By the end of the week, everyone was wondering how to reveal to Superintendent Welsh the fact that he was being led gently along a path that led to nowhere in a wonderfully false world. It was learned that he would be going home on the Sunday, and in order to make the necessary impact upon him, the truth should be revealed.

The opportunity came during the dinner on Saturday night. It was made known that the Chief Constable of Newcastle upon Tyne City Police would be attending the evening dinner as a guest of the Home.

He was chairman of the management committee and was attending in that capacity. Chief constables were regular visitors, for most of them served on the management committee or supported the work of the convalescent home in various ways. As the dinner gong sounded, therefore, the residents moved into the dining-room and Superintendent Welsh made sure he shared a table with Keith. There was an even more important reason for this because Welsh realised that Keith was from the Newcastle force. Perhaps he thought the Chief Constable would come over and express interest in the health of one of his most senior officers. Everyone was seated prior to the Chief Constable's entry and, as was his custom, he toured the tables to speak to the guests before settling down to eat.

When he arrived at Keith's table, his eyes lit up.

'Ah, PC Burton, good to see you. How's it going?'

'Fine, sir,' beamed Keith. 'This break has done me a world of good. I feel much better now.'

'Summonses and Warrants is having a busy time without you, you know. I'll tell Sergeant Helm you're doing fine; I know he's anxiously awaiting your return!'

'Another week should do it, sir,' said Keith, pleased his Chief had recognised him.

'Good, well, nice to have seen you looking so fit. And you,' he now addressed Welsh. 'Are you recuperating nicely?'

'Yes, sir,' beamed Welsh.

And before Welsh could announce his name and rank, the Chief Constable moved on and stopped at Bill Short's table.

'Bill, good to see you! Are you coping with these rebels around you? It's time you were getting back, you know, your Chief hasn't had a day off since you went sick!'

Everyone in the room heard his friendly exchanges and all eyes were now on Superintendent Welsh. For a long time, he said nothing, his eyes flickering as the full import of the Chief's words began to register.

'PC Burton?' Eventually he quietly asked Keith to tell the truth. 'Did I hear your Chief correctly?'

'You did, Mr Welsh,' said Keith with an air of pride. 'I am PC Keith Burton of the Summonses and Warrants Department of Newcastle upon Tyne City Police.'

'And that other man, that Bill Short, he led me to think he's a constable at Scarborough. If my ears don't deceive me, your Chief knows him well and that smacks of a rank much higher than constable! The others haven't mentioned their ranks.' Already there was a look of impending horror on Welsh's pale face; he realised he had been deliberately tricked.

'He's a deputy chief constable, Mr Welsh. With the local force.'

For a long time, Superintendent Welsh did not speak. He ate his dinner in silence, often playing with his food and allowing the conversation to bubble around him. No one could tell what thoughts were buzzing through his head.

At the end of the meal, the Chief Constable left the room with other members of staff, and only then did the grim-faced Welsh make his move.

'I would like a word with all of you,' he said to the residents. 'In the lounge, if you don't mind, in five minutes.'

It was almost like a command, but it was clearly tempered with a note of sorrow and even regret. As the others looked to him for guidance, Bill Short nodded his agreement to Welsh's request and they all assembled, wondering what was in store. They settled on the easy chairs which lined the walls, awaiting Welsh's comments. He came in and stood before them, a tall, pale and now rather fragile figure. The arrogance had been knocked out of him.

'You've made a fool of me,' he said, without smiling. 'I fell into your trap. I am a fool,' he suddenly added with a smile. 'An utter stupid fool. It's people that matter, not ranks. So if anyone wants to go out for a drink, there's a nice hostelry down the road, and the drinks are all on me. I am sorry for my behaviour.'

There was a momentary silence, then Bill Short said, 'It takes a man to admit he's wrong, so you're on – er, sir!'

'Thanks – er, Bill,' smiled Welsh. 'You've made me realise we're human beings, not machines with pips on our shoulders!'

Everyone started chattering and then Welsh turned to Keith Burton. 'Coming – er, sir?', he asked with a smile.

'You try and stop me – er, Adam,' said PC Burton.

8

'I have considered the days of old,
and the years that are past.'
The Book of Common Prayer

In previous 'Constable' books, I have provided accounts of fascinating people in the twilight of their years; some of their stories are included in *Constable around the Village* and I thought I would elaborate upon one or two of those tales and include a few new ones.

So far as old folk are concerned, caring for them is very much a part of the village constable's life. This is not formal care of the kind expected from the multitude of welfare and charity services nor does it impinge upon their family's own responsibilities, but it means that the village constable, while on patrol, does keep an eye open for signs of need or distress among the older folk. Sometimes this continuing observation results in a telephone call to the family concerned or perhaps to one or other of the welfare services or charitable organisations. More often than not, however, the constable is able to cope with any immediate need and his work goes unpublicised, save for a word of thanks, or a cup of tea, from a grateful senior citizen.

I found that the elderly who lived in and around Aidensfield were highly independent country folk who hated the idea that they might have to depend on charity or the welfare state. In helping them, there was a need to exercise discretion and to show them that any help given was not an adverse reflection upon their own capabilities.

Having led a life of self-sufficiency founded upon hard work

153

and enterprise, their advancing years made them less able to cope physically, although their mental state and belief in themselves remained undimmed. Many of them felt they could achieve just as much at eighty years of age as they had done at thirty, and that did cause some worries.

One shining example of this philosophy was eighty-three-year-old Jacob Broadbent. Officially, he was a retired farmer and he and his wife, Sissy (81), lived in a neat bungalow in Aidensfield. Built specially for them in their retirement, it was fitted with the latest work-saving ideas and boasted a large garden full of mature soft-fruit bushes, fully grown apple and plum trees and a patch for vegetable cultivation. The garden had once been part of a larger house and Jacob's son had succeeded in buying the plot upon which to build his parents' retirement home.

The inclusion of a large garden had been a brilliant idea by Jacob's son, Jesse, a man in his late fifties. Jesse knew that his father would require something to occupy him during his so-called retirement, and this was the garden's purpose. In spite of tending his little patch, however, Jacob made regular visits to the farm where Jesse found the old man various jobs to keep him busy. Jacob, as one would have expected, couldn't understand the new ideas and machinery that Jesse introduced, but contented himself by looking after the pigs and sheep, feeding the hens and recording their egg production as he had in years past.

The result was that in his retirement, Jacob was kept busy and that made him very happy. Sissy, his down-to-earth wife, kept out of his way. She knew better than to interfere with his daily routine. Always on the go, she fussed over her new bungalow, visited people in the village and, even at eighty-one, made sure she was involved in village activities such as the church and the Women's Institute. This kept her fully occupied, and for a couple in their eighties, they were remarkably alert, active and energetic.

There is no doubt that one of Jacob's joys was his orchard. Having grown apples at the farm, he had continued this enterprise at his new bungalow, another example of Jesse's foresight in providing something for his father to do. And so, in the autumn, Jacob supplied the local shops, hotels and village people with a variety of fresh and tasty apples. It provided him with some pocket money, out of which he enjoyed a regular pint in the Brewers Arms, a daily pipe or two of strong-smelling tobacco and weekly trips to all the local cattle markets and, where possible, sales of antiques or house-contents.

It was during a late September afternoon that I was attracted to his orchard by a cry for help. By chance, I was walking through Aidensfield, intending to call at the garage on a routine enquiry about a recent accident. The garage had recovered from the scene the vehicles which had been damaged, and because I needed precise details of the damage for my report I was on my way to inspect them.

As I walked beneath the high wall which concealed the Broadbents' home from the street, I became aware of a hoarse cry. It was very faint. At first, I could not decide what it was or where it was coming from, but as I stopped to listen more carefully, I realised it was a man and it was coming from Jacob's orchard. Sensing trouble, I rushed into the garden and hurried around the back of the bungalow to the orchard from where the calls were being repeated. And there, as I rounded the corner past the greenhouse, I found Jacob.

'Mr Rhea!' he breathed as he saw me. 'By, it's good thoo's come along now . . . '

He was lying on his back beneath a tall, sturdy apple tree and his right leg was held high in the air among the lower branches. A basket of apples was lying upturned near by with its contents spilled across the grass.

'What's up, Jacob?' I asked, hurrying to his aid.

'I tummled doon this tree, Mr Rhea, and that trouser leg's gitten hooked up somewhere . . . '

'Jacob!' I tried to sound angry as I examined his elevated leg. How did he come to tumble down the tree? But I had no time to ask that sort of question just yet. I had to release him first. The material of his trousers had "snagged" on a short, strong stump of a branch, and it had pierced the cloth. This now held Jacob's leg in the air and from his position on the ground, he could not free himself. He was a prisoner of his own apple tree!

'This is a right mess you've got yourself into, Jacob!' I said, trying to free his leg. 'Are you hurt?'

'It winded me, Mr Rhea,' he said. 'Knocked the stuffing out of me, landing flat on my back like this. But I've got me breath back now. I think I'm all right.'

'No injuries, then?' I was struggling to free the trouser leg from the tree but his weight made it difficult.

'Nay, nowt.'

'How long have you been lying here then?' was my next question.

'Ages, Mr Rhea. She's out, you see, our Sissy, I mean. Gone to see a friend, she has. I've been laid here shouting for hours . . . nobody heard me . . . I got frightened, thoo knaws.'

'Lift your backside in the air a bit, can you?' I asked him. 'Then it'll take some of the weight off this leg and I'll be able to lift you off this branch.'

His overall trousers were made of tough denim and I had to cut the cloth to effect his release. My pocket knife made short work of that problem and once his leg was free, I lifted him to his feet. He hobbled around a bit, stamping his foot and holding his aching back with his hand. I looked around for a ladder, but found none. Maybe a rung had snapped or its wood was rotten?

'How did you get up that tree, Jacob?' I asked.

'Climbed up,' he said.

'Without a ladder or steps?' I put to him.

'There's no need for owt like that, Mr Rhea,' he said with just a trace of contempt. 'Why bother with ladders when t'trees grow their own steps?'

'You shouldn't be climbing trees at your age!' I shook my finger at him in a mock rebuke. 'You could break a leg or something if you fall down – these are big trees and it's a long fall from the top! Look how a tumble bruises apples that come down! You'll be covered with bruises tonight, I shouldn't wonder.'

'Thoo'll not tell our missus, wilt thoo?' he asked with a note of pleading in his voice.

'Why not?' I put to him.

'Well, she's allus going on at me about climbing trees and picking apples, Mr Rhea, and it's only way I can pick 'em. So say nowt to her, eh? About me tummling doon.'

'So long as you're not hurt!' I submitted.

'Fit as a fiddle,' he said, straightening his back as if to emphasise his words. 'There's nowt ailing me.'

'OK, but remember, no more climbing trees!'

'You sound just like my missus!' he grumbled as he stooped to begin picking up the spilt apples, groaning with pain as he did so. I helped him and when we'd collected the lot, he went indoors.

'Thoo'll come in for a cup o' tea, Mr Rhea?' he invited me.

'No thanks, Jacob,' I said. 'I'd love to, but I've got to get on. I'm supposed to be visiting the garage!'

Happy that his fall had not resulted in any permanent damage, I left him to recover over a cup of tea. I thought little more about the incident until I saw his wife, Sissy, in the village street a couple of weeks later.

'How's your Jacob these days?' I asked after a general chat.

'Fine,' she said, 'But his rheumatics is bothering him a bit. He reckons his back hurts; I say it's with climbing apple trees but he says it's not. Mr Rhea, mebbe you'd have a word with him about climbing trees at his age. He'll fall down one of these days, mark my words, and that could be t'end of him. I shouldn't want to deal with him if he cripples hisself cos he's tummled oot of a tree at eighty-three, Mr Rhea. He's a bit awd for that sort of a caper.'

'I'll have a word with him,' I promised her.

I did speak to him and said he was too old for that sort of a caper, as Sissy had put it. But it made no difference. He continued to climb apple trees until his death at ninety-two.

Another tale involved Sidney Latimer who was eighty-six. A retired lengthman, his work had involved keeping the roads tidy and well maintained. And, so I learned from the older folks, Sidney had done a very thorough job. In winter especially, he had kept them gritted and open when others near by had been closed in the grip of the weather. Sidney had always taken a pride in "his" roads.

He lived alone in a pretty cottage just off the main street at Aidensfield and he coped very well with his daily chores, albeit with the help of a lady who popped in to care for him. Like so many of the elderly in and around Aidensfield, he would emerge on a fine day to sit on the bench near the war memorial, there to observe the passing show and to chat with three or four pals of similar age.

Then he became ill. I was not aware of this for some time, but realised that he was not enjoying his daily walk or his sojourns to the village seat and so I asked after him from his cleaning lady.

'Oh, he's in hospital, Mr Rhea, at York.'

'Oh, I had no idea! What's wrong with him?' I asked.

'Old age mainly,' she said without a hint of sympathy. 'And his waterworks are giving him pain. They're seeing to him there, he might be in for a week or two.'

I rang the hospital to enquire after his progress and was given the usual response, 'Mr Latimer is as well as can be expected.'

That did not say a great deal so, one afternoon when Mary and I, with the family, went shopping to York, I decided to pop in and see Mr Latimer. I found him in a ward full of elderly gentlemen, some in a very poor state and clearly approaching the end of their lives. Assailed by the distinctive smell from this geriatric ward, I settled at Sidney's bedside.

'Now, Mr Latimer,' I said. 'How's things?'

'Hello, Mr Rhea.' His old eyes twinkled with delight because he had a visitor. 'You are looking slim. How's Mrs Rhea?'

This was his usual greeting; whenever he met anyone, man or woman of any shape or size, he complimented them upon looking slim.

'She's fine thanks,' I told him, pulling up a chair. 'She's in town, shopping, she sends her best wishes and hopes you'll be home soon.'

'It's my waterworks, Mr Rhea, they say. I reckon I need a good plumber not a doctor. But they say I'll be home before long.'

He was very alert and we chatted for some time about village matters. He was a big man, well over six feet tall, and in his younger days must have been an impressive sight. He had married, I knew, but his wife had died several years earlier and, so far as I knew, there had been no children. Sitting propped up on that hospital bed, he did look rather vulnerable and somewhat smaller and more fragile than usual. During the course of our conversation, he said he got a bit lonely.

'It's not like being at home, is it? At home I can pop out and
see folks, there's allus somebody about, or something to do,
even if it's just popping into a shop or the post office for my
pension. Here, I just have to lie down and do as I'm told. These
old lads in here aren't much company, are they?'

He looked along the ward at his companions and sighed.

'Just lying there fading away, that's all they're doing. There's
not a lot of excitement unless it's some poor sod who's cocked
his toes.'

It must be awful, seeing one's companions dying one by one,
but he seemed unperturbed. He was fully convinced he would
be allowed home very soon.

'There must be somebody I can tell about you being in here,
Mr Latimer,' I suggested. 'The village folks know you're
here . . . '

'They never come!' he grumbled.

'Relations, then? Old friends? Shall I write to them and say
you're here?'

'Apart from folks around Aidensfield, there's only my old
schoolteacher. Taught me when I was a lad, she did. You might
tell her, I allus send her a Christmas card.'

Now I thought he was going senile but wary of his reactions if
I showed disbelief, I said, 'Where's she live? I'll tell her.'

He delved into his bedside cabinet and pulled out a battered
old pocket diary, years out of date. Flicking through the pages
until he found the place, he said, 'No 18 Ryelands Terrace,
Eltering. Miss Wilkinson. Taught me my three Rs at Ashfordly
Primary she did. 1886 she was there. Lovely woman. Lovely as
they come. She'll be interested to know I'm here. Allus kept in
touch, she has.'

To humour him, I made a note of the name and address in my
private diary and promised I would tell her. This seemed to
please him greatly and our next half-hour was spent in casual
chatter about nothing in particular. I could see he was tiring so I
said my goodbyes.

'Goodbye, Mr Rhea,' he smiled as I stood up. 'My word, you
do look slim. Now, you won't forget to tell Miss Wilkinson, will
you? And you will come again?'

'Yes, I'll come again,' I assured him, and left to collect my wife and family from the cafe where they'd been having tea with one of Mary's friends.

I must admit I gave no more thought to Mr Latimer's supposed schoolteacher, but a few days later, I was patrolling Eltering. I had driven there in my mini-van because I was scheduled for a two-hour foot patrol in the town; there was a shortage of local officers that afternoon. And then, quite unexpectedly, I found myself walking along Ryelands Terrace. The name had meant nothing until now and when I saw the nameplate on the wall of one of the houses, it caused a flicker of reaction in my mind. At first, I could not determine why it should interest me and then I recalled my chat with old Mr Latimer.

Pulling out my diary, I found my note about Miss Wilkinson, the primary schoolteacher who'd taught him around 1886; she had lived at No 18. Now full of curiosity, I decided to walk along to No 18.

When I got there, I found an elderly lady tidying her front garden. She was slender and small, with a neat head of tidy grey hair and she carried a paper sack. She was collecting fallen leaves which had been blown from some nearby sycamores. She smiled warmly as I approached.

'Leaves are such a nuisance, Constable, aren't they? Every autumn, they blow into my garden, and every autumn I clean them out!'

'They are!' I sympathised with her. 'My wife makes compost from them, we find them a nuisance really, but we can make use of them!'

'Yes, I give mine away,' she smiled. 'To the old gentleman who lives next door. My garden is much too small for me to worry about compost.'

I wondered if I dare ask about Miss Wilkinson, Mr Latimer's old teacher, for it was such a long time ago that she'd taught the old man. Maybe she had married and this was her daughter? Or a younger sister? Maybe this lady had no idea who lived here before her . . .

'Excuse me,' I said, 'But now that I'm here, I wonder if you know of a Miss Wilkinson who used to live here. She was a teacher in the primary school at Ashfordly in 1886.'

'That's me,' she said primly. 'I'm Miss Wilkinson.'

'You!' I did not know what to say. 'But, she must be older than you . . . she taught a friend of mine, a Mr Latimer . . . '

'Sidney Latimer,' she smiled. 'Yes, of course. He was in my class, a very good pupil and very bright. He did nothing with his life, Officer, he could have done anything he wanted, that man. Wasted his talents. Such a shame.'

I was still not sure we were discussing the same Sidney Latimer, so I said, 'Well, he's in hospital actually, in York. He's had a minor operation and asked if I would inform Miss Wilkinson, his teacher . . . '

'Yes, that's me. He must be, oh, what? Eighty-six now? He was eight when I taught him, Constable, and I would be getting on for twenty, I think.'

'So you really were his teacher?' I was astounded.

'Yes, of course! I'm well into my nineties now, you know, but still going strong!'

'But . . . '

'Sidney was a nice boy, Constable, and I've always been interested in his welfare. Always. I shall go to visit him in hospital.'

'Shall I arrange a lift for you?' I heard myself offering.

'Thank you, but no. I will use the bus. There is a very good bus service from Eltering to York and I will enjoy the outing. Thank you for telling me about Sidney, I will certainly pay him a call.'

And so she did. He was delighted and I was amazed.

I sat down and worked it out; if he was eight in 1886, he'd been born in 1878 and at the time I met him, he was about eighty-six. If she was twenty in 1886, which was feasible for a teacher in a primary school, she'd have been born in 1866 which meant she was around ninety-eight!

Even now, I find myself surprised that a man of eighty-six could keep in touch with his primary school teacher. And, following her visit, Sidney Latimer did get well and returned home to continue his life in Aidensfield.

Another sad but funny tale occurred during a summer soon after I arrived at Aidensfield. It involved a pair of twin bachelor brothers and their aged father who farmed in an isolated dale to the north of Aidensfield. The sons were Angus and Fergus MacKenzie, and their father was Alexander Cameron Mac-Kenzie, a man in his eighties. No one was quite sure of the twins' age, but they must have been around sixty years old.

In spite of their names, they were Yorkshiremen, although I'm sure a distant ancestor must have journeyed this way from the Highlands. They occupied one of the most remote farms in the moors; it was called Dale Head and it stood high on the slopes of Lairsbeck, at the end of a long, rough track. The MacKenzies dealt chiefly in sheep, although they did breed Highland cattle, and seemed to scrape some kind of a living from their lofty farmstead. Theirs was a life of constant work with no time for relaxation.

Money was always short; they were clearly hard up and were seldom seen in the village or nearby market towns. Mrs Mac-Kenzie had died some years ago, but the twins had never married; they'd never seen the point of having to keep one or two extra people in the house. And so, over the years, they existed in the little stone farmhouse with its stupendous views across the moors. I called infrequently to check their stock register, and that was my only contact with them. I called, drank a mug of tea, signed their book and departed. I probably called once every month or even once every two.

On one occasion when I called in late May, Angus met me and produced the necessary book which I signed. I had seen Fergus in the foldyard and on this occasion, I was not invited to stay for a cup of tea in spite of my long drive.

'We're getting set up for haytime, Mr Rhea,' Angus told me. 'It's allus a thrang time for t'likes of us.'

I knew what he was saying. Thrang is the local word for "busy", and for a moorland patch like this, every day counted. Haytime up here was fraught with risk from the weather, and so they had to work rapidly and positively to succeed, taking swift advantage of the limited sunshine and drying winds. And with only two fit men and one old man to do all the work, it was a lengthy procedure. Later, however, I thought about that missing mug of tea. It was unusual, but at the time I did not pay any heed to this departure from the normal.

Later, I realised I had not seen the old man around the buildings either, and once more, this was unusual. Down in the dale and in the surrounding hamlets, no one thought it odd that old Mr MacKenzie had not been seen. He seldom ventured out anyway, his lads making sure they did any shopping that was necessary. I must admit that his absence did not bother me, for I knew of his habits and routine. It was more unusual to see him than not to see him! It was only after the events which occurred later that I realised the significance of all these odd facets.

It began with a call from Harold Poulter, the undertaker.

'Mr Rhea,' he said quietly over the telephone. 'I've a rum sort of a job on. I thought I'd better give you a call.'

Harold dealt with most of the local funerals and we had a good working liaison due to my own official involvement in the investigation of sudden, violent or unusual deaths. Harold knew which deaths should be investigated by the police and so a call from him had to be taken seriously.

'Yes, Harold, what is it this time?'

'It's poor awd Alex MacKenzie, you know, from Lairsbeck. He's tipped his clogs.'

'Ah', I said partly to myself, 'that's why I haven't seen him around, he must have been ill.'

'Well, I'm not so sure about that, Mr Rhea,' he said. 'But it's a funny affair if you ask me.'

'Go on, Harold,' I invited him to continue.

'Well, them twin lads of his, they've had him up there for weeks, Mr Rhea, never got around to fixing a funeral. I mean, I wonder if you fellers'll need a PM or inquest or summat. Seems he's been dead for weeks.'

'Weeks? How many weeks, Harold?' I asked.

'Dunno, and they're not sure either,' he said. 'They've had no doctor in, they say they know when a pig's dead or a cow, so they know when a feller's gotten his time overed.'

I groaned.

'Where is the body now?'

'In a pigsty,' said Harold. 'They put him there because it's a cool spot and he would keep a while. He wouldn't stink the

163

bedroom out, so they said.'

'I'd better get up there,' I said. 'Have you told Doctor McGee?'

'No, I thought you'd best know first.'

'OK, right, I'll have a ride up to Dale Head and let you know what happens. I'll ring Doctor McGee before I go.'

When I spoke to Doctor McGee, he asked whether I thought it was a suspicious death, like a suicide, or even murder. I had to say I had no idea at this stage; a visual examination would help to determine the future police action, but in view of what Harold had told me, I felt the presence of a doctor was advisable.

'Right, I'll see you there,' he said.

I arrived in advance of Dr McGee and knocked on the tatty kitchen door. In need of a coat of paint, it was opened by Angus, a thin, large-boned fellow with gaunt cheeks and an unkempt head of sparse ginger hair which was greying around the temples. He smiled a welcome, showing a mouth full of huge yellowing teeth which looked as solid as the rocks around the farm and which had probably never seen a dentist in half a century.

'Noo then, Mr Rhea,' he said, opening the door. 'We was expecting thoo.'

Inside, Fergus, who was almost identical to his brother, albeit perhaps a little more robust in his appearance, was sitting at the end of the plain wooden kitchen table. Around him was a collection of mugs along with the teapot, a half-full milk bottle and a sugar bowl.

'Thoo'll have a cup o' tea, Mr Rhea?' Fergus asked. I was pleased to see this routine had been re-established.

'Thanks, Fergus,' and I settled at the table with Angus at my side. I waited until I had the mug in my hands and said, 'Harold Poulter would tell you why I had to come?'

'Aye, 'e did, Mr Rhea. Unusual death, 'e said. But, Mr Rhea, there's nowt unusual aboot oor father's death. 'E just passed on, like awd folks do. In 'is sleep, no fuss or bother. We've 'ad cows pass on like yon. Nice as yer like, Mr Rhea, so, well, Ah'll be honest, Ah can't understand why awd Harold wouldn't just let us git on wi' t'funeral and git t'awd man buried. It's time we did summat wiv 'im.'

'There are always formalities when a person dies.' I tried to be courteous. 'Forms to fill in, a doctor's certificate to obtain, the registrar to see, things like that. You can't bury a human being like you'd bury a sheep.'

'When they're dead, they're dead,' said Angus. He was probably harking back to the days when the procedures surrounding death were less strictured. Certainly in some remote places, people died in circumstances which today would warrant a full investigation – but all that was in the past.

'Doctor McGee is following me along,' I said. 'He must see the body . . . er . . . your father . . . and certify that he is dead. That's his first job. Then if he cannot certify the *cause* of death, I'm afraid a post-mortem must be held. That means examination by an expert who determines precisely what caused death; he'll find out if it was a heart problem, or something else. Once that's been established, the funeral can go ahead, with the permission of the coroner.'

''E's as dead as a doornail,' cried Angus. 'There's neea need for t'doctor to come and tell us that! And as for t'reason 'e died, it was age, nowt else. 'E was tonned eighty-eight, and 'e just faded away in 'is sleep.'

'I'm sure you're right, but we do have to do things the proper way.'

I could see they did not understand the need for all the fuss, and then Dr Archie McGee arrived. Fergus took him to the table and he sat down with a mug of tea, then looked at me for guidance.

'Well, Mr Rhea, what's the score on this one?'

'It seems that Mr MacKenzie, senior, died in his sleep, Doctor.'

'He'll be upstairs now, is he? I'll have a look.'

'No, he's outside, in a pigsty,' I said. 'We are waiting to take you there, after you've had your cuppa.'

'Pigsty? Did he die there?' he asked the twins.

'Nay!' said Fergus shortly. ''E died in bed, but because it was haytime, we couldn't stop work to git 'im buried. There was no time, Mr Rhea, not a minute to spare. You'll know what t'weather's been like, we daren't miss a day just for a funeral. So we laid 'im in yon pigsty till we got finished haytiming; it's not in use and we cleaned it out, them put 'im in straw and salted 'im, making sure we turned 'im twice a week. 'E's out there, as fresh as a posy, waiting to be buried. I mean, there's nowt wrang wiv 'im, except he's dead o' course. 'E didn't suffer, 'e wasn't badly, 'e never fell off a ladder or banged 'is head on owt . . . 'e just faded away like Ah said.'

Doctor McGee raised his eyes as if to heaven. 'And how long has he been there?'

'Since just afore we started haytime. Four or five weeks, mebbe. Actually, Doctor, we got finished haytiming a while back, and we was that relieved we'd got all t'hay ladened in, we forgot aboot 'im for a day or two. It was only when Ah went in t'sty for summat that Ah saw 'im there, so Ah turned him over and rang Harold to git 'im buried.'

Dr McGee grinned ruefully at me, as Fergus continued,

'I thought it was time we were gitting summat done with t'awd feller. Not that 'e'd have minded waiting, thoo knaws, 'e allus was a patient chap, oor dad.'

'You are supposed to organise the funeral straight away, gentlemen,' Doctor McGee sighed. 'You must call a doctor who'll certify death and get things moving.'

'We couldn't see t'point in that,' said Fergus. 'Ah mean, once 'e was dead, there was nowt 'e could do and nowt we could do, and besides, 'e wouldn't take any 'arm waiting awhile to get buried. Ah reckon this is a fuss about nowt.'

McGee drained his tea. 'I'd better have a look at him. Take us to him, gents.'

The brothers led us to a row of pigsties and pointed to one with its door closed. 'In there,' said Fergus.

'You wait outside,' he said to them. 'I'll have a look at him, PC Rhea had better come with me.'

Inside, there was the stench of death which is always present around a corpse, but it was tempered by the stronger smell of salt and there, packed in lots of dry straw, was the body of old Mr MacKenzie. It had not decomposed as one would have expected, and no doubt the salt treatment had done something to preserve it. And the straw had kept it cool too, rather like the old system of storing blocks of ice in straw deep within the ice-houses of country mansions. Ice blocks kept in straw could survive for many months without melting . . .

Corpses were kept in mortuary fridges for months or even years, and those old ice-houses would keep game fresh for months too. This pigsty was beautifully cool and dry; it was also rat-proof and I wondered how long old Mr MacKenzie would have kept 'as fresh as a posy' in here. Maybe for months, even if it was an English summer.

Dr McGee began his examination; it was very thorough due to the curious circumstances, and he stripped the nightshirt off the stiff old man to check for wounds or marks of violence, turning the body over and meticulously inspecting it. From where I stood, I saw no marks likely to raise suspicion, but I watched the doctor's careful work.

'You never treated the old man, Doctor?' I asked as he conducted his examination.

He shook his head. 'Once, years ago, he went down with a stomach problem, but that was ten or twelve years since. Looking at him, and bearing in mind he's been out here for weeks, I'd say he died from old age, from natural causes.'

'Would you certify that?' I put the important question to him.

'It would require a postmortem to determine that with any accuracy.' He spoke honestly. 'The pathologist would have to examine the heart, brain, internal organs, lungs, throat muscles, the lot – you know the routine as well as I do. There are ways of despatching old folks, as you well know, to make it look like a natural death.'

'So do you think this is a suspicious death?' I put him on the spot once again.

'To be honest, no. These chaps are too basic for that. Besides, if they had done the old chap in, they'd have got rid of the body, not kept it in cold storage until they could fix a proper funeral. Look, PC Rhea, if we go through all the official motions, with a PM, the coroner, publicity and so forth, these old characters are going to be made to look fools, aren't they? And nothing will be achieved.'

'Yes,' I agreed. 'They will look a bit daft.'

'I am prepared to certify first, that he is dead, and second, that he died from natural causes, from old age in fact. In spite of these odd circumstances, there is no doubt in my mind that the old boy died naturally, although, to be totally honest, we should really have a post-mortem due to the time lapse since he died. But I will stick my neck out and issue the necessary certificate, without going through all those formalities. I think it is totally unnecessary in this case.'

'Fine, that's all I need, and thanks. We can get this over now. That's all Harold needs to organise the funeral.'

And so Dr McGee wrote out the necessary certificate and gave it to the brothers.

'That's all you require,' he said. 'Give this to Harold Poulter and he'll attend to the rest of it. He'll see the registrar for you as well, leave it all in his hands.'

'Thanks, Doctor,' said Fergus. 'Ah never realised dying meant sike a carry-on.'

'I've dated the death certificate for today,' said McGee. 'That means the official date of your dad's death is today, do you understand?'

Angus nodded. 'A bit like t'Queen, eh?' he said slowly. 'She's got an official birthday and a real one, so our dad's got an official day for dying and a real one.'

'Yes,' said McGee, 'but don't mention the real one!'

'Do we 'ave to do owt else, then?' asked Angus. 'Is that it? Is t'official bit ovver with?'

'Nearly, but Harold the undertaker will see to the rest of it for you. You've done your bit.'

'Dying's fussier than Ah thought it would be,' said Angus to his brother. 'So think on, and get me buried quick if Ah goes afore thoo!'

'And we'll 'ave to get yon pigsty disinfected, we've a sow due to farrow next week, and we can't let t'young 'uns live in a sty that needs disinfecting. It's time we got oor awd dad shifted somewhere more permanent.'

And so the funeral went ahead and they made their 'more permanent' arrangements for their father's long-term rest. So if you visit the churchyard at Lairsbeck, you will see the tombstone of Alexander Cameron MacKenzie who died aged eighty-eight. The date on his tombstone is 4th July, but that is neither the date of his actual death nor of his funeral.

It is the date Dr McGee examined him in that pigsty.

9

'Something very childish, but very natural.'
Samuel Taylor Coleridge, 1772-1834

Children take part in a large proportion of a police officer's work, sometimes through the fault of others such as cases of neglect or cruelty, sometimes as victims through the commission of crimes, sexual assaults, family arguments and maintenance defaulters, sometimes by accident when they are knocked down by motor vehicles or suffer death by drowning or from any other cause. Other matters within our scope were the employment of children, dangerous performances in places like circuses or theatres, harmful publications which might affect them, smoking by juveniles, their general care and protection, their education and a whole host of other matters. Abortion, child destruction, infanticide, concealment of birth and the abandonment of children all came with the realm of our duties.

Our law books and police procedural volumes devoted entire chapters to the law, practice and procedure relating to children and young persons but I cannot determine precisely what proportion of my duty time was spent on matters relating to them. It was certainly a substantial amount and indeed, the criminal law of England does rightly devote many statutes or parts of statutes to children and young persons. Indeed, it divides them into neat categories and we had to learn, parrot fashion, a table of relevant ages at which certain crimes and offences might be committed against youngsters.

For example, a mother causing the death of her child under 1 year old could be convicted of infanticide; it was an offence to abandon a child under 2 so as to endanger life or health; there was a crime committed by suffocation of a child under 3 when it was in bed with a drunken person over 16; intoxicants must not be given to a child under 5 unless for medicinal reasons, and children over 5 must receive a proper education. It was an offence to be drunk in charge of a child under 7 in a public place or on licensed premises and, at that time, a child under 8 was not held criminally responsible for his or her acts. That age was subsequently raised to 10.

This table of ages included youngsters up to 24, with a mass of information concerning those in their teens – there was drinking in pubs, owning and using firearms, driving motor vehicles, marriage, betting, pawning goods or dealing in rags plus a list of penalties open to them if they committed offences or crimes. Much of this legislation was designed for the care and protection of children and young persons and it was our duty to enforce those laws.

In criminal law, the word 'child' meant a person under the age of 14, and 'young person' meant a person who had attained the age of 14 but was under the age of 17. The term 'juvenile' included both children and young persons, thus referring to all those under 17, while 'adult' was a person aged 17 and upwards, but aspects of these definitions have now been changed.

It follows that we spent a lot of time learning the mass of laws which affected children and young persons, and we also spent considerable time enforcing the awkward laws which seemed to attract rebellious youngsters, such as drinking under age, driving under age, betting under age, smoking under age, using firearms under age, having sex under age and being employed under age. There were times when even police officers felt the law was silly – for example, a person can take the responsibility for getting married and having children at 16, but cannot buy a pint of ale in the bar of a pub until reaching 18. A person of 17 could be in sole charge of an aircraft in motion but should not be sent betting circulars until reaching 21.

However, it was not the task of the police service to question the laws of the realm, however illogical they might be, for those laws were made by Parliament and our job was to enforce them without fear or favour. In fact, our enforcement of the law is always tempered with discretion for without that, the country would become a police state. If we rigidly enforced every law, life would be intolerable; imagine the furore if we prosecuted everyone who drank, smoked or placed bets while under age or experienced their first groping sexual encounter with someone under the permitted age. One learned judge made it clear that the latter laws were not for the prosecution of youngsters having a tumble in the hay.

But many of our dealings with youngsters were outside the scope of the law; they were simply ordinary everyday happenings which involved a policeman and a child, and I had a marvellous example of this when Mrs June Myers lost her purse. A pretty young mother with two children, she came to my police house at Aidensfield to report the loss.

When the doorbell rang that Saturday lunchtime, I answered it to find the fair-haired June standing outside with her daughter; this was Melanie and she was seven. I invited them into the office, but June turned to look behind herself, and there, hiding behind the hedge at my gate, was her son. This was Joseph and he was nine.

'I won't come in, thanks, Mr Rhea, it's Joseph, he won't come near you.'

'Why not?' I asked as the little face peered at me through the foliage.

'He's frightened of policemen,' she said. 'He thinks you'll lock him up!'

'I'm not frightened!' beamed Melanie from her mother's side.

'Of course you're not,' I smiled, 'so what on earth's given Joseph that idea?'

'Some of the kids at school, I think. He won't say much about it, but I don't like to leave him there with all the traffic passing . . . so . . . '

'Joseph is silly,' said Melanie.

'Be quiet, Melanie,' said her mum.

'I won't hurt him,' I said loudly so he might hear, 'so what's the problem, June?'

She explained how she had been to Ashfordly on the bus only

this morning to do some shopping and had lost her purse. It contained a few personal belongings and about £10 in cash, too much for her to lose.

With Melanie adding her comments, I took details and promised I would see if it had been handed in. As she waited at the door, I rang Ashfordly Police Station, but at that stage, there was no record of it. However, I assured her that if it was handed in, it would be restored to her in due course. Off she went, with Joseph running ahead to keep out of my clutches and Melanie waving a brave goodbye.

That afternoon I had to visit Ashfordly Police Station on a routine matter and was in time to see a middle-aged lady departing. As I entered, PC Alwyn Foxton said,

'Ah, Nick! Just in time. That purse you rang about, it's just been brought in. Found in the market place under a seat. The finder's just left.'

I checked the contents and sure enough, it belonged to June Myers, and the money was intact. I told Alwyn I'd deliver it to Mrs Myers later in the day, and would provide her with the name of the lady who had been so honest in handing it in. And, of course, I would obtain the necessary official receipt for it and its contents.

I knocked on the door of the Myers' council house at teatime and it was opened by young Joseph.

Upon seeing me standing there in full uniform, he gave a sharp cry of alarm and bolted back indoors, shouting and crying for his mother. Alarmed at his outburst, she rushed from the kitchen and expressed relief when she saw me at the door. I gave her the good news about her purse and she invited me in while she signed my official receipt. During this short item of business, Joseph hid behind the settee, peering out at me with tearful eyes. I learned that Melanie was out playing with friends.

'Mr Rhea isn't going to hurt you!' she said to the child. 'He's brought mummy's purse back, look!'

He looked at it, apparently puzzled that a policeman should be doing something helpful, and then he retreated behind his protective settee.

'I'm not here to hurt you, Joseph,' I spoke to the unseen lad.

'I'm here to help your mum, we've brought her purse back.'

There was no reaction from him. I didn't seek him out; that would have raised his fears even more, so I left quietly with June's delight being my reward. She said she would write a letter of thanks to the finder.

It was some three weeks later when I received a phone call from Alan Myers; he was June's husband and he worked at an agricultural engineers' depot in Ashfordly. I think he was a welder and he rang me from work.

'It's Alan Myers, Mr Rhea,' he said. 'I've just had a call from our June. Somebody's pinched Joseph's bike, it's a new one an' all. We got it for his birthday . . . '

'Where did it go from?' I asked.

'Outside our house, sometime since last night. It got left out, Mr Rhea, by accident; it's our own fault, but I thought you might come across it.'

'I'll have a walk down there this morning, Alan,' I assured him. 'Is June in? I can see her for a description of it.'

'Aye, she rang me from a neighbour's, said she'd be in all day.'

'Good, I'll do my best.'

When I arrived, both Joseph and Melanie were at school and I obtained the necessary written statement from June Myers. This included an account of the bike's location, its description and a sentence to say that no one had any authority to remove it. It was a Hercules, a small blue cycle with white mudguards and a white pump. The seat was white too and it had a chainguard and lamps back and front. Almost new, it was clean and in very good condition. It was the miniature of a gents' full-size bicycle.

I promised June I would circulate its description to all local police stations and patrolling officers, and that it would appear in our monthly Stolen Cycles Supplement which was distributed to all cycle dealers. But, in my heart of hearts, I was doubtful if we could recover it.

Having undertaken these routine matters, I decided I would tour the area around Aidensfield, making a search of hedge-backs and likely dumping places. An adult could not have ridden it away; it was far too small for that, but another child might have taken it for a joy ride and abandoned it. Or, of course, a thieving adult could have picked it up and transported it away to sell for cash.

But I was lucky, or rather, Joseph was lucky. Later that afternoon, I decided to visit the village sports field at Maddleskirk, a couple of miles away. I knew it attracted youngsters from the local villages and many rode there on cycles. And there, parked behind the cricket pavilion, I found Joseph's bike. It was undamaged and there was no one on the field at the time. I was tempted to leave it and keep observations upon it, for the thief would probably return and collect it. Then he could be dealt with. But there was no hiding-place for me here and if I left it unsupervised in the hope that I might later catch the thief riding it, it might be stolen again or lost forever. I decided against those risks. I had found it and it was safe, so I put it in the van and drove to the Myers' home.

When I arrived, the family was having a cooked tea and Alan answered the door.

'Hello, Alan,' I smiled. 'I've good news,' and I led him to my van. I lifted out the cycle and, of course, he was delighted. He looked at it and was pleased it had suffered no damage.

'Come in, Mr Rhea, and show it to our Joseph. He's scared of blokes like you, this might make him appreciate you fellers a bit more.'

Following Alan indoors, I wheeled the little bike into the front room and Alan called for Joseph, Melanie and June. They came from the kitchen, and when Joseph saw me holding his precious bike, his little brown eyes showed a mixture of fear and amazement.

'Here, Joseph,' I invited him to come closer. 'Come and have a look – is this your bike?'

'Go on, Joseph,' urged his mother. 'Tell Mr Rhea if it's yours.'

The little lad, brave but somewhat shy, moved towards me and I crouched down to welcome him. 'Well?' I asked. 'Is this yours, Joseph? I found it on the cricket field.'

He took hold of its handlebars and nodded.

'Yeth,' he said.

'Say thank you to PC Rhea,' said his mother. 'Thank you for finding my bike.'

'Thank you for finding my bike,' he said.

'There,' said his mother. 'That wasn't bad, was it? You see, policemen are not here to hurt you, Joseph, they're here to help you.'

'Shall I ride it for you?' He suddenly asked me.

'Can you ride a two-wheeler?' I asked.

'Yeth, of courth I can,' and he proudly wheeled it outside as I followed with June and the others.

Melanie suddenly decided she should ride a bike too, for she said, 'I can ride a bike, Mr Rhea,' and dashed back indoors for her red three-wheeler. On the footpath, I was then treated to a display of cycle-riding by Joseph who did tricks like ringing his bell while riding with one hand, riding with his feet lifted from the pedals and doing rapid turns around the lamp-posts. His shyness had evaporated; now he was a show-off. Melanie did her best to outdo him with her skills, and for me it was a pleasant few moments. Quite suddenly, Joseph decided he was unafraid of me. He halted at my side and asked, 'Do you arretht naughty boyth? There are thome very naughty boyth at our thchool.'

'We only arrest very naughty people,' I said. 'We are here to help people, really, like your mum when she lost her purse or you, when somebody took your new bike.'

'I'm ten now,' he said proudly. 'I'm big now and I'm not frightened of you any more!'

'Good, then I am very pleased. Now, you must look after your bike . . . '

I gave him a short lecture on caring for his belongings and bade the family farewell. I thought no more of the incidents until, around half past five one evening, I heard a knock at my office door. I went outside to find Joseph standing there clutching a small boy by the collar.

'Thith ith a very naughty boy,' Joseph announced as the other cringed and protested beneath my gaze. 'I've brought him for you to arretht!'

'What's he done?' I asked.

'He thtole thome thweets from a girl at thchool, I thaw him,' he said. 'That ith very naughty!'

'Really, well, you'd better come in, both of you.'

I was uncertain how to cope with this development, but the other little lad, a six-year-old whose name I learned was Simon, denied the charge.

'I never,' he said. 'She gave me them.'

I lectured Simon against ever stealing sweets and congratulated Joseph on his community spirit, albeit couched in terms he would understand, and packed them off home. I wondered if he knew what was meant by the word 'arrest' – perhaps he thought it involved nothing more than a telling off by a policeman? In that case, I had done as he had expected and honour had been satisfied. Two days later, Joseph returned with another arrested child. This time it was a girl who'd torn another girl's dress in a fight.

'Thhe'th very naughty,' Joseph told me. 'Thhe'th tore Fiona'th dreth fighting when Mith Clement said not to.'

I gave Fiona a lecture about damaging the belongings of her friends, and she cried a little. I told Joseph to take her home. Now I had a problem, because he turned up with other 'arrested' children and probably thought he was doing a good job as a very special constable. I didn't want to hurt the child by telling him off, for that might destroy all his new-found confidence and the good work that had been achieved in removing his fears of policemen.

So, in an attempt to solve this little dilemma, I decided that the easiest way was to be 'out' whenever he arrived with one of his arrests. I explained the situation to Mary and so during the following few weeks, whenever we heard his knock at the office door around teatime, she answered it. For a short time afterwards, she was confronted by Joseph and his many prisoners. One some five or six occasions that followed, she explained that PC Rhea was out on patrol and suggested that Joseph and his prisoner return later. This had the desired effect. Joseph ceased his one-man vigilante campaign, but he always spoke to me when he saw me. In fact, he matured into a fine young man and became a detective chief inspector in the London Metropolitan Police with his own lovely children. And he always pops in to see me when he's in the area – but now he doesn't bring his prisoners for me to deal with!

A farmer's eight-year-old son caused something of a flap one Christmas Eve, but it was a short-lived panic. I learned that the little boy, who was called Jonathan, had been suffering from teasing at school because he believed in Father Christmas when some of the others claimed he did not exist. Determined to settle the issue in his own mind, young Jonathan had not mentioned his doubts to anyone, not even to his parents, but after they had tucked him into bed that night, he had secretly gone out to seek Santa Claus.

I learned of his disappearance about ten o'clock on Christmas Eve when his father, Howard Sinclair, rang me. I hurried straight to the farm, which was only five minutes drive from my own home, and was ushered into the living-room. There, with the help of Jonathan's older brother, Andrew, I learned of his worries.

Andrew told us that, at school, several of the lads in Jonathan's class were boasting that they had discovered the truth about Father Christmas and Jonathan had championed those who still believed in him. Jonathan had said, before the holidays, that he would find out for sure whether Father Christmas really existed.

'Did he say how he would do this?' I asked Andrew, an alert eleven-year-old.

'No, he never said. I thought he'd forgotten all about it, Mr Rhea, 'cos it was at school, before the holidays when he was on about it.'

At my instigation, we checked Jonathan's clothes and found he had dressed in his warm clothes which comprised a pair of small jeans, warm jumper, wellingtons, scarf, gloves, balaclava and overcoat.

'Let's search the farm buildings first,' I suggested.

'We've had a look around,' said Howard.

But if a policeman learns anything, it is how to conduct a thorough search of houses and buildings, especially for people who are deliberately concealing themselves.

I was sure the lad was out of doors, because of the clothing he had taken, and so we began our hunt. I allowed the parents to go one way while I went elsewhere, then I would retrace their steps, searching for the tiniest and most unlikely of hiding places. There was no snow yet, but it was crisp and frosty outside, so there'd be no footprints to provide any clues. After some twenty minutes of searching outbuildings, sheds and parked vehicles, I found myself in the hayloft. It was dry and cosy, with the scent of the hay filling my nostrils as my powerful torch picked out the stacked bales with hollows and passages between.

And then, as my torch beam moved across the surface of the bales, someone hissed for me to be silent.

'Sssh!' demanded the child's voice. 'You'll frighten 'em off!'

'Jonathan?' he would not know my voice.

'Who's that?' he demanded.

'The policeman, PC Rhea, we're looking for you.'

'I'm all right, leave me alone. I'm busy.'

My torch picked him out now. He was lying fully clothed on some bales of hay, peering through the loft window in the gable-end of the hayshed. The window was normally closed, having a small door to cover the gap, but now it was standing wide open. It gave him a perfect view of the farmhouse and at his side was a carpet brush and dustpan.

I knelt beside him. 'What are you doing here?'

'Waiting for Father Christmas,' he said.

'He never comes when children are awake and waiting for him,' I said gently. 'He will know you are here, so he'll keep away till you go to sleep in bed. Why do you want to see him?'

'To see if he's real,' he said simply.

'Well, as I said, Jonathan, he won't come while you are here, so you'd better come home. Your mum and dad are worried about you.'

'Are you sure he won't come?' he asked me, standing up and collecting his brush and dustpan.

'Yes,' I said, pointing the way out with my torch. 'But why have you got that brush and dustpan?'

'For reindeer droppings,' he said. 'I know Father Christmas will come to that chimney over there,' and he pointed at the house. 'And I know his reindeer like our hay, 'cos mum and dad said so; we always leave this hayloft window open so them reindeer'll come here for a feed. And I know how cows and horses make droppings, so I'll pick 'em up and show 'em to my pals. Then they'll know Father Christmas is real, won't they?'

'If you can find some reindeer droppings, I'm sure you'll convince them,' I said, accepting the brush from him and taking his hand. 'Come on, time for bed.'

'I'll never know, will I?' he said slowly.

'One day you will,' I told him, as I led him back to the house.

If young Joseph Myers misunderstood the meaning of 'arrest', it was understandable that little Martin Stokes, a small-built ten-year-old, should misunderstand one of this nation's best-known phrases. Most grown-ups know what is meant by 'London's streets are paved with gold' but Martin's vision of that big city was one of a glistening fairy-tale lane with golden footpaths and houses which contained everything a family could ever wish for, especially a dad.

Martin's mother had no husband. Martin was the result of a brief encounter with a young man who had vanished immediately after the act which had created Martin, and so the little fellow was reared by his loving and caring mother who was called Rosemary. She provided her sole offspring with lots of affection and as much comfort as possible.

She worked in a local shop which provided the barest of necessities, but at least she did work and she did attempt to give Martin the best that was within her very limited means. When the village primary school announced it was organising a trip to London for some ten- and eleven-year-olds, therefore, Martin said he would like to go. The trip was a form of celebration of the conclusion of their primary school education because next term, they would begin a new life at either a Grammar School or a Secondary Modern. In spite of the expense, Rosemary wanted Martin to go to London and she raided her meagre savings for his fare. Happily, a local businessman had said he would match fifty per cent of the total cost if the parents would raise the rest themselves.

The outcome was that a dozen children found themselves embarking on the trip of a lifetime. None had ever been to London and so the teacher, Miss Clement, told them about it. She explained about the Houses of Parliament, Big Ben, the Queen and Buckingham Palace, the Horse Guards, the River

Thames and all the traditional tourist sights. She showed them photographs too and a short film about London. And it was Miss Clement, in her lecture about the delights of our capital, who quoted from the poet George Colman (1762–1836), when she said,

'Oh, London is a fine town,
A very famous city,
Where all the streets are paved with gold,
And all the maidens pretty.'

At home that evening over his tea, Martin told his mum all about the golden streets of London but she tried to explain that they weren't really made of gold. She told Martin that London was the town of opportunity, where people could become rich if they worked hard because there was a lot of money in London. It was there for everyone if they worked hard and took the opportunities to find it. Martin said he understood, and the night before the trip, she'd bathed him, got his best clothes ready and packed him an old army knapsack full of sandwiches and drinks.

'Will I be rich if I go to London?' he had asked her as she'd tucked him into bed.

'Maybe when you are grown up,' she'd said. 'If you go to London and work.' Poor Rosemary; money was so short for her that her worries about it must have made an impression upon her young son. He was always anxious to earn lots of money. 'But if the streets are made of gold, there must be some for me?' he'd said.

'No, darling, I've told you. The streets aren't made of gold, not really. They're stone like our streets, but there is lots of money in London, there's lots of it about and people can find ways of getting a lot, earning a lot, if they live and work there.'

He hadn't quite understood it all, but had fallen into a fitful sleep, dreaming of the fabulous town he would visit tomorrow. Next morning at six, a small coach left Aidensfield for York Station where the train departed just before seven o'clock, thus allowing them a day in London under the guidance of the teachers and one or two volunteer helpers. They were all so eager to see the sights and to bring back lots of souvenirs. All had little bags containing their sandwiches and drinks, and I knew these would be full of trinkets and leaflets upon their return.

I was aware of the trip – a village bobby should know everything that is happening on his patch – but as none of my own children were old enough to join it, I was not really involved. The trip was an unqualified, if exhausting, success and my professional involvement came the following morning.

I received a phone call from Rosemary Stokes asking if I could call at the shop where she was working as she had a matter to discuss with me. Not knowing what this matter could be, I drove along to Maddleskirk where I found her behind the counter of the post-office-cum-grocery store. She was alone, the proprietor having gone into York to buy his weekly stock of groceries, and the morning was quiet.

'Hello, Rosemary,' I greeted her. 'What's bothering you?'

'Would you like a coffee, Mr Rhea? I've got the kettle on?' This was a good start!

I let her make the coffee without asking more questions and she settled on a stool behind the counter as I settled on another at the customers' side. If a customer entered, she would deal with him or her, and I would enjoy my drink.

'I hope you don't mind me calling you like this,' she apologised. 'But I am very worried about Martin.'

'Why, what's he done? He went to London yesterday, didn't he? He has come back, hasn't he?' I suddenly had an awful thought that he might not have returned.

'Oh, yes, he's back. He's asleep, he went straight to bed last night when he got back, Mr Rhea, he was utterly worn out. I've never seen him so tired,' and she bent to withdraw something from under the counter. It was a small khaki-coloured knapsack of the type soldiers used to carry for their rations and it was evidently very heavy. As she passed it over to me, I heard the rattle of coins.

'Look inside,' she invited.

Resisting its weight as I accepted it, I pulled open the stout press-studs and saw it was half full of coins. Threepenny bits, sixpences, shillings, florins, half-crowns, pennies and ha'pennies. There was a small fortune.

'Somebody's been saving fast!' I laughed. 'Who's is all this?'

'I don't know,' and she looked sorrowful. 'Martin brought it back from London. He said he'd found it all. I didn't give him that money, Mr Rhea, nothing like that. I don't know where it's come from. I do hope he hasn't been stealing. I thought I'd better hand it in.'

I fingered through it; there were no £1 notes or ten-shilling notes, merely a large amount of cash. I didn't count it and learned Rosemary hadn't done so either, but there would be several pounds.

'Did you quiz ..im closely about it?' I asked.

She shook her head. 'No, he was too tired, he just fell into bed, exhausted and besides, I didn't like to upset him after his day out. I do know it's not his money and as he said he'd found it, I thought I'd better hand it in. I wondered if anybody had said anything to you about it.'

'No, they haven't,' I told her. 'I'm not surprised he was tired, carrying this around! I'll have to ask him about it.' I was worried in case he had taken it off the other children, although I doubted it. Martin was an honest little fellow, I was sure.

'He's in bed, at home, Mr Rhea, my mother's looking after him today, he's got the day off school. I didn't wake him to ask about it this morning. Should I come with you?'

'Your mother's there, so I'll be fine. I'll take the money to remind him!' I said, and so I returned to Aidensfield to have a chat with Martin.

Mrs Stokes, senior, Rosemary's mother, opened the door and was aware of the reason for my visit. She took me into her house, for Rosemary still lived at home, and said Martin was now out of bed and in the front room, playing with his souvenirs of yesterday in London. I went in. He was a happy boy, with a mop of curly blond hair and bright blue eyes, and showed no apprehension at my arrival.

'Hello, Martin,' I squatted on the carpet at his side. 'What have we got here?'

'Things from London,' he told me proudly. 'Pictures, books, flags; look, that's where the Queen lives and that's Big Ben . . . there's boats on the river and that's the Tower where the two princes were killed . . . '

I let him tell me all about his journey and it was clear it had made a tremendous impression upon him. At this stage, I knew nothing of his vision of golden pavements, but when I presented the knapsack full of coins, he said, 'I got them from London, Mr Rhea.'

'Did you?' I expressed surprise. 'Where from?'

'The streets,' he said. 'Everybody said the streets were paved with gold, well, they weren't, they were stone like ours, and it was mum who said there was money on the streets for everybody who could find it, so I found all that, Mr Rhea. I looked for it, and brought it home.'

'You mean you found all this, Martin?' I ran my fingers through the coins.

'Yes, Mr Rhea. On the pavements. I told mum that.'

'Was all this money lying on the pavements?' I asked, surprised at the amount. Finding the occasional coin was not unusual, but to find all these . . .

'Yes, it was,' he said. 'People were throwing money down and other people were picking it up.'

'Whereabouts was this happening, Martin?'

'Oh, all over. Everywhere we went.'

'And who was picking it up?'

'Sometimes nobody, it was just left there. But those men playing music and drawing things on the pavements, they were keeping some. And sometimes, people threw it in boxes and hats and things on the pavements. I saw a lot of money thrown away like that, Mr Rhea, so I thought I'd have some.'

'You helped yourself from the boxes and hats, then?'

'Not really, 'cos I thought it must be somebody's, but I did pick some up from the pavements when it was just lying there. There was lots lying about, Mr Rhea.'

'I'm sure there was!' I had now guessed the source of his cash flow!

And so, by asking more questions, I came to realise that Martin, through the legend that the streets of London are paved with gold, had honestly thought money was being thrown on to the pavements to be collected by poor people like himself. And so, during that trip, he had picked up pounds' worth of coins from the feet of pavement artists, buskers and newspaper vendors and no one had noticed.

Martin's grandmother overheard this and was shocked.

'Martin!' she shouted at him. 'That's stealing . . . '

'He wasn't to realise that,' I said. 'But Martin, this money did belong to those people playing the music and doing the drawings. That's how they earn their money.'

I don't think he fully understood, but his grandmother asked, 'You're not going to take him to court, surely?'

'No,' I said. 'I wouldn't, not for this! But I couldn't take official action anyway, not without a complaint from those buskers and pavement artists! And I hardly think I'll get one from them!'

'What do we do with the money, then?' asked Mrs Stokes.

'I'll leave Rosemary to decide,' I said. 'She might give some to a charity, but I'm sure if those artists and buskers knew the struggle she was having, they wouldn't mind it going into Martin's Post Office Savings Account. He can always pay some back next time he's in London.'

I left, not wishing to know more about Martin's money-making but hoped he would learn that, even in London, cash was not there for the taking. It had to be earned.

On another occasion, anxiety was caused after Miss Alice Calvert retired as Headmistress of Ashfordly Primary School. Because she had served there during her entire teaching career, a matter of some forty years, her retirement created a lot of interest in the town and surrounding area, and resulted in wide local press coverage. There were presentations to her, one from her pupils past and present, and another from the governors and parents. Then, on the last day of her career, there was a social evening in the school with speeches and yet more gifts for Miss Calvert from her small staff and numerous associates, both within the teaching profession and from the townspeople.

She announced that next year she would be taking a long holiday to tour Europe by car, and she hoped to take an extended break to visit her sister and her family in Australia. She hoped to enrol at night-school to study pottery and promised that her retirement would enable her to undertake all those things she'd been unable to do while working.

Alice Calvert was of very distinctive appearance. Now sixty years old, she was a very tall and heavily built lady with a habit of wearing long, colourful and flowing dresses which concealed any hint of her feminine shape. Some of the crueller senior boys would call her Bell-Tent Alice, and few people really knew whether she was slim on top with big hips, or big on top with narrow hips. Almost invariably, she wore flat-heeled shoes or sandals and lots of bangles.

Her face, however, was beautiful. Embraced by a mop of pure white hair, it was round and cheerful with rosy cheeks and a constant smile. Miss Calvert radiated happiness and love and I, for one, often wondered why she had never married. She loved children and was completely happy in her work. Retirement, and the subsequent parting from the children, would not be an easy adjustment to make. But Alice Calvert could cope and would make the necessary adaptations without grumbling or self-pity.

She lived in Aidensfield, where she had a neat little bungalow not far from the church. I would see her pottering around the place at weekends, for she kept an immaculate garden full of flowers and shrubs, somehow guiding her massive bulk between the plants without causing damage. The bungalow was called Honeymead and during her long school holidays, she would ask me to keep an eye on the house whenever she was away. She was always careful to lock it against intruders. I was pleased that, during her frequent absences, she did notify me and so allow me to keep a careful watch on her property. I knew that during her longer absences overseas or indeed any other travelling she undertook in Britain, she would keep me informed when the bungalow was empty. I knew she would worry about the effect of her recent publicity, and whether this would attract undesirables who would snoop around her premises. In an attempt to offset this concern, I assured her that my colleagues and I would pay regular visits when on duty.

Knowing this background, it was with more than a little concern that at four o'clock on the morning following her farewell party, I received an urgent telephone call from her. It took a long time to arouse me but by the time I reached my cold office downstairs, I was fully awake.

'Mr Rhea,' she hissed into the phone. 'There's a man out-side . . . he's been trying to break into my bungalow . . . What shall I do?'

'Is he still there?' I asked, speaking in a hoarse whisper.

'Yes and it's funny, I think he's gone to sleep outside, on the patio . . . '

'Asleep? Right, don't make a sound. I'm coming straight away. Look out for me . . . '

Pausing only to call Divisional Headquarters with an urgent request for the Police Dog Section and any other handy mobiles to be available at the bungalow in case the villain ran away or there was trouble, I dressed and hurried out. I did not take the mini-van, because a stealthy approach seemed vitally impor-tant. Instead, I used a pedal cycle I'd just acquired and, after riding without lights for half a mile in the semi-darkness of that summer morning, I arrived at Honeymead within minutes. Parking my bike several doors away. I radioed Divisional Head-quarters to announce my arrival at Honeymead and to inform them I was about to search for, and hopefully arrest, the re-ported intruder.

Calls of this kind were made as a form of security so that if I failed to respond to radio calls in the ensuing drama, assistance would be sent. I knew the dogs and maybe other crews were already *en route*, and that gave me some comfort. I could wait for them, but I would hate to lose this prisoner; he might be frightened off at the approach of their vehicles, and so I made my move. My heart was pounding and I made sure I had my handcuffs and truncheon, my only defence against attack.

As I crept up to her back door in the near-darkness, I thought it odd that her burglar had gone to sleep, but I knew that sillier things had happened. Burglars often went to sleep inside a deserted house or even cooked meals there. Maybe this was just a drunk who'd read about her in the papers? The bungalow was in complete darkness, but in the approaching light of morning, she had seen my arrival. She unlocked her back door and opened it silently to admit me.

'Thank goodness you've come, Mr Rhea!'

I did not make the mistake of switching on my torch but

186

could see she was enveloped in a huge flowing dressing-gown and had a heavy poker in her hand. If he'd got in here, he would have had a shock and a few bruises into the bargain.

'Where is he? Is he still here?' I whispered.

'On the patio, fast asleep. Maybe he's drunk.'

'Can I get there by going through the house?'

'No, he's lying against the french windows. You'll have to go round the side and through the garden.'

'Right,' I whispered and began my move. I knew the way, I'd been around her bungalow many previous times.

'What shall I do?' she asked.

'Stay here. Keep an eye on me from inside; it's not too dark. If I get attacked or anything, dial 999 and tell the police what's going on.'

'Be careful!' she whispered. And so I left. I crept around the side of her house, trying not to make a sound, and then, as I reached the front, I could see the dark shape of the sleeping intruder. It was a bulky man and he was huddled on the patio, lying fast asleep against her french windows. In the dim light, I could see he was very casually dressed in jeans and a sweater, and that he carried a back-pack comprising a sleeping-bag and rucksack, and this was forming his pillow. His hair was tousled and I could just discern a thick brown beard . . .

Wondering how long it would take for my assistance to arrive, I halted to take a deep breath. Miss Calvert was nearby with her poker but in cases like this, there was no knowing how a suspect would react; he might have a gun or a knife, he might be armed with a knuckleduster or a club. I began to think it would be wiser to await the dogs, but I could not flinch from my task.

I approached the sleeping form.

'Hey!' I moved his foot with my boot. 'You, hey, wake up . . . it's the police . . . '

I stood back in case of a violent reaction.

'Hmm?' he stirred but did not arouse. I kicked his boot again, shouting at him and keeping my distance.

'Police . . . wake up . . . ' and now I shone my torch full in his eyes. 'Hey, come on, who are you? Stand up . . . '

In the reflected light of my torch, I could see Miss Calvert just inside her french windows, wringing her hands and wondering what she should be doing. I just hoped she did not go away – that poker might be my salvation! But the fellow was now rising to his feet, sleepily and without any sign of antagonism. He made no effort to run off, but stood there, blinking at me and apparently quite docile.

'Who are you?' I demanded loudly, hoping to penetrate his weariness. 'This is the police . . . '

'Huh?' He blinked against the light of my torch and covered his eyes. 'Who?'

'Police,' I said. 'Who are you? What are you doing here?'

'Oh God,' he muttered and his deep voice emerged with a strong Australian accent. 'Streuth, I'm shattered, I really am . . . is this Miss Calvert's house? Alice Calvert's house?'

'Yes, it is,' I said. 'So who are you?'

'G'day. I'm her nephew . . . from Adelaide . . . Derek's the name . . . I knocked but she was asleep . . . I didn't like to rouse her so I kipped here . . . she always left a key under the stone when I was little so I could get in, but it's not there, Officer. Sorry, have I upset things?'

'You've been travelling long?'

'Couple of weeks or so,' he said. 'Flew a bit, caught ferries and hitched most of the way; I aimed to get here as a surprise, for her retirement party, do you know . . . '

'Wait there,' I said, and I knocked on her window. 'It's all right, Miss Calvert. You can put the light on and open this door.'

Even with my approval, she was nervous, but she obeyed. When the door was fully open, Derek said, 'Aunt Alice!' and threw his huge arms around her.

'Derek! It is you, isn't it? Derek!'

'Yes, it's me . . . '

I maintained a discreet distance during their dramatic reunion and then she invited me inside to have a cup of tea with her nephew. I learned it was seventeen years since she'd last seen him; he was then twelve and was now twenty-nine and approaching thirty. This had been his retirement surprise . . .

'And you're coming back to Australia,' he said eventually, delving into his baggage. 'I've a return ticket for you, starting

188

five weeks from now. For a whole month . . . you're coming to stay with us . . . '

I felt I ought to leave this scene of domestic happiness, but at that moment, the bungalow was suddenly surrounded by cars, flashing blue lights and lots of police officers . . .

'Oh crumbs!' I said. 'I forgot to cancel the cavalry!'

'Bring them in for a drink,' said Alice Calvert happily. 'It's a good job he wasn't a burglar!'

'It is,' I laughed. 'They'd have frightened him off!'

Half a dozen policemen and two dogs came into the house and filled the place with blue uniforms as I explained what had happened. They were delighted with the truth.

'Look,' said Alice, addressing us all in her school-ma'am voice, 'I know you're not supposed to drink on duty, but I do have a bottle of wine . . . perhaps a glass each, just to celebrate? My nephew has come rather a long way, half-way round the world, and he did miss my party . . . '

And so, in the early hours of that morning, seven policemen and two police dogs, aided by glasses of wine, slices of her farewell cake and cups of coffee, helped Miss Calvert to celebrate her nephew's arrival. It was a lovely night's work!

As we prepared to leave, I said to my colleagues, 'Miss Calvert's going away soon, lads, can I ask you all to keep an eye on her bungalow when I give you the word, just in case some burglar shows an unhealthy interest in it?'

'Sure,' they said. 'So long as we can have another party when she gets back!'

'That's a promise,' she beamed, hugging her nephew.

My reinforcements left in a procession of cars, doubtless rousing and puzzling the entire village, and I returned to my parked bike. Derek followed me out.

'Thanks, Mr Rhea,' he said. 'Thanks for looking after Aunt Alice. It could have been nasty, eh? A real intruder?'

'It's all part of the job,' I said, shaking his hand.